COOK SMART

FOR A HEALTHY **HEART**

With Fran Berkoff, R.D.

COOK SMART
FOR A HEALTHY
HEART

Reader's
Digest

MONTREAL

COOK SMART FOR A HEALTHY HEART

© 2007 The Reader's Digest Association, Inc.
© 2007 The Reader's Digest Association (Canada) Ltd.
© 2007 Reader's Digest (Australia) Pty Limited
© 2007 Reader's Digest Association Far East Ltd.
Philippine Copyright 2007 Reader's Digest Association
    Far East Ltd.

All rights reserved. No part of this book may be reproduced, stored in a retrieval system, or transmitted in any form or by any means, electronic, electrostatic, magnetic tape, mechanical, photocopying, recording or otherwise, without permission in writing from the publishers.

Reader's Digest and the Pegasus logo are registered trademarks of The Reader's Digest Association, Inc., of Pleasantville, New York, USA.

Library and Archives Canada Cataloguing in Publication

Cook smart for a healthy heart: more than 240 good-for-your-heart recipes that taste great too / from the editors at Reader's Digest.

Includes index.
ISBN 0-88850-797-6

1. Heart—Diseases—Diet therapy—Recipes. I. Reader's Digest Association (Canada)

RC684.D5E38 2006   641.5'6311   C2005-907454-X

We are interested in receiving your comments on the content of this book.
Write to: The Editor, Books and Home Entertainment, Reader's Digest (Canada) Ltd.
1100 René-Lévesque Blvd. West, Montreal, Quebec H3B 5H5

To order additional copies of *Cook Smart for a Healthy Heart* or to request a catalogue, please call our 24-hour Customer Service hotline at 1-800-465-0780.

For more Reader's Digest products and information, visit our website at **www.rd.ca**

Front cover Rustic broiled vegetable and rigatoni salad, p. 225
Back cover (top to bottom) Beef in red wine and brandy, p. 191; Garlicky tomato salad, p. 223; Rich chocolate torte, p. 287
Title Stir-fried beef with fine noodles, p. 95
Foreword Rice with shrimp and dill dressing, p. 102
Contents (left) Leek and prosciutto pizza muffins, p. 48; (right) Spanish orange and almond cake, p. 301

Printed in China

Contributors

Chief Nutritionist
Fran Berkoff, R.D.

Writers Catherine Atkinson, Shirley Bond, Anna Brandenburger, Sara Buenfeld, Carole Clements, Linda Collister, Gail Duff, Christine France, Anne Gains, Carole Handslip, Beverly LeBlanc, Sara Lewis, Sally Mansfield, Janette Marshall, Maggie Mayhew, Kate Moseley, Jenni Muir, Angela Nilsen, Maggie Pannell, Anne Sheasby, Marlena Spieler, Susanna Tee, Judith Wills

Recipe Testers Pat Alburey, Catherine Atkinson, Juliet Barker, Valerie Barrett, Anna Brandenburger, Bridget Colvin, Christine France, Emma-Lee Gow, Bridget Jones, Clare Lewis, Jane Middleton, Heather Owen, Maggie Pannell, Anne Sheasby, Gina Steer, Susanna Tee

Photographers Sue Atkinson, Martin Brigdale, Gerry Colley, Gus Filgate, Amanda Heywood, Graham Kirk, William Lingwood, Sean Myers, Simon Smith

Stylists LJ Crompton, Michelle Lucia, Penny Markham, Helen Payne, Sue Russell, Helen Trent, Jody Vassallo

Home Economists Caroline Barty, Jules Beresford, Maxine Clark, Joanna Farrow, Nicola Fowler, Lisa Heathcote, Joss Herd, Justine Kiggen, Lucy McKelvie, Lucy Miller, Louise Pickford, Bridget Sargeson, Joy Skipper, Linda Tubby, Sunil Vijayakar

For Reader's Digest Canada

Senior Project Editor Pamela Johnson

Senior Designer Andrée Payette

Contributing Editor Robert Ronald

Assistant Editor Jim Hynes

Copy Editor Gilles Humbert

Indexer Diane Harriman

Production Manager Gordon Howlett

Reader's Digest Association (Canada) Ltd.

Vice President, Book Editorial
Robert Goyette

The Reader's Digest Association, Inc.

Editor-in-Chief Neil Wertheimer

President and Chief Executive Officer Eric Schrier

about this book

With all the publicity given to diseases such as cancer, it is sobering to realize that diseases of the heart and blood vessels are in fact the leading cause of death in Canada today. All too often, the victims are relatively young people.

One of the main reasons for this high rate of heart disease is a global epidemic of a condition known as metabolic syndrome, a disorder that occurs with great frequency in people who are overweight. It has been estimated that more than 25 per cent of Canadians have this condition, and the number is growing daily. It is appearing in younger and younger people, even in children.

People with metabolic syndrome can suffer from elevated blood pressure, high levels of triglyceride, low levels of "good" or HDL cholesterol and inflamed arteries. They are also in greater danger of developing diabetes. Most importantly, people with this condition run a high risk of having a heart attack while still relatively young. Unless we act now, the situation will only become worse.

Researchers around the world are looking for new ways to reduce the risk of heart disease in those who have the condition. But it is even more important to prevent metabolic syndrome from occurring in the first place. The good news is that the epidemic can be defeated if we return to a life which features daily physical activity and healthier food choices—like those used in the recipes in this book.

Working with a team of health and food professionals, the experts at Reader's Digest have taken familiar family favourite recipes, along with many new ones, and made them "heart-healthy"—and still full of delicious, robust flavours and textures. All the recipes have been kitchen-tested. Included is invaluable, up-to-date information on the latest nutritional research and incorporates the benefits of certain foods into your diet—ones that can dramatically lessen your risk of heart disease.

contents

foreword

We've known for a long time that food is an integral part of health and well-being. As the science of nutrition grows, we're learning more and more about the role food plays, not in just treating disease but in keeping you healthy. In recent years, scientists have been able to identify risk factors for heart disease, such as obesity, diabetes and high blood pressure, as well as strategies to alter your diet and lifestyle to lower these risks. Armed with this information, it is now possible to individualize your eating habits to alter your heart disease risk.

Eight in ten Canadians have at least one risk factor for cardiovascular disease, and 11 per cent have three risk factors or more. Obesity, one of these risk factors, is growing in epidemic proportions in Canada. Of more concern is the appearance of obesity, diabetes and high blood pressure in young people. It's critical to act now to reverse these alarming trends. This can be achieved, in part, through a heart-healthy diet and regular exercise.

When it comes to a heart-healthy diet, there are a number of well-known truths. Eating more fruits and vegetables, more fish (especially fatty fish), sufficient soluble fibre, more whole grains and less fat (especially saturated fat and trans-fatty acids) are all associated with reducing the risk of heart disease and other illnesses associated with heart disease. Exercising regularly, achieving a healthy weight and maintaining a healthy weight are also part of the heart-healthy lifestyle.

But, while the information is available, actually taking the important nutritional steps remains difficult for many people. These days it seems more challenging than ever to be a smart consumer. Pick up any newspaper or magazine or turn on the television or computer and you will likely find at least one or two new ways that food is said to lower your cholesterol or prevent heart attacks and strokes. The more information you have, the more difficult it can be to sort out the best and most reliable information. And, once you've sorted through all this information, the next challenge is incorporating it all into your lifestyle.

So, it's wonderful when you can pick up a cookbook that takes the most current heart health principles and applies them to tasty and easy-to-prepare dishes. *Cook Smart for a Healthy Heart* has over 240 recipes that will help you develop a taste for heart-healthy cooking and the information that you read alongside will give you much of the latest science on this important topic. This book is one of those important steps on the path to your heart-healthy life.

Fran Berkoff, R.D.
Consulting Dietitian
Toronto, Ontario

you &
your heart

heart health

Heart disease is the single largest cause of death in Canada. Here are the statistics:

- Every day, more than 200 Canadians die from some sort of cardiovascular disease.

- The death rate from heart disease has fallen 56 per cent since 1969, but it remains the leading cause of death, responsible for 32 per cent of male deaths and 34 per cent of female deaths each year—more than three times the numbers of deaths caused by lung cancer and breast cancer combined.

- Over 30 per cent of men and women in their twenties are overweight and young people make up the largest proportion of smokers.

- The cost of heart disease is high. It is estimated that heart disease costs the Canadian economy approximately $18 billion annually. This includes the costs of medical treatment, medications and lost work time.

How heart disease develops

Heart disease develops slowly over many years. Fatty deposits gradually build up on the inner walls of arteries, which thicken and stiffen, losing their elasticity and ability to "flex." Eventually, the artery narrows or stops the flow of blood. This process is called "atherosclerosis."

Blood clots can lodge in the narrowed artery and cut the blood supply—and therefore the oxygen supply—to the heart muscles. When this happens, a heart attack can occur. Which artery is affected, and how severe the blockage is, will determine how serious this is, or even whether it's fatal. If the blockage is in the brain, it can trigger a stroke.

Preventing heart disease

However, there is good news. You can lower your risk of developing heart disease by adopting a heart-healthy lifestyle, which includes regular exercise, a heart-healthy eating plan and a desire for change.

The importance of diet

Heart-healthy eating doesn't mean an end to delicious food. You'll discover that you can still cook your favourites, but enjoy them in a heart-healthy form. The recipes in this book are low in saturated fat and salt, and include plenty of fibre and whole grains. And these days you have a lot more choice at the grocery store with the ever-growing range of heart-healthy products.

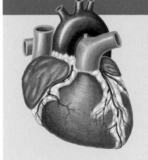

YOUR CARDIOVASCULAR SYSTEM

Blood provides your body's cells with the vital nutrition they need to survive and function. Your heart is the powerful "pump" that drives the blood through your blood vessels—a vast plumbing network that stretches into every nook and cranny of your body. Together, the pump and plumbing make up your cardiovascular system.

By following the nutrition guidelines outlined in this book, you'll find that:

- Losing weight is easier.

- Keeping your weight in check is easier.

- You can help lower your blood cholesterol levels.

- Your blood pressure will be easier to keep in control (if it's too high).

- Your meals will be healthy and balanced, ensuring you get all the important vitamins, minerals, fibre and antioxidants.

- And, if you suffer from diabetes, you will find this condition is better managed.

risk factors

Don't leave your heart health to chance. Brush up on your knowledge of risk factors. Work with your doctor and make sure you have regular screening tests, including blood pressure and cholesterol checks.

Are you at risk of heart disease?

There are many risk factors that contribute to heart disease. Some, such as obesity, smoking and high blood cholesterol, can be controlled or eliminated while others, such as age and family medical history, are inherited.

Here are the risk factors. Take steps to reduce your risk of heart disease by working to control those risk factors that you can change. If you have two or more, your risk rises sharply.

Inherited risk factors:

1 Family history If a close relative of yours has died from heart disease or had heart problems before the age of 60, you're at greater risk.

2 Age and gender The risk of heart disease is greater for men than for women up until menopause, when women "catch up" to men.

Modifiable risk factors:

1 Cigarette smoking Smoking contributes to the narrowing of blood vessels and loss of lung function. It also lowers your overall fitness. The link between smoking and heart disease is too well proven to ignore. If you smoke, take steps today to quit. Speak to your doctor or pharmacist for smoking cessation options. Enlist support from family and friends. Try to quit with a friend.

2 High blood pressure High blood pressure puts extra strain on the heart and blood vessels. Talk to your doctor about managing this via changes to your lifestyle, such as healthy eating, less salt, less alcohol and weight loss.

3 High blood cholesterol High levels of total cholesterol and the "bad" LDL cholesterol put

you at risk of heart disease. Have a blood test and discuss the results with your doctor. A heart-healthy diet can help to lower your LDL-cholesterol.

4 Diabetes Having diabetes increases your risk of heart disease by two to four times. Many of the problems of heart disease overlap with those of diabetes, such as obesity, high blood pressure, high triglycerides and circulation problems, so their treatment is similar. If you have diabetes, follow the guidelines in this book and they will help manage both conditions. A consultation with a dietitian is a must to plan a suitable diet.

5 Being overweight Carrying too much weight, especially around your abdomen, increases your chance of heart troubles as your heart has to pump harder. And you're more likely to have high blood pressure, high cholesterol and diabetes. Therefore, aim for the healthy weight range by eating right and keeping fit. Following the healthy eating principles in this book will help.

6 Being inactive Our sedentary lifestyle and technology, such as computers and remote controls, cause us to move about less. But physical activity is essential for a healthy heart. It can raise the "good" HDL cholesterol, lower blood pressure and burn off calories. Therefore, try and incorporate some regular exercise into your schedule. Find ways to be active—try taking the stairs rather than the elevator and walking rather than driving.

7 High triglycerides Triglycerides, another type of blood fat, are often elevated if you have diabetes or are overweight, or consume too much alcohol. High triglyceride levels increase the chance of heart disease. You can lower triglycerides by reducing or avoiding alcohol consumption, losing weight, minimizing your intake of simple sugars and eating more foods rich in omega-3 fatty acids such as fish.

DID YOU KNOW?

The total length of all the thousands of blood vessels (arteries, veins and capillaries) in your body is around 96,000 km—which is long enough to encircle the Earth more than twice.

know your fats

It's critical to look at the types and amounts of the fats you eat if you have high cholesterol, or need to eat for a healthy heart. There are four different types of fats—saturated, trans, mono-unsaturated and polyunsaturated.

Saturated fats

Saturated fats raise both the total cholesterol and the LDL cholesterol. Eating less saturated fat is one of the most important things you can do for your heart. Saturated fats predominate in animal fats such as fatty meat, poultry with skin, full-fat dairy products and in certain tropical oils such as coconut and palm oil. It is suggested that you reduce saturated fats to less than 10 per cent of the total calories consumed. To do this, buy lean meat, remove the skin from poultry and use lower fat dairy products.

Trans fats

Trans fats act like saturated fats by raising LDL cholesterol and lowering HDL cholesterol. A natural component of animal fat, trans fatty acids are found in all meat and milk products but in small quantities.

However, trans fats can also be made synthetically during hydrogenation (see the "Hydrogenated Fats" box right), so they may be found in commercially produced cookies, cakes, snack foods and fried foods. Some margarines and spreads in Canada are produced with hydrogenated fats, so they contain trans fats. Health Canada's new food labels make it mandatory to declare the amount of trans fats in all packaged foods.

Monounsaturated fats

Monounsaturated fats lower the total cholesterol and the "bad" LDL cholesterol when they replace saturated fats in the diet. Monounsaturates are found in all fats but are particularly high in olive, canola and peanut oils, some non-hydrogenated margarines, avocados and most nuts. The abundance of the monounsaturated olive oil in the Mediterranean diet is thought to be one of the factors responsible for the low rate of heart disease in Italy and Greece.

Polyunsaturated fats

Polyunsaturated fats lower the undesirable total cholesterol and the LDL cholesterol in the blood and reduce the risk of heart disease. They are found in all fats and exist as two distinct types:

Omega-3 fats such as eicosapentaenoic acid (EPA), docosahexaenoic acid (DHA) and alpha-linolenic acid (ALA). EPA and DHA are found primarily in the fat of fish, particularly deep sea oily fish. ALA is found in flaxseed and flaxseed oils, canola oil, soy oil and walnuts. There are now a number of new products that contain omega-3 fats such as omega-3 eggs, dairy products and some breads. Omega-3 fats are important for your heart.

Omega-6 fats such as linoleic acid are the main polyunsaturated fatty acids of common vegetable oils (sunflower, safflower, corn and sesame), some nuts and seeds (walnuts, almonds, pecans, Brazil nuts, sunflower seeds and sesame seeds) and some non-hydrogenated margarines. Aim to eat a little of these but more omega-3 fats.

CALORIES AND FAT

Remember all types of fat have the same amount of calories. They all supply 9 calories per gram, which is twice as many as from protein or carbohydrate. So if you have a weight problem, aim to cut down on ALL fats but especially saturated and trans fats.

HYDROGENATED FATS—WHAT THEY ARE

Hydrogenation is a process used to solidify vegetable oils for commercial use. It turns liquid oils into a more solid fat, which is more suited to frying and baking. The process greatly improves the stability and shelf life of processed foods and many baked goods. Many manufacturers are now producing cookies, crackers, snack foods and other processed foods that are free of trans fats. Since trans fats appear on food labels, it is easier to significantly reduce or avoid processed foods that contain them.

DO YOU EAT TOO MUCH FAT?		
Take our quick test and see whether you are cutting back enough on saturated fat and trans fats for your heart. Simply answer Yes or No to each question and add up your score at the end.		
Do you trim all visible fat from your meat?	Yes	No
Do you use non-hydrogenated margarine?	Yes	No
Are cream and sour cream items you buy only rarely?	Yes	No
Do you limit fast food (pizza, burgers, french fries, fried chicken) to no more than once a week?	Yes	No
Have you swapped your milk for a low-fat or skim variety?	Yes	No
Do you buy yogourt and cheese in a reduced-fat or low-fat form?	Yes	No
Do you have a nonstick pan for cooking or frying?	Yes	No
Do you roast your meat on a rack to allow the fats to drip away?	Yes	No
Do you buy snack foods that are trans fat free?	Yes	No
Do you avoid cooking with lard and shortening?	Yes	No
Do you use reduced-fat cooking methods such as broiling, roasting, grilling or steaming?	Yes	No
Do you say "no" to potato chips and corn chips and other high-fat snack foods?	Yes	No

How did you score?

Add up all your Yes answers.

If you scored 8 or more: You're doing well and reducing the main sources of saturated and trans fats from foods. Keep going.

If you scored 4 to 7: You've made a good start but you need to be a little more vigilant if you want to protect your heart.

If you scored 0 to 3: You're not doing enough. Start today to rethink your food choices and use the suggestions in this book to cut back on saturated fat.

MAKE THE FAT SWITCH

Replace your saturated fat with the healthier unsaturated types. Here's how:
- Dip your bread in olive oil instead of using butter.
- Cook with healthy oils.
- Add nuts or seeds to stir-fries and salads.
- Spread avocado on sandwiches instead of cheese.
- Pop corn with canola oil and skip the melted butter.
- Snack on nuts instead of potato chips and corn chips.

But, remember, even though they are healthier fats, they are fats and should be used moderately.

All about cholesterol

Cholesterol finds its way into the body from your diet (dietary cholesterol) and it is also made by the liver (blood cholesterol), where it is used by the body to maintain cell structure. While cholesterol is important for body function, it can be unhealthy. Cholesterol can build up on the walls of blood vessels. This buildup causes blood vessels to narrow, making it harder for blood to pass through. The end result can be a heart attack or stroke.

There are two types of blood cholesterol: high-density lipoprotein (HDL) and low-density lipoprotein (LDL). LDL cholesterol is known as "bad" cholesterol since it increases the deposit of cholesterol in the blood vessel wall. HDL cholesterol is known as the "good" cholesterol because it picks up the cholesterol from around your body and takes it to the liver for disposal. The object of a healthy diet is to lower your LDL levels and raise your HDL levels.

Food sources of cholesterol are animal products such as egg yolks and fatty meats.

the glycemic index (GI) and how it can help your heart

What is the glycemic index?

The glycemic index (or GI) is a ranking of carbohydrate-containing foods, from 0 to 100, according to their effect on your blood sugar after they are eaten and digested. Carbohydrate foods that are digested and absorbed slowly, such as oatmeal or lentils, release glucose into the blood gradually. These are low GI carbohydrate foods. They have a GI value of 55 or less. Carbohydrate foods that are digested and absorbed quickly, such as potatoes and white bread, cause a fast release of glucose. These are high GI foods, with a value of 70 or higher.

How low GI helps your heart

Most people know about GI due to its benefits in diabetes and blood sugar control. What many do not realize is that the GI of their diet can also influence the health of their heart, just like the type of fat. Recent research shows that a diet based on slowly digested foods can lower total and LDL cholesterol, raise HDL cholesterol and help to lower body weight.

What to aim for

Not every carbohydrate you eat needs to be a "slow carb." Just aim for one low GI food at each meal and you will significantly lower the GI of your total diet and improve heart health. For example, make your sandwich on pumpernickel bread or eat brown rice instead of a potato or finish off with cherries in place of watermelon.

Making the change

Read the following information to see how easy it is to make your diet lower in GI, or refer to the table opposite to see the figures. Look for the "low GI" symbol in the recipes of this book— these recipes have had particular ingredients included to ensure a low GI result.

Seven key foods to change

Certain high GI foods may feature prominently in your diet but can easily be substituted with a low GI option. Do you base your meals around potatoes? Are you a big bread eater? Do you love rice? You don't have to look up a table of figures each time. Just follow the food swaps outlined here for the key carbohydrate foods you eat and that will influence the final GI of your diet.

Bread White bread and fine whole-wheat bread are typically high in GI, meaning they are rapidly absorbed. Swap these for grainy varieties with visible grains or "heavier" breads. Pumpernickel and rye are good bets.

Cereal Switch to less processed whole-grain cereals, such as rolled oats or muesli or high-fibre bran types. Or sprinkle oat bran or psyllium fibre over your usual cereal.

Rice Low-grain rice, such as basmati, is the best options. Other low GI choices are pearl barley, wheat noodles or cracked wheat (bulgur).

Potatoes Most—but not all—potatoes are rapidly absorbed (high GI). Improve your GI rating by making mashed potatoes with low-fat milk, choosing baby new potatoes or cooking sweet potatoes instead.

Legumes All legumes (lentils, chickpeas, dried peas and beans) have a small effect on blood sugar and insulin. Use them in soups, casseroles and salads to lower the overall GI of your favourite dish. In addition, they are rich in fibre and an excellent vegetarian protein source.

Fruit With the exception of some of the tropical fruits, most fruits have a low GI. Eat at least two pieces each day. Fruit juices are nutritious but can be too high in calories—it is better to eat whole fruit and quench your thirst with water.

Pasta All pasta and noodles, when cooked al dente, are low in GI. Enjoy them as an alternative to potatoes.

GLUCOSE LOAD

Not only is the nature of the carbohydrate important (whether it is slow or fast), but so is the actual amount of carbohydrates you eat. Even if a food is low GI, if you consume large quantities, your blood sugar will rise.

FOODS AND THEIR GI FACTORS

The following table lists a variety of common food items, both fresh and commercially prepared, together with their GI factor. Remember, foods with a low GI are the ones to include more of, and foods with a higher GI are the ones to reduce. Whether the GI is low, moderate or high, it is based on a standard one-person serving. Use this table as a guide to help you switch to a low GI diet.

FOOD	GI

LOW—55 OR LESS

Peanuts*	14
Cherries	22
Grapefruit	25
Lentils, red, boiled	26
Chickpeas, boiled	28
Prunes, pitted	29
All Bran™ breakfast cereal	30
Apricots, dried	30
Milk, homogenized	31
Fettuccine, egg	32
Milk, skim	32
Yogourt, low-fat flavoured	33
Custard (homemade with powder)	35
Apple, raw	38
Pear, raw	38
Spaghetti	38
Tomato soup	38

Plum	39
Apple juice, unsweetened	40
Pumpernickel	41
Chocolate, milk	42
Orange	42
Peach	42
Oatmeal	42
Apple muffin	44
Sweet potato	44
Grapes	46
Noodles, 2-minute*	46
Corn kernels, canned	46
Baked beans, in tomato sauce	48
Peas, green, boiled	48
Carrots, boiled	49
Banana	52
Kidney beans, canned	52
Coca Cola®	53
Honey	55

MODERATE—56 TO 69

Muesli, untoasted	56
Kiwi	58
Rice, basmati, boiled	58
Rye bread	58
Ice cream, regular fat	61
Raison Bran™	61
Beets, canned	64
Shortbread cookies*	64
Cantaloupe	65

Couscous	65
Pineapple	66
Croissant*	67
Mars Bar*	68
Sugar (sucrose)	68
Crumpet	69
Special K™	69

HIGH—70 AND OVER

Bread, white	70
Popcorn	72
Bagel, white	72
Rice, parboiled	72
Watermelon	72
Sultana Bran™	73
Pumpkin	75
Bread, whole-wheat	77
Coco Puffs™	77
English muffin	77
Jelly beans	78
Lychees, canned	79
Rice Krispies™	82
Pretzels	83
Potato, baked	85
Rice Chex	89
Parsnip	97

* These are foods high in fat. Use them only occasionally and count them as part of your fat allowance.

If you want to know more about the GI rating of foods, visit the website of *The American Journal of Clinical Nutrition* at www.ajcn.org.

Reprinted with permission from The American Journal of Clinical Nutrition.

eat less salt

Except for some of the breads, our recipes do not call for any added salt and, where we can, we've substituted salt-reduced products. It is important to cut down on the amount of salt you eat, as too much salt can contribute to high blood pressure (hypertension), which in turn increases your risk of heart disease, stroke and kidney failure.

Five easy steps to cut back on salt

1 Stop sprinkling salt on your food.

2 Use herbs and spices that don't contain sodium. Boost flavour by adding plenty of pepper, onion, garlic, ginger, curry powder, dry mustard, lemon, basil, bay leaves, chili powder, cumin and cilantro.

3 Buy salt-reduced and no-added-salt products at the grocery store whenever you can. Products regularly available are margarine, canned vegetables, soy sauce, soups and soup stock, ketchup, canned salmon and peanut butter. If you do purchase regular canned vegetables or canned fish, rinse them in cold water before you prepare them.

4 Eat more fresh or frozen vegetables that are lower in sodium than the canned varieties. And, use fresh or frozen meat and fish instead of those that are smoked, cured or processed.

5 Try to avoid heavily salted ingredients, such as anchovies and olives (see the panel right).

Salt-reduced products we've used

To make our recipes a little lower in sodium content, we found it essential to buy three ingredients in a reduced-salt version—soy sauce, liquid stock and margarine.

Reduced-salt soy sauce Contains significantly less sodium than regular soy sauce but with no noticeable drop in flavour. It's still salty but nowhere near as much.

Reduced-salt liquid stock Commercial liquid stock, or stock powder or cubes, quickly increases the sodium level of a dish. It's worth shopping for the salt-reduced versions of stock. Many manufacturers have reformulated their stocks in recent years, making them less "artificial" tasting and better-flavoured with less salt. Alternatively you can make your own stock at home by simmering a pot of beef or chicken bones, with celery, carrot, parsley, a bay leaf and pepper.

Reduced-salt margarine Margarine that is labelled as "reduced-salt" will have different amounts of salt reduction. Check the labels and pick the one with the lowest amount of salt.

Sodium or salt?

Chemically, salt is sodium chloride. It is actually the sodium part that can affect blood pressure and other problems of fluid balance. The recommended maximum intake is 2300 mg a day, which is equivalent to slightly more than a teaspoon of salt. If all our sodium came just from the salt you add, then you could limit it to a teaspoon a day. But because most of it is "hidden" in bought foods, it's impossible to tell how much you're really eating. Thus nutritionists recommend using no added salt in cooking or at the table and buying lower-salt foods. And the good news is that your desire for salty-tasting food will diminish over time.

SEA SALT

Sea salt, made by evaporating sea water, comes in either fine or coarse grain and has a slightly different taste because of the other minerals it contains. However, it is not a healthy substitute for table salt, as it is still high in sodium.

FOODS HIGH IN SODIUM

Snack foods such as chips, pretzels, salted nuts

Olives

Capers

Pickled vegetables

Processed and smoked meats such as salami, bacon, bologna, hot dogs, sausage, pickled meats

Salty and smoked fish such as anchovies, caviar, herring

Ketchup

Pickles

Canned soups

Processed cheese

Worcestershire sauce and barbecue sauce

Tomato sauce

weight management

Together with regular physical activity, a sensible eating plan will help you to lose weight. Be sure to include plenty of vegetables, legumes, fruit, fish, lean meat, whole-grain cereals and low-fat dairy products.

Keeping your weight in the healthy range is important for your heart. If you are overweight, your heart has a greater workload to carry and your health suffers. Being overweight also puts you at greater risk of high blood pressure and diabetes—two other risk factors for heart disease.

Over the last 10 years, we have witnessed an epidemic of obesity where the proportion of people—both adults and children—classified as overweight or obese has risen dramatically. Researchers believe that not only are we eating too many fatty, calorie-dense foods, but also our levels of physical activity have dropped.

Automation and technology have made it easy for us to be inactive—we hardly have to move much anymore thanks to computers and remote controls—and this lack of exercise means we are not burning off what we eat. Researchers coined the term "obesogenic environment" to describe this fat-inducing environment where everything is contrived to make you put on weight.

Assess your lifestyle

Look at your current lifestyle and consider these reasons why you could be overweight.

- Watching too much television.
- Driving everywhere—less walking or cycling.
- Labour-saving gadgets (remote controls, food processors, cordless tools) in the home.
- Less manual work, more technology.
- Little or no time for exercise.
- Lack of time to cook healthy meals.
- Wide availability of cheap junk food and soft drinks.
- Bigger portion sizes.
- Marketing of high-calorie, nutrient-poor snacks and takeout food.
- Eating out frequently.

BLOOD PRESSURE

Raised blood pressure or hypertension is a massive problem in the developed world and 5 million adult Canadians suffer from it. Hypertension is a major risk factor for cardiovascular disease but fortunately there are plenty of things you can do to improve the condition. Blood pressure increases somewhat with age in most populations in the developed world but research suggests this is not inevitable. While no one fully knows exactly what leads to hypertension, a combination of factors seem to be involved. Diabetes, obesity and certain other disorders increase the risk. Other contributors include smoking, excessive alcohol consumption and a sedentary lifestyle.

Give up the dieting mentality

Rather than going "on a diet" for a week or a couple of days, try to change your vision so that you think of your eating as part of an overall healthier lifestyle. You're eating to look after your body and feed it well, not just to lose weight. Give up counting fat, counting calories, following a set diet. Instead, reset your mind to healthy eating—for life. You don't have to cut out all treats for ever. Enjoy them occasionally but make good, healthy foods the centrepiece of your eating habits.

Doctors and nutritionists are concerned not only about your excess weight, but also where the fat is distributed in your body.

People who are "apple shaped" and carry most of their weight around the middle (abdominal fat), are more prone to develop health problems such as heart disease or diabetes. In contrast, people with "pear shapes," where their weight is largely around the hips and thighs, have much less trouble.

This book offers recipes that are low in saturated fat and total fat. Most are high in fibre or have low GI ingredients to keep you feeling fuller for longer. The recipes that are lower in calories are flagged so you know they are ideal to cook if you want to shed excess weight.

Portion distortion

Don't deprive yourself. It only sets the scene for binge eating later on. If there's something special that you really want, enjoy a few mouthfuls and have a small indulgence. Often that's all you will need and it will be guilt-free.

Super-sized servings and "two-for-one" meal deals encourage people to eat more than they need—and therefore contribute to their weight problem. Since 1985 research has shown that food portions have become bigger and, therefore, it is no coincidence that so has the rate of obesity. If bringing your own reasonably sized lunch to work is not an everyday possibility and eating out is necessary, choose smaller dishes or leave some of the meal on the plate. You don't have to finish it.

Look at these examples. What used to be considered a family-sized bar of chocolate is now the standard size and soft drinks come in huge

2-litre bottles. Movie popcorn is sold in buckets, muffins balloon out of their paper cases and fast food outlets supersize your burgers and fries for a fraction more money. It represents value for money—but it's a bargain that our waistlines simply do not need.

In addition, many researchers have shown that the bigger the portion size, the more we tend to eat.

How to cope with large portions:

- If there's a choice, opt for the smaller size.
- Share large portions with a friend.
- Ask for a doggie bag to take leftovers home for later.
- Don't get fooled by supersized meals when you order out. It might cost only 30 or 40 cents more, but it costs you a lot in extra calories and fat that you don't need.
- If you do buy a two-for-one offer, don't eat it all at one sitting.
- Serve meals on smaller plates so the serving looks more generous.

Exercise will help

Exercise burns off fat, helps raise the "good" HDL cholesterol, keeps your bones strong (if it's weight-bearing) and leaves you feeling good. Try to find some form of exercise that you like to do and that you can fit into your life a few times a week. Walking, swimming, dancing or gym classes are all good choices. Aim for around 30 minutes of more vigorous exercise—it should be vigorous enough so that you are a little out of breath, but not too exhausted to talk. If you are unfit or have not been on an exercise program previously, it is a good idea to get advice from your doctor as to which exercise is best for you.

healthy eating—the basics

As well as reducing saturated fats and salt in your daily diet, you should eat plenty of the nutritious foods across all the food groups. This will give you variety and ensure you obtain all the essential vitamins, minerals, protein and antioxidants that your body needs for health and energy. Choose foods from these seven basic food groups each day.

TWO MENUS FOR YOUR HEART

Menu 1

Breakfast

whole-grain cereal with low-fat milk and a banana, or muesli with strawberries and hazelnuts (see page 36)

Lunch

sandwich with whole-grain bread and tuna (not oil-packed), red onion, sliced green pepper and tomato, or tarragon chicken with baby spinach (see page 144)

piece of fresh fruit

Dinner

chargrilled salmon cutlet with potatoes and a large salad, or grilled swordfish steaks with tomato and pepper salsa (see page 122)

double raspberry sorbet (see page 284)

Menu 2

Breakfast

baked beans on toasted whole-grain bread or English muffin, or egg-white omelette with spinach, tomato and Cheddar (see page 32)

Lunch

thick bean soup such as Tuscan mixed bean soup (see page 60)

whole-grain roll

fresh fruit salad with low-fat ice cream

Dinner

baked chicken and vegetable casserole, or beef in red wine and brandy (see page 191)

large serving of assorted vegetables

low-fat berry yogourt with additional fresh seasonal berries

Basic foods to include in your diet:

Vegetables Choose at least five servings of vegetables and salad a day. Vegetables have almost no fat and are good sources of fibre, vitamins and antioxidants. One serving is one cup of salad or half a cup of cooked vegetables.

Legumes Rich sources of plant protein, legumes are also valuable for their soluble fibre, B vitamins, minerals and heart-friendly phytonutrients. Try to eat lentils, beans or peas at least twice a week.

Fruit Two servings of fruit a day—fresh, canned or dried—will boost fibre, vitamin C, beta carotene and antioxidant intakes. One serving is equal to one medium or two small pieces of fruit.

Fish/lean meat/chicken Providing important protein, B vitamins and the minerals zinc and iron, these foods are a valuable inclusion in your healthy-heart eating plan. Fish and seafood also contribute omega-3s. Trim meat free of all fat. One serving is 150–175 g raw weight (125–150 g when cooked).

Cereals and grains Aim for at least four servings of whole grains each day. Rich in fibre, B vitamins and polyunsaturated fats, most whole-grain cereals are also more slowly digested than the refined types, resulting in more sustaining meals and snacks. One serving means one slice of bread, half a cup of cooked rice, pasta or noodles, or 40 g of ready-to-eat cereal.

Low-fat dairy Rich in bone-building calcium, low-fat dairy also has a role to play in keeping blood pressure down. Make sure you get two to three servings each day. One serving is equal to one cup of milk, a 175-g container of yogourt or 40 g (2 slices) of cheese.

Healthy fats By using monounsaturated and polyunsaturated fats, you can reduce your risk of heart disease. Have one to two tablespoons a day of heart-healthy oil or swap for avocado or nuts.

heart-friendly foods

As researchers uncover evidence of the "healing" role of natural compounds in foods, here is a list of the many foods now being hailed as valuable weapons in the war against heart disease. Make sure that you include these nutritional superstars in your daily diet.

Fish and seafood

Eat fish two to three times a week and you make a significant investment in your heart's health.

The high omega-3 fat content of fish, particularly the oily types such as mackerel, salmon and sardines, can help steady the heart beat, lower blood pressure and keep the blood free of clots.

Best of all, fish is low in calories and cooks in minutes. If you find fish difficult to cook, our book offers plenty of ideas to get you started on preparing fish simply and quickly. Fish doesn't have to be fresh. Frozen fillets and canned salmon and sardines are also rich in omega-3s.

Whole grains

Numerous studies have shown that a diet rich in whole grains significantly diminishes the risk of death from heart disease and reduces the risk of some cancers. Most whole-grain foods have a lower glycemic index (GI) than white or refined products so will keep blood sugars on an even keel and leave you feeling full for longer. They are a rich source of B vitamins, vitamin E, fibre and important antioxidants.

Oats

Eating about one to one and a half cups of rolled oats a day has been shown to have noticeable effects on blood cholesterol. Two factors are believed responsible. First, oats are high in a type of soluble fibre called beta glucan that prevents the breakdown products of cholesterol from re-entering the system via the intestine, with the result that less cholesterol is made by the body. Second, oats are slowly absorbed into the bloodstream, which lessens the glucose load (see the panel on page 14). Therefore, include oats with your breakfast as oatmeal or an oat-based muesli and substitute oats or oat bran for some of the flour when baking muffins or breads.

Garlic

Garlic has a long medicinal history, having been used by the ancient Egyptians, Vikings and Chinese to ward off illness and stay in good health. Both fresh and dried garlic have been shown to lower the "bad" LDL cholesterol, lower high blood pressure and help dissolve blood clots, although the dose required is quite large for most of us—you'd need to take in three or four cloves a day or 600–900 mg powdered garlic. Researchers believe that garlic's strong sulphur compounds are the active agents. They also impart its pungent odour and flavour. Add as much as you can to your cooking and help your heart.

Linseeds

Small, shiny, dark-brown seeds about the size of sesame seeds, flax is rich in two heart-healthy compounds. The first is alpha-linolenic acid (ALA), a plant version of the omega-3 oils found in fish. ALA has been linked to a reduced risk for heart disease and heart attack. The second is soluble fibre that can help lower cholesterol levels.

BEST SOURCES OF OMEGA-3*
Atlantic salmon
Salmon, canned
Salmon, smoked
Sardines, fresh and canned
Trout
Tuna, fresh
Mackerel
Herring
Cod

* Note: Oily fish are richer than white fish, having four to five times more omega-3 oils than sole and perch.

Soy is a heart superfood. In fact, scientists think that the significantly lower rate of heart disease among Asian populations may be related to the soy protein in their diet.

Sprinkle the seeds over cereal, toss them through salads, add them to muffin dough and look for the soy-linseed breads. One or two tablespoons a day is all it takes to boost your intake. You can buy whole flaxseed but there is some advantage to using it ground. The whole flax will give you the fibre but grinding will release more of the other healthy ingredients.

Almonds, pecans, macadamias and other nuts

Munching on a handful of nuts (around 50 g) a day is now one of the strategies nutritionists recommend for your heart. Are you surprised? Most of us will be, as for years we've been told that nuts are too high in fat and will make us put on weight, and are certainly not part of a heart-smart diet.

However, a wave of studies over the past few years has changed the thinking on nuts. They're now considered a healthy, energy-packed snack that will outperform potato chips any way you look at it!

Despite having more than 50 per cent total fat content, the fat in nuts is heart-friendly. It is either predominantly monounsaturated or polyunsaturated—not saturated fat, the bad fat to avoid in frequency and amount—both of which will keep your cholesterol in check. Nuts also boast a good dose of vitamin E (a well-established antioxidant), fibre, many important minerals and essential fatty acids.

In a recent study, almonds were shown to lower blood cholesterol levels significantly. (But there was a catch: They were eaten instead of some of the usual spreads and fatty foods—not as an extra.)

The best way to consume nuts is light-roasted but not salted. You can toss them through salads and stir-fries or use them, as we have in our recipes, in baking or as a crunchy topping. Enjoy the great variety of nuts on the market, but watch how many you eat.

Soy beans

Soy protein lowers the harmful LDL cholesterol and prevents artery "clogging," according to more than 38 soy trials spanning 20 years. In fact, one study showed that eating half a cup of dry-roasted soy nuts every day can drop blood pressure readings as much as some prescription blood pressure medications.

Soy's heart-healthy attributes are credited to its protein and isoflavone content. Researchers think that the protein in soy binds cholesterol in the intestine and therefore prevents its absorption and the isoflavones have important antioxidant properties. A regular intake of soy may also raise HDL cholesterol, lower blood pressure and keep blood vessels healthy.

To achieve heart benefits, you need to eat around 25 g of soy protein a day, which you can get in half a cup of cooked soy beans plus half a cup of soy bran cereal OR 2 cups of soy milk. Tofu is a handy ingredient, too. You can use soft tofu as a cream substitute, or toss firm diced tofu into stir-fries and noodle soups.

Health food stores have long had a wide variety of soy products available, but it is no longer necessary to make a special trip. All grocery stores now carry soy products from both Canadian and international companies.

Tea

People who regularly drink tea (green or black) are reported to have significantly lower risks of heart troubles than those who don't. Tea's powerful protective effects are believed to be due to flavonoids, substances shown to be strong antioxidants. It seems that tea flavonoids help maintain heart health by decreasing inflammation, lowering the tendency for clotting (an early factor in heart attacks) and by keeping the arteries more "elastic." These effects are obtained regardless of whether you add milk or sugar.

There are other benefits. Tea contains tannins, which may be responsible for protecting against tooth decay. It is also believed that tea may be a weapon against infection and possibly fighting tumors. Perhaps best of all, if you take it black with no milk or sugar, tea has no calories and has the ability to both relax and revive you.

Wine

In modest amounts, red wine is good for your heart. Red wine has been part of the answer to the so-called "French paradox"—why the French have one of the lowest rates of heart disease in the world, despite their love of rich, cholesterol-laden fare such as pâté, croissants and many high-fat cheeses.

Wine's secret is more than 50 phenolic compounds known as polyphenols. These act as antioxidants, reduce thickening of the arteries, and keep the blood "thin" and smooth-flowing—an effect similar to aspirin. Red wine, made with the skins and seeds of grapes, has nine to ten times more of these natural chemicals than white wine. One phenolic, resveratrol, has been intensively studied but others, such as epicatechin and quercetin, are emerging as important. But all things should be taken in moderation—a glass a day is fine, but any more can put you at risk of other illnesses, such as breast cancer or liver disease.

Olive oil

Believed to be one of the reasons for the low rate of heart disease and general good health of those from the Mediterranean, olive oil is a rich source of monounsaturated fat and contains vitamin E. Extra virgin olive oil is also rich in antioxidants. One tablespoon of olive oil has only 1.8 g of saturated fat, but like all oils it is high in calories (120 per tablespoon).

Psyllium

Psyllium seeds contain both soluble and insoluble fibre, so they do two jobs—they keep you regular and can lower your blood cholesterol (both total cholesterol and LDL cholesterol). Psyllium is the key ingredient of some laxative products sold by pharmacies.

GUIDE TO HEART-HEALTHY EATING

Keep your intake of saturated fats to a minimum. Foods rich in saturates (and trans fats) raise your LDL cholesterol, increasing heart disease risk.

- Include the healthy fats that contain monounsaturates and polyunsaturates. Use oils such as olive, canola or safflower in salad dressings or stir-fries and choose a soft, non-hydrogenated margarine in cooking or as a spread.

- Eat fish and seafood twice a week.

- Eat foods high in soluble fibre such as oats, barley, legumes, vegetables and fruit.

- Go for the heart-friendly carbo-hydrates. These are the whole-grain and/or low GI varieties of breads, cereals and grains.

- Eat plenty of vegetables and fruit.

- Choose lower fat dairy products such as skim or 1% milk, low-fat cheeses and yogourts.

- Cut down on salt.

eating lighter and healthier

Eating for a healthy heart needn't be hard work. Make simple food changes to tip the scales in favour of a diet that's low in saturated fat and your heart will reap the benefits. Put into practice these healthy tips for eating less saturated fat when shopping, cooking and eating out.

Out shopping

- Choose lean cuts of meat, such as sirloin or inside round, skinless chicken and pork tenderloin.
- Opt for skim or low-fat milk, reduced-fat cheeses and low-fat yogourt.
- Stock up on low-fat snacks such as pretzels, yogourt, low-fat bars and dried fruit instead of chips, chocolate and cookies.
- Choose low-fat spreads or non-hydrogenated margarines that help lower cholesterol levels.
- Read labels and check for the amount of fat per serving, especially on products claiming to be "light," "low fat" and "cholesterol-free."

- Look for ingredients to make your cooking interesting without too much fat and salt, such as fresh herbs, mustards, chutneys, balsamic vinegar, salad dressings, spices (nutmeg, ginger, chili and cumin) and heart-friendly garlic.

Label watch

No cholesterol or cholesterol-free Cholesterol-free foods also must be low in saturated fats but they may still have a higher total-fat content. Remember, "no cholesterol" does not mean "no fat."

Light If it is referring to a specific nutrient, such as "light in fat" or "light in calories," it means that food is reduced in fat or calories. But, it can also be used to describe a feature of the food such as "light in colour." Always check the label to find out what makes the food light. It might be something that you don't want to consume.

Reduced-fat or reduced in calories This means that the product has at least 25 per cent less fat or calories than the food to which it is compared. But, you still must read the label to see how much fat and/or calories are in it. There may remain a lot of fat in the product and/or the sugar content may be high to compensate for the reduction of fat. A low-fat yogourt, for example, may actually be fairly high in calories because it has been sweetened.

Serving size The serving size tells you how much of that food you need to eat to get the calories and nutrients shown on the nutrition facts table. Always check this serving size against the serving size that you actually eat. If a package of four sausages lists a serving as one sausage and each serving has 24 g of fat and you eat two sausages, you will have consumed 48 g of fat. Remember too, that if you eat double the amount of the suggested serving, you should also double up the daily value count.

CHECK OUT THE CONTENTS

Learn to read the figures on the nutrition facts table when food shopping, so you know exactly how much fat—including saturated fat—cholesterol, sodium and carbohydrates are present in a suggested serving. Compare brands and purchase products that are lower in fat—especially saturated and trans fats—calories and sugars. Pay special attention to cholesterol and sodium contents and use the daily value reading to set your nutrient goals for each day.

Nutrition Facts		
Per 125 mL (87 g)		
Amount		**% Daily Value**
Calories 80		
Fat 0.5 g		1%
Saturated 0 g + Trans 0 g		0%
Cholesterol 0 mg		
Sodium 0 mg		0%
Carbohydrate 18 g		6%
Fibre 2 g		8%
Sugars 2 g		
Protein 3 g		
Vitamin A	2%	Vitamin C 10%
Calcium	0%	Iron 2%

In the kitchen

- Always remove skin from chicken and trim off any visible fat from meat before cooking.
- Grill, steam, poach, microwave, stir-fry, boil or bake in preference to frying or deep-frying.
- Avoid adding or cooking in unnecessary fat— for example, spray a thin film of oil into the pan when cooking, don't pour it in.
- Dry-roast meats on a roasting rack to allow the fat to drain away.
- Skim fat from meat juices before making gravy.
- Use unsaturated cooking oils such as canola, olive, safflower or soybean.
- Replace some of the meat and chicken in curries and casseroles with a handful of chickpeas, lentils or other legumes.
- Let homemade soups and casseroles cool before serving so that any fat can solidify on top. Remove this fat layer before reheating.
- Substitute low-fat natural yogourt for sour cream in casseroles or dips.
- In place of a melted cheese topping on baked pasta dishes, use a little shaved Parmesan or mix together whole-wheat breadcrumbs with reduced-fat Cheddar.
- Use low-fat evaporated milk or soft tofu as a replacement for cream.
- Cut in half the amount of cream added to a cup of coffee or replace cream with reduced-fat or skim milk.

Dining out

- Order fish and seafood as often as you can— restaurants cook them well, and it saves you having to cook them at home if you find fish difficult to handle.
- Avoid high-fat starters such as pâté or anything deep-fried—opt for soup, salad, seafood cocktail or smoked salmon.

- Don't be afraid to ask for vegetables served without butter, or meat and fish with sauce on the side.
- Avoid creamy sauces, pastry and fried foods.
- Vegetarian options are not always lower in saturated fat—avoid vegetable dishes with a lot of cheese.
- You don't have to miss out on dessert if you choose wisely. Fruit-based puddings, sorbets and meringues are delicious, heart-healthy choices. Or, if you want a richer offering, share the dessert with a friend.
- Eat small. Some restaurants offer the option of a reduced-sized portion—usually half or two thirds—at a slightly reduced price.
- Eat smaller. Order two entrees or share an entree and then enjoy your main dish. Ask for a doggie bag if you can't finish everything at one sitting.
- Eat slowly and enjoy the conversation with others. This will help you to not overeat.
- Watch your alcohol intake. Enjoy a drink or two but sip slowly and intersperse with a mineral water or diet soft drink.

Stir-frying is a healthy cooking method as the ingredients cook quickly while being stirred rapidly in a hot wok or nonstick pan, thereby needing only a spray of oil.

HEALTH CHECK

The Heart and Stroke Foundation of Canada launched a Health Check™ food information program in 1999. The Health Check symbol was designed to help consumers identify healthy food choices in the grocery store. The logo means the product has been reviewed by the Foundation and meets specific nutrition criteria that are based on Canada's Food Guide to Healthy Eating.

how to use the recipes

Next to each recipe is a panel with at-a-glance icons to help you select quick recipes, low-calorie recipes, high-fibre recipes and recipes with a low glycemic index. Also provided are full nutritional statistics per serving. These analyses are based on the ingredients listed in each recipe. They do not include the serving suggestions.

Quick recipes

Recipes that have this icon at the top of the nutritional statistics panel can be both prepared and cooked in 30 minutes or less.

Calories

Calories are a measure of food energy. We've highlighted those recipes that are "lighter" or lower in calories for those trying to lose weight or just counting calories.

Mains 400 calories or less
Light meals/lunches 300 calories or less
This will fit within a standard fat loss diet of 1200 calories for most women and 1800 calories for most men.

Fibre

We've highlighted those recipes with 3 g or more of fibre per serving. These are usually recipes that contain beans, lentils, whole-wheat flour or bread, brown rice, oats, high-fibre vegetables such as corn, peas or cabbage, and fruit. Aim to eat as much fibre as you can. At least 30 g a day is suggested for good health, more if you want to lose weight. High-fibre foods are nutritious and filling. For few calories, you get to eat more.

STATISTICS PANEL

30 · C · Fb · GI

preparation time **10 mins**
cooking time **15 mins**
serves **4**

PER SERVING

341 calories

11 g protein

6 g total fat
1 g saturated fat

2 mg cholesterol

60 g total carbohydrate
8 g sugars

7 g fibre

204 mg sodium

GI (glycemic index)

Recipes with a low glycemic index (GI) are marked. This means that the overall GI of all the ingredients is low, so the carbohydrates will be slowly digested and absorbed. Low GI recipes are ideal for anyone with diabetes or wanting to lose weight. They cause only a small rise in blood sugar levels and fill you up for longer, so you're less inclined to snack between meals.

Fat

Both the total fat and the saturated fat are listed. The total fat is handy to check if you're counting fat grams or trying to lose weight. Some recipes are higher in fat than others because they contain avocado, olive oil, hummus or nuts. These are okay as they're high in the "healthy" fats (monounsaturated and polyunsaturated) and yet low in unhealthy saturated fat. Be sure to eat smaller portions of these if you're trying to lose weight because low fat or "healthy" fat does not necessarily mean low calorie.

How much fat you should eat will depend on how active you are. No more than 30 per cent of the calories you eat should come from fat, which means around 50 to 70 g fat a day for a moderately active person.

Cholesterol

Cholesterol has been listed for those people who need to watch their levels. Recipes with eggs or shrimp will have a higher cholesterol content but are lower in saturated fat.

Sodium

Except for some of the bread recipes, none of the recipes contains any added salt (sodium chloride), and salt-reduced products have been used wherever possible to minimize the final sodium content of the recipes. Remember to use only small quantities of salty ingredients such as cheese, olives, capers, stock and sauces.

breakfast
& brunch

banana and peach smoothie

Bursting with vitamins and minerals, this smoothie is ideal when you have little time for breakfast, and it makes a great snack.

1 Place the bananas, peaches and juice, yogourt, mint and honey in a food processor or blender and blend to a smooth purée, scraping down the sides of the container once or twice. Add the orange juice and blend briefly until mixed.

2 Pour the smoothie into tall glasses and garnish with sprigs of mint, if desired.

Variation For a strawberry and banana smoothie, instead of peaches use 220 g strawberries. Reserve 4 strawberries and blend the remainder with the bananas and yogourt (there is no need to add honey or mint). Mix in apple juice in place of the orange juice. Stir in the grated rind and juice of 1 lime. Pour into glasses and decorate each one with a reserved strawberry skewered on a cocktail stick, if desired.

2 large bananas, thickly sliced
1 can (398 ml) peach halves in natural juice
200 g plain low-fat acidophilus yogourt
⅓ cup chopped fresh mint
1 tablespoon clear honey
1¼ cups freshly squeezed orange juice
sprigs of fresh mint to garnish (optional)

preparation time **10 mins**
serves **4**

PER SERVING
173 calories
5 g protein
0.3 g total fat
0.1 g saturated fat
2 mg cholesterol
37 g total carbohydrate
33 g sugars
4 g fibre
47 mg sodium

strawberry yogourt smoothie

This refreshing drink takes only a few minutes to prepare, and is ideal as a nourishing start to the day.

1 Place the strawberries in a food processor or blender and add the grated orange rind, orange juice and yogourt. Blend to a smooth purée, scraping down the sides of the container once or twice during blending.

2 For a really smooth consistency, press through a nylon sieve to remove the strawberry pips.

3 Pour into glasses and garnish with strawberries, if desired.

Variation Add a slice of fresh mango to the smoothie. This will add natural sweetness.

450 g ripe strawberries, hulled
grated rind and juice of 1 large orange
150 g plain low-fat yogourt
strawberries to garnish (optional)

preparation time **5 mins**
serves **4**

PER SERVING
54 calories
4 g protein
0.2 g total fat
0.1 g saturated fat
2 mg cholesterol
8 g total carbohydrate
8 g sugars
3 g fibre
34 mg sodium

melon boats with orange glaze

Fresh melon boats are the perfect refresher. A sweet-and-sour glaze gives the fruit unexpected zest and dresses it up for a summery lunch. This recipe is low in calories and provides 7 g fibre per serving.

1 To make the glaze, combine the vinegar, orange rind and juice and brown sugar in a microwavable dish. Microwave on High until syrupy, about 2–3 minutes. Or, cook over medium-high heat in a small saucepan, 4–5 minutes. Set the glaze aside.

2 Make melon balls with a melon baller, and prepare the melon boats by hollowing out wedges of cantaloupe (see the photograph below). Put the melon balls, strawberries, blueberries, raspberries and kiwi fruit in a bowl.

3 Drizzle the fruit with the glaze. Toss to coat evenly. Spoon the fruit into the melon boats and serve immediately.

1 large cantaloupe
2 cups strawberries, hulled
and quartered
1 cup blueberries
1 cup raspberries
2 kiwi fruit, peeled, halved and
cut into thin wedges

ORANGE GLAZE
¼ cup balsamic vinegar
¼ teaspoon grated orange rind
2 tablespoons fresh orange juice
2 teaspoons brown sugar

30 C Fb GI

preparation time **20 mins**
cooking time **5 mins**
serves **4**

PER SERVING

115 calories

3 g protein

0 g total fat
0 g saturated fat

0 mg cholesterol

23 g total carbohydrate
23 g sugars

7 g fibre

27 mg sodium

HEALTH HINT

Like all yellow and orange fruit and vegetables, cantaloupe is rich in beta carotene, an antioxidant converted by the body to vitamin A. Beta carotene may provide protection against heart disease by preventing LDL (low-density lipoprotein, known as "bad" cholesterol) from oxidizing and promoting the development of artery-clogging plaque.

eggs Benedict

This dish traditionally uses ham or bacon and a rich butter sauce. Here, a yogourt and chive hollandaise sauce contrasts with the richness of poached eggs and lean prosciutto, to make a lighter, but equally special version.

1 teaspoon vinegar

4 eggs

4 whole-wheat English muffins, halved

4 slices prosciutto, about 50 g in total, trimmed of all visible fat

pepper to taste

paprika to garnish

1 tablespoon snipped fresh chives to garnish

YOGOURT AND CHIVE HOLLANDAISE SAUCE

2 egg yolks

1 teaspoon Dijon mustard

150 g Greek-style yogourt

1 tablespoon snipped fresh chives

pepper to taste

1 To make the hollandaise sauce, whisk together the egg yolks, mustard and yogourt in a heatproof bowl. Set over a saucepan of barely simmering water and cook for about 12–15 minutes, stirring constantly, until thick—the sauce will become thinner at first, but will then start to thicken. Stir in the chives, and season with pepper. Remove from the heat and keep the sauce warm over the pan of hot water.

2 Half-fill a frying pan with water. Bring to a boil, then add the vinegar. Reduce the heat so the water is just simmering gently, then carefully break the eggs into the water, one at a time. Poach for 3–4 minutes, spooning the hot water over the yolks toward the end of cooking.

3 Meanwhile, preheat the broiler. Lightly toast the muffin halves for about 1 minute on each side. Place one half on each of 4 warmed plates and top each with a slice of prosciutto, crumpled slightly to fit. Season with pepper.

4 Using a slotted spoon, remove the poached eggs from the pan, one at a time. Drain on paper towel and, if desired, trim off any ragged edges of egg white with scissors. Place an egg on each prosciutto-topped muffin half.

5 Spoon the warm hollandaise sauce over the eggs, and sprinkle each serving with a pinch of paprika and the chives. Serve immediately with the remaining toasted muffin halves.

Variations Instead of chives, add 1 tablespoon chopped fresh tarragon to the hollandaise, and garnish with sprigs of tarragon. • You can also use thin slices of lean cooked ham instead of prosciutto.

preparation time **5 mins**

cooking time **20 mins**

serves **4**

PER SERVING

291 calories

19 g protein

12 g total fat
5 g saturated fat

333 mg cholesterol

25 g total carbohydrate
5 g sugars

3 g fibre

590 mg sodium

HEALTH HINT

Like other animal foods, eggs provide useful amounts of vitamin B_{12}. Free-range eggs tend to contain more than eggs from battery hens. All the fat in eggs is found in the yolk (around 6 g per average-sized egg) and is predominantly unsaturated fat.

eggs Florentine

The term "Florentine" in a recipe title indicates that the dish uses spinach. This updated version of the classic eggs Florentine uses a sauce thickened with cornstarch rather than a butter and flour roux. Serve with whole-wheat toast.

30 **C** **Fb**

preparation time **10 mins**

cooking time **20 mins**

serves **4**

PER SERVING

278 calories

17 g protein

18 g total fat
5 g saturated fat

224 mg cholesterol

14 g total carbohydrate
7 g sugars

3 g fibre

229 mg sodium

HEALTH HINTS

Spinach is a good source of nutrients with antioxidant properties, including vitamins C and E and carotenoid compounds.

Leeks belong to the onion family. They provide vitamin E, and the green part of the leek is a good source of beta carotene.

1 To make the cheese sauce, mix the cornstarch to a paste with a little milk. Pour the remaining milk into a nonstick saucepan and bring to a boil. Stir the boiling milk into the cornstarch mixture, then pour back into the pan. Bring to a boil, stirring. Once it has thickened, simmer for 2 minutes. Remove from the heat, stir in the Gruyère cheese, and season with nutmeg and pepper. Cover the surface of the sauce with parchment paper to prevent a skin from forming and set aside in a warm place.

2 Heat the margarine with the oil in a saucepan. Add the leeks and cook for about 3 minutes, until beginning to soften. Add the spinach and stir. Cover the pan and cook over medium heat for 2–3 minutes until the spinach has wilted and the leeks are tender. Drain the vegetables in a sieve, pressing down with the back of a spoon to remove any excess moisture. Return to the pan and season with pepper. Cover and keep warm.

3 Meanwhile, half-fill a large frying pan with water and bring to simmering point. Add the vinegar. Break in the eggs, and cook gently for 3–4 minutes, spooning the hot water over the yolks. Lift out the eggs with a slotted spoon and drain on paper towel.

4 Preheat the broiler. Spread the leek and spinach mixture in an even layer in a large flameproof dish. Make 4 hollows in the vegetables using the back of a spoon and place a poached egg in each hollow. Spoon the cheese sauce over the eggs. Lightly dust with paprika, then place the dish under the broiler. Cook for 3–4 minutes until lightly browned. Serve at once.

1 tablespoon reduced-salt margarine

1 tablespoon extra virgin olive oil

200 g small leeks, thinly sliced

800 g baby spinach leaves

pepper to taste

1 teaspoon vinegar

4 eggs

paprika to garnish

CHEESE SAUCE

2 tablespoons cornstarch

1¼ cups low-fat milk

50 g Gruyère cheese, finely grated

⅛ teaspoon grated nutmeg

pepper to taste

egg-white omelette with spinach, tomato and Cheddar

A delicious basic omelette minus the fat and cholesterol—that's the kind of recipe every health-conscious cook needs. To make it even more delicious, you can embellish the dish in creative, savoury ways with simple fillings.

3 egg whites

2 teaspoons chopped fresh dill

pepper to taste

½ cup loosely packed, thinly sliced fresh spinach

1 Italian tomato, chopped

2 tablespoons grated 25% reduced-fat Cheddar cheese

1 Whisk the egg whites, 1 teaspoon water, dill and pepper in a medium bowl until soft peaks form.

2 Toss the spinach, tomato and Cheddar in a small bowl.

3 Lightly coat a small nonstick frying pan with nonstick cooking spray and set over medium heat for 1 minute. Pour the egg mixture into the pan and cook until the eggs begin to set on the bottom. Lift up the edge of eggs with a spatula, pushing the cooked part toward the centre of the pan and letting the uncooked portion run underneath. Cook until the eggs are almost set and the bottom is just lightly browned.

4 Spread the spinach filling over half the omelette, leaving a 1 cm border and reserving 1 tablespoon of the mixture for the garnish. Lift up the omelette at the edge nearest the handle and fold in half, slightly off-centre, so the filling just peeks out. Cook for 2 minutes. Slide the omelette onto a plate and garnish with the reserved filling. Serve at once.

preparation time **5 mins**

cooking time **5 mins**

serves **1**

PER SERVING

121 calories

18 g protein

4 g total fat
2 g saturated fat

12 mg cholesterol

2 g total carbohydrate
2 g sugars

5 g fibre

287 mg sodium

COOK'S TIP

Fill the omelette with reduced-fat cheese and vegetables. Cooking the omelette in a nonstick frying pan or omelette pan coated with nonstick cooking spray eliminates the need for butter or margarine, which many similar recipes use.

noodle-stuffed Thai omelette

For these delectable chili-flavoured omelettes, the eggs are whisked with cornstarch to give them a slightly firmer texture, suitable for folding around a colourful filling of stir-fried rice noodles and vegetables.

30 **Fb**

preparation time **15 mins**
cooking time **15 mins**
serves **4**

PER SERVING

306 calories

17 g protein

21 g total fat
4 g saturated fat

430 mg cholesterol

13 g total carbohydrate
4 g sugars

4 g fibre

509 mg sodium

HEALTH HINT

Rice noodles contain no gluten and are therefore suitable for people with celiac disease who are unable to tolerate gluten-containing food.

1 Mix the cornstarch with 4 tablespoons cold water in a bowl. Add the eggs and whisk together until mixed. Stir in the chilies and season with pepper.

2 Heat 1 teaspoon of the canola oil in a 20 cm (8 in.) nonstick frying pan over medium heat. Pour in one-quarter of the egg mixture, tipping the pan to spread out the egg in a thin, even layer. Cook for 2 minutes or until set and golden-brown.

3 Slide the omelette out of the pan onto a plate. Make 3 more omelettes in the same way, stacking them up interleaved with parchment paper. Set aside and keep warm.

4 While making the omelettes, soak the rice noodles in boiling water to cover for 4 minutes, or according to the package instructions, then drain.

5 Heat the remaining 2 teaspoons canola oil with the sesame oil in a wok or large frying pan. Add the mushrooms, carrots, pepper and cabbage and stir-fry for 4–5 minutes or until just tender. Add the soy sauce, vinegar, ginger and rice noodles. Gently toss together until hot.

6 Divide the vegetable and noodle mixture among the omelettes and fold them over in half. Sprinkle with the sesame seeds, if using, and serve at once.

1 tablespoon cornstarch
8 eggs
¼–½ teaspoon crushed dried chilies
pepper to taste
6 teaspoons canola oil
120 g fine rice noodles
1 teaspoon sesame oil
110 g button or Swiss brown mushrooms, sliced
2 carrots, cut into 5 cm long matchstick strips
1 small green pepper, seeded and cut into thin strips
170 g white cabbage, finely shredded
2 tablespoons reduced-salt soy sauce
2 teaspoons white wine vinegar
2 teaspoons chopped fresh ginger
1 tablespoon sesame seeds to garnish (optional)

fresh fruit muesli

Fresh muesli, moist from soaking and rich with juicy fruit, is a revelation to those who have only eaten dried muesli. It has the consistency of oatmeal with the freshness of raw ingredients. It makes a satisfying way to start the day.

preparation time **15 mins** plus 30 mins soaking

serves **6**

PER SERVING

394 calories

8 g protein

14 g total fat

1 g saturated fat

0 mg cholesterol

60 g total carbohydrate

43 g sugars

12 g fibre

29 mg sodium

HEART SUPERFOOD

Sunflower kernels are a rich source of vitamin E, an antioxidant that helps to protect cells from damage by free radicals (thus helping to protect against heart disease and cancer). They also provide useful amounts of niacin, thiamine and zinc.

HEALTH HINT

Dried figs are a good source of potassium, with small amounts of calcium as well as fibre, both soluble and insoluble.

1 In a large bowl, combine the bulgur with about 1 cup water and stir to combine. Cover and leave to soak for 30 minutes to soften the bulgur. Drain well in a sieve and return to the bowl.

2 Add the rolled oats, apple juice, almonds, pine nuts, sunflower kernels, apricots, figs, brown sugar, grated apple and diced persimmon. Fold into the bulgur.

3 Cut the passion fruit in half. Place a sieve over the bowl of muesli and spoon the passion fruit pulp and seeds into it. Press until the juice has passed through the sieve and only the seeds are left behind. Discard the seeds.

4 Add the almond extract, if using, and a little more apple juice, if needed, to make a moist but not sloppy consistency. Keep, covered, in the fridge until ready to eat, then serve topped with pomegranate seeds or blueberries, plus additional persimmon. The muesli can be kept in the refrigerator, tightly covered, for up to 2 days. Stir it well before serving, and then add the fresh fruit garnish.

Variations This muesli makes a wonderful breakfast for those who do not eat dairy products. However, if you do eat dairy products, you can serve a large spoonful of plain low-fat yogourt on top of your muesli or perhaps layer the muesli with yogourt, like a sundae.
• You can also decorate each serving with fresh cherries instead of pomegranate seeds or blueberries, if desired.

½ cup bulgur (cracked wheat)

¾ cup rolled oats

1 cup apple juice

½ cup slivered unblanched almonds

4 tablespoons pine nuts

2 tablespoons sunflower kernels

10 dried apricots, diced

10 dried figs, stalks removed and diced

4 tablespoons soft brown sugar

2 green apples, cored and coarsely grated

1 large or 2 small persimmons, peaches or nectarines, about 200 g in total, peeled and diced

1 passion fruit

few drops of pure almond extract (optional)

pomegranate seeds or blueberries to garnish

extra diced persimmon, peach or nectarine to garnish

muesli with strawberries and hazelnuts

 The original recipe for this nutritious breakfast cereal was developed more than a century ago, by Dr. Bircher-Benner at his clinic in Zurich. The technique of soaking the cereal, here using milk, makes it easier to eat and digest.

¾ cup rolled oats

¾ cup sultanas

1 cup low-fat milk

1 crisp green apple

2 teaspoons freshly squeezed lemon juice

¼ cup hazelnuts, roughly chopped

1 tablespoon pumpkin seeds

1 tablespoon sesame seeds

100 g strawberries, hulled and chopped

5 tablespoons plain low-fat acidophilus yogourt

4 teaspoons clear honey

1 Place the oats and sultanas in a large bowl and add the milk. Stir to mix evenly, then cover and place in the refrigerator. Leave to soak overnight.

2 The following day, just before eating, grate the apple, discarding the core. Toss the apple in the lemon juice to prevent the apple from browning.

3 Stir the hazelnuts, pumpkin seeds and sesame seeds into the oat mixture, then stir in the grated apple and strawberries.

4 To serve, divide the muesli among 4 cereal bowls, and top each with a spoonful of yogourt and honey.

Variation To make a mixed grain muesli, soak ½ cup rolled oats, 1 cup malted wheat flakes, 2 tablespoons flaked rice and ½ cup raisins in 1 cup buttermilk. Just before eating, stir in 2 tablespoons roughly chopped almonds and 2 tablespoons sunflower kernels, then add 1 roughly mashed banana and 1 chopped mango. Serve with plain low-fat acidophilus yogourt.

 Fb GI

preparation time **10 mins** plus overnight soaking

serves **4**

PER SERVING

330 calories

10 g protein

9 g total fat

1 g saturated fat

4 mg cholesterol

52 g total carbohydrate

40 g sugars

5 g fibre

69 mg sodium

HEALTH HINT

Oats have a low glycemic index (GI), which means they are digested and absorbed slowly and therefore produce a gentle, sustained rise in blood glucose levels.

breakfast muffins

Muffins are perfect for breakfast, providing the energy boost the body needs to start the day. This particular recipe is packed full of good ingredients that add fibre, vitamins and minerals, too.

1 Preheat the oven to 400°F (200°C). Grease a 12-cup muffin pan (each cup should measure about 6 cm across the top and be about 3 cm deep).

2 Sift the flours, baking soda and cinnamon into a bowl. Stir in the sugar, wheat germ and raisins, and make a well in the centre.

3 Lightly whisk together the yogourt, oil, egg and orange rind and juice. Pour into the well in the dry ingredients and stir together, mixing only enough to moisten the dry ingredients. Do not beat or overmix.

4 Divide the mixture among the muffin cups, filling them about two-thirds full. Bake for 15–20 minutes or until the muffins are well risen, peaked in the centre and springy to the touch. Leave them to cool in the pan for 2–3 minutes, then turn out onto a wire rack. The muffins are best eaten still slightly warm, but they can be cooled completely and then kept in an airtight container for up to 2 days. Or, you can freeze them for up to 3 months.

Variation To make blueberry and walnut muffins, instead of raisins use 200 g blueberries, and add ³⁄₄ cup chopped walnuts in step 3.

²⁄₃ cup whole-wheat all-purpose flour
1¼ cups white all-purpose flour
2 teaspoons baking soda
¼ teaspoon ground cinnamon
¼ cup soft dark brown sugar
⅓ cup wheat germ
1½ cups raisins
220 g plain low-fat yogourt
5 tablespoons canola oil
1 egg
grated rind of ½ orange
4 tablespoons freshly squeezed
   orange juice

preparation time **15 mins**
cooking time **20 mins**
makes **12 muffins**

PER MUFFIN

226 calories

5 g protein

7 g total fat
1 g saturated fat

19 mg cholesterol

35 g total carbohydrate
19 g sugars

3 g fibre

145 mg sodium

HEALTH HINT

Wheat germ is the embryo of the wheat grain and contains a high concentration of nutrients. Just 1 tablespoon wheat germ provides around 25 per cent of the average daily requirement for vitamin B$_6$. Wheat germ is also an excellent source of folate, vitamin E, zinc and magnesium.

apricot and pecan muffins

Packed with fresh fruit and nuts, and delicately spiced with cinnamon, these homemade apricot and pecan muffins are lower in fat and sugar than store-bought muffins, and contain no trans fats or preservatives.

2⅔ cups all-purpose flour
2 teaspoons baking powder
½ cup soft light brown sugar
1 teaspoon ground cinnamon
4 tablespoons wheat bran
½ teaspoon grated lemon rind
1 cup low-fat milk
2 eggs
¼ cup reduced-salt margarine, melted
220 g ripe but firm apricots, pitted
   and diced
½ cup pecan nuts, chopped

1 Preheat the oven to 400°F (200°C). Using nonstick cooking spray, grease a 12-cup muffin pan (each cup should measure about 6 cm across the top and be about 3 cm deep).

2 Sift the flour, baking powder, sugar and cinnamon into a bowl. Stir in the wheat bran and lemon rind. Combine the milk, eggs and margarine in a bowl, mixing well. Pour into the dry ingredients and add the diced apricots and pecans. Stir just until the dry ingredients are moistened, leaving some small lumps of the flour mixture in the dough. Do not overmix.

3 Spoon into the prepared muffin pan, filling the cups two-thirds full. Bake for 20–25 minutes or until the muffins are well risen, peaked in the centre and springy to the touch. Leave to cool in the pan for 2–3 minutes, then turn out onto a wire rack. The muffins are best if served within a few hours of baking, but they can be stored in an airtight container for up to 2 days, or frozen for up to 3 months.

Variation Blueberries, strawberries, peaches or nectarines can also be used, but the fruit must not be too ripe and mushy or it will make the muffin mixture too wet.

preparation time **25 mins**
cooking time **25 mins**
makes **12 muffins**

PER MUFFIN

243 calories

6 g protein

9 g total fat
1 g saturated fat

38 mg cholesterol

33 g total carbohydrate
10 g sugars

2 g fibre

285 mg sodium

HEALTH HINT

Health experts regularly recommend that we increase the amount of fibre in our diet. This recipe shows an easy way to achieve this—substitute 2 or 3 tablespoons of wheat bran for some of the flour in your favourite recipe. And try to include fruits or nuts in your baking which boost both soluble and insoluble fibre—good for digestion and controlling blood sugar levels.

fruity vegetable muffins

Not only do grated vegetables and dried fruit add food value and flavour to these muffins, but they also make them deliciously moist. Unlike many muffins, these are not too sweet, so they are as good in a packed lunch or as a snack.

C

preparation time **15 mins**
cooking time **25 mins**
makes **12 muffins**

PER MUFFIN

247 calories

4 g protein

12 g total fat
2 g saturated fat

54 mg cholesterol

32 g total carbohydrate
17 g sugars

2 g fibre

180 mg sodium

HEALTH HINT

Combining whole-wheat flour with white flour increases the fibre content of baked goods without making them too heavy.

1 Preheat the oven to 350°F (180°C). Using nonstick cooking spray, grease a 12-cup muffin pan (each cup should measure about 6 cm across the top and be about 3 cm deep).

2 Sift the flours and cinnamon into a mixing bowl. Add the sugar. Stir in the dried mixed fruit or raisins, and make a well in the centre.

3 In another bowl, beat together the carrot, zucchini, oil and eggs. Pour this mixture into the well in the dry ingredients and stir until almost blended, but with a small amount of dry flour still visible in places.

4 Divide the mixture among the muffin cups, filling them about two-thirds full. Bake for 20–25 minutes or until the muffins are well risen, peaked in the centre and springy to the touch. Transfer the muffins to a wire rack to cool.

5 Serve the muffins warm or at room temperature. They are best eaten on the day they are made, but they can be stored in an airtight container for up to 2 days. Alternatively, you can freeze them for up to 3 months.

1 cup white self-raising flour
1 cup whole-wheat self-raising flour
2 teaspoons ground cinnamon
⅔ cup caster (superfine) sugar
½ cup dried mixed fruit or raisins
1 large carrot, finely grated
1 medium zucchini, finely grated
½ cup sunflower oil
3 eggs

waffles with glazed nectarines

Waffles aren't just for weekends any more! You can dig into this hot breakfast any weekday morning. Light and simple ingredients and plenty of juicy nectarines make these wonderful waffles a heart-healthy way to start the day.

3 medium nectarines, about 480 g in total, thinly sliced
¼ cup soft dark brown sugar
½ cup freshly squeezed orange juice
2 tablespoons cornstarch
8 waffles

1 Lightly coat a large nonstick frying pan with nonstick cooking spray and set over medium heat. Sauté the nectarines until they are lightly browned, about 5 minutes. Stir in the brown sugar and cook until the sugar dissolves and becomes syrupy, about 2 minutes. Transfer the nectarines to a bowl with a slotted spoon.

2 Whisk the orange juice and cornstarch in a small bowl until smooth, then add 1 cup cold water. Whisk this mixture into the frying pan. Bring to a boil over medium-high heat and cook, whisking constantly, until the sauce boils and thickens, about 2 minutes. Return the nectarines to the frying pan and allow to heat through.

3 Toast the waffles in a toaster. Serve 2 waffles per person, topped with about 6 slices nectarines. Serve hot.

preparation time **20 mins**
cooking time **20 mins**
serves **4** (makes 8)

PER SERVING

398 calories

9 g protein

14 g total fat
6 g saturated fat

67 mg cholesterol

60 g total carbohydrate
28 g sugars

4 g fibre

676 mg sodium

HEALTH HINT

Nectarine skins are high in pectin, a soluble fibre that aids in controlling your blood cholesterol level and keeping your heart healthy.

blueberry popovers with berry salad

 Similar to Yorkshire puddings, popovers are a much-loved treat, and the sweet version here is perfect for breakfast or brunch. The batter is baked, and the popovers are served with sweet, fresh berries to add extra vitamin C.

preparation time **20 mins**

cooking time **30 mins**

serves **4** (makes 8)

PER SERVING

260 calories	
12 g protein	
4 g total fat	
1 g saturated fat	
110 mg cholesterol	
44 g total carbohydrate	
19 g sugars	
5 g fibre	
70 mg sodium	

HEART SUPERFOOD

Blueberries contain antibacterial compounds called anthocyanins. These are powerful antioxidants that prevent LDL ("bad") cholesterol from being oxidized and deposited on artery walls.

1 Preheat the oven to 425°F (220°C). Using nonstick cooking spray, grease 8 cups of a 12-cup muffin pan (each cup should measure about 6 cm across the top and be about 3 cm deep).

2 Sift the flour into a mixing bowl, add the caster sugar, and make a well in the centre. Break the eggs into the well, add the milk and beat together with a fork.

3 Using a wire whisk, gradually work the flour into the liquid to make a smooth batter.

4 Divide the batter evenly among the prepared muffin cups—they should be about two-thirds full. With a spoon, drop a few blueberries into the batter in each cup, dividing them equally. Half-fill the 4 empty cups with water.

5 Bake in the centre of the oven for 25–30 minutes or until the popovers are golden-brown, risen and crisp around the edges.

6 Meanwhile, to make the berry salad, purée two-thirds of the raspberries by pressing them through a nylon sieve into a bowl. Add the remaining raspberries to the bowl, together with the blueberries and strawberries. Sift the icing sugar over the fruit and fold gently to mix everything together.

7 Remove the popovers with a round-bladed knife, and dust with the icing sugar. Serve the popovers hot, with the berry salad.

1 cup all-purpose flour

1 teaspoon caster (superfine) sugar

2 eggs

1 cup low-fat milk

70 g blueberries

1 tablespoon icing sugar to dust

MIXED BERRY SALAD

150 g raspberries

100 g blueberries

200 g strawberries, hulled and thickly sliced

1 tablespoon icing sugar

caramelized banana crumpets

Forget about smothering toasted crumpets in butter; this low-fat topping is yummy and much healthier. Mashed bananas are mixed with ricotta and spices and piled onto crumpet fingers, then drizzled with honey and broiled.

4 crumpets

2 bananas

5 tablespoons reduced-fat ricotta, cream cheese or plain yogourt

seeds from 4 cardamom pods, crushed

½ teaspoon ground cinnamon, plus extra to sprinkle

1 teaspoon finely grated orange rind

2 tablespoons clear honey

1 Preheat the broiler. Cut round crumpets in half to create 8 crumpet fingers. Place crumpets under the broiler and toast for 2–3 minutes on each side or until browned and crisp.

2 Meanwhile, mash the bananas with a fork, keeping them a little textured. Add the ricotta, crushed cardamom, cinnamon and orange rind, and mix well together.

3 Spread the banana mixture over the toasted crumpets, levelling the surface, then drizzle each with 1 teaspoon honey.

4 Return to the broiler and cook for 2–3 minutes or until the tops are lightly browned and the honey is bubbling. Leave the crumpets to cool slightly, then sprinkle over a little extra cinnamon and serve at once.

Variations Use whole-wheat crumpets for added fibre. • Instead of cardamom seeds, use ¼–½ teaspoon ground cardamom.

preparation time **5 mins**

cooking time **10 mins**

serves **4**

PER SERVING

237 calories

6 g protein

2 g total fat
1 g saturated fat

9 mg cholesterol

48 g total carbohydrate
22 g sugars

3 g fibre

665 mg sodium

HEALTH HINT

Bananas are a concentrated source of carbohydrates and one of the best fruit sources of potassium, which is vital for muscle and nerve function—this is why bananas are so popular with athletes.

herbed French toast with mushrooms

Give breakfast or brunch a new twist with this savoury version of French toast. Triangles of bread are dipped into a fresh herb and egg mixture, then fried until crisp and golden. Serve with mushrooms and lean bacon.

1 Combine the eggs, milk, most of the parsley, the chives, thyme and paprika in a shallow dish. Season with pepper and set the mixture aside.

2 Preheat the broiler. Remove the stalks from the mushrooms. Using 1 tablespoon of the oil, lightly brush the gill sides of the mushroom caps. Place them gill-side up on the broiler rack. Add the bacon to the rack. Broil the bacon and mushrooms until cooked, remove from the oven and keep warm.

3 Meanwhile, cut each slice of bread into 4 triangles. Heat a large nonstick frying pan over medium heat and add 1 tablespoon of the remaining oil. Dip about one-third of the bread triangles into the egg mixture to moisten on both sides, then place in the hot pan. Cook for 1–2 minutes or until golden-brown. Remove from the pan and keep warm while you cook the rest of the bread, adding the remaining oil as needed.

4 To serve, arrange 5 triangles of French toast on each plate. Cut the mushrooms into thick slices and add to the plates, together with the bacon. Sprinkle with the remaining parsley

4 large eggs

5 tablespoons low-fat milk

1 tablespoon finely chopped parsley

1 tablespoon finely chopped fresh chives

½ tablespoon chopped fresh thyme or ⅛ teaspoon dried thyme

⅛ teaspoon paprika

pepper to taste

4 large flat mushrooms, about 250 g in total

4 tablespoons canola oil

4 strips bacon, trimmed of visible fat

5 thick slices whole-wheat bread

preparation time **10 mins**

cooking time **15 mins**

serves **4**

PER SERVING

393 calories

23 g protein

26 g total fat
5 g saturated fat

275 mg cholesterol

17 g total carbohydrate
3 g sugars

4 g fibre

862 mg sodium

HEALTH HINT

This hearty breakfast dish contains fewer calories than the traditional version of French toast, which is often served with melted butter and maple syrup.

lima beans and bacon on toast with red leaf salad

Here's a new version of beans on toast, combining creamy lima beans with crisp bacon, cottage cheese and mustard. Accompanied by a fresh salad, this makes a fabulous meal that is ready to serve in about 15 minutes.

1 tablespoon reduced-salt margarine

4 strips bacon, trimmed of visible fat and chopped

1 bunch green onions, sliced

80 g arugula or watercress, tough stalks removed, roughly chopped

2 cans (398 ml each) lima beans, drained and rinsed

50 g reduced-fat cottage cheese

1 teaspoon Dijon mustard

pepper to taste

8 thick slices whole-wheat bread

RED LEAF SALAD

2 tablespoons extra virgin olive oil

2 teaspoons lemon juice

1 teaspoon clear honey

pepper to taste

1 small head red-leaved radicchio, cut into thin wedges

1 small red leaf lettuce, leaves separated

1 To make the salad, put the oil, lemon juice and honey in a salad bowl and add pepper. Whisk together. Add the radicchio and lettuce to the bowl and set aside (do not toss yet).

2 Preheat the broiler. Melt the margarine in a large nonstick frying pan until it begins to sizzle. Add the bacon and green onions, and cook over medium heat for about 3 minutes, stirring frequently, until the bacon begins to colour and the green onions are just tender.

3 Add the arugula or watercress and cook for a few seconds, stirring, then add the lima beans, cottage cheese, mustard and pepper. Lower the heat and cook for 2 minutes, stirring constantly, until the mixture is hot.

4 While the bean and bacon mixture is cooking, toast the slices of bread under the broiler or in a toaster. Spoon the bean and bacon mixture onto the hot toast. Quickly toss the salad, and serve while the lettuce is still crisp.

Variation For pinto bean and blue cheese Italian rolls, place 2 cans pinto beans, 540 ml each, drained and rinsed, in a saucepan with 80 g crumbled Gorgonzola cheese, 2 tablespoons plain low-fat yogourt and 2 tablespoons ricotta cheese (or 2 extra tablespoons yogourt). Heat very gently, stirring frequently, until the cheese melts and the beans are hot. Stir in 1 tablespoon sundried tomato pesto and serve on crusty Italian rolls, split in half and lightly toasted. You can accompany the toasted rolls with an Italian-style fennel and arugula salad. For the dressing, whisk 2 tablespoons extra virgin olive oil with 1 teaspoon balsamic vinegar, 2 tablespoons freshly squeezed orange juice and pepper to taste. Add 1 thinly sliced fennel bulb, 80 g arugula leaves, 1 thinly sliced small red onion and 30 g pitted black olives, and toss just before serving with the Italian rolls.

30 **Fb** **GI**

preparation time **5 mins**

cooking time **10 mins**

serves **4**

PER SERVING

350 calories

21 g protein

18 g total fat
4 g saturated fat

26 mg cholesterol

26 g total carbohydrate
8 g sugars

9 g fibre

903 mg sodium

HEALTH HINTS

Lima beans have a buttery flavour. They offer plenty of dietary fibre, essential for a healthy digestive system.

Trimmed of fat, lean bacon is a high-protein, low-fat ingredient that provides particularly useful amounts of thiamine which is essential for maintaining a healthy nervous system.

potato cakes with baked tomatoes

Potato and leek cakes, flavoured with tasty cheese and fresh herbs, make a satisfying vegetarian meal served with baked tomatoes and accompanied by a simple leaf salad.

1 kg potatoes, washed

1 large leek, sliced

2 tablespoons low-fat milk

2 teaspoons whole-grain mustard

$\frac{2}{3}$ cup 25% reduced-fat Cheddar cheese, grated

6 tablespoons chopped parsley

1 tablespoon chopped fresh thyme

all-purpose flour for dusting

1 egg, beaten

1 cup fresh whole-wheat breadcrumbs

4 large tomatoes, halved

2 tablespoons ready-made garlic-flavoured olive oil for brushing (or, to make your own, add 1 crushed garlic clove to 2 tablespoons olive oil)

1 Cut the large potatoes into halves or quarters. Bring a large saucepan of water to a boil and add the potatoes. Bring back to a boil, turn down the heat and cook for 15 minutes or until tender. Add the leek to the pan for the last 5 minutes. Drain the vegetables, then spread them out on a plate and leave them to cool. Preheat the oven to 425°F (220°C).

2 When the potatoes are cool, peel and place in a bowl with the leek, and mash. Add the milk, mustard, cheese, parsley and thyme, and mix well. Divide the mixture into 8 portions. Shape each into a ball, then press on a floured surface into a flat cake about 10 cm across and 3 cm thick.

3 Set the cakes on a clean plate. Brush with the beaten egg and sprinkle over half the breadcrumbs. Turn the cakes and coat the other side with egg and breadcrumbs. Transfer them to a nonstick baking sheet and bake for 15 minutes.

4 Meanwhile, place the tomatoes in an ovenproof dish, cut-side up. Brush them with the garlic oil and sprinkle over any remaining breadcrumbs.

5 Turn the potato cakes over carefully. Place the tomatoes in the oven with the potato cakes and bake for a further 10 minutes or until golden. Serve hot.

preparation time **35 mins** plus cooling

cooking time **40 mins**

serves **4** (makes 8)

PER SERVING

401 calories

18 g protein

16 g total fat
5 g saturated fat

69 mg cholesterol

44 g total carbohydrate
7 g sugars

8 g fibre

314 mg sodium

HEALTH HINT

Potato cakes are often fried in oil or butter. Here they are oven-baked to produce cakes that are equally tasty but with a lower fat content.

preparation time **15 mins**

cooking time **20 mins**

serves **8**

PER SERVING

175 calories

9 g protein

12 g total fat
3 g saturated fat

169 mg cholesterol

9 g total carbohydrate
1 g sugars

2 g fibre

203 mg sodium

HEALTH HINT

Zucchinis are a good source of vitamin B$_6$ and niacin. The skin contains the greatest concentration of these vitamins.

potato and zucchini tortilla

Tortilla is made from the simplest of ingredients—eggs, onions and potatoes—cooked like a flat omelette and served warm or cold, cut into wedges. All kinds of extra ingredients can be added, such as asparagus, peas and mushrooms.

1 Add the diced potatoes to a saucepan of boiling water. Bring back to a boil, then lower the heat slightly and cook for 3 minutes. Drain thoroughly.

2 Heat the oil in a heavy-based nonstick frying pan that is about 25 cm (10 in.) in diameter. Add the potatoes, onion, zucchini and bacon, and cook over medium heat for 10 minutes, turning and stirring from time to time, until the potatoes are tender and lightly golden.

3 Preheat the broiler. In a bowl, beat the eggs with 1 tablespoon cold water. Add the parsley and pepper. Pour the egg mixture over the vegetables in the pan and cook for 3–4 minutes or until the egg has set on the bottom, lifting the edges to allow the uncooked egg mixture to run onto the pan.

4 When there is just a little uncooked egg on the top, place the pan under the broiler and cook for a further 2 minutes to set the top. Slide the tortilla out onto a plate or board and allow to cool for 2–3 minutes. Cut into small wedges or other shapes and serve warm, or leave to cool completely before cutting and serving.

600 g potatoes, peeled and diced 1 cm thick

2 tablespoons extra virgin olive oil

1 red onion, finely chopped

1 zucchini, diced

2 strips bacon, trimmed of visible fat and chopped

6 eggs

2 tablespoons chopped parsley

pepper to taste

leek and prosciutto pizza muffins

Leeks, basil and prosciutto combine with mozzarella to make a sophisticated pizza-style topping for whole-wheat muffins. Serve with a simple salad of arugula and grated carrot tossed with extra virgin olive oil and lemon juice.

1 tablespoon extra virgin olive oil

2 leeks, thinly sliced

pepper to taste

4 whole-wheat English muffins, halved

5 tablespoons shredded fresh
  basil leaves

4 slices prosciutto, about 50 g in
  total, trimmed of visible fat and
  halved crosswise

100 g mozzarella cheese, cut
  into thin strips

¼ cup coarsely chopped arugula
  to garnish

1 Heat the oil in a saucepan, add the leeks and cook over medium-high heat, stirring frequently, for about 5 minutes or until the leeks are tender and the juices have evaporated. Season with pepper.

2 Preheat the broiler. Place the muffins, cut-side down, on the broiler rack. Toast the bases, then turn the muffins over. Divide the leeks equally among the muffins. Top with the basil, then place a piece of prosciutto on each muffin half. Gently pinch the prosciutto up into loose folds. Scatter the strips of mozzarella cheese over the top.

3 Cook the muffin pizzas under the broiler until the mozzarella cheese has melted and is bubbling. The prosciutto and cheese should be lightly browned in places. Sprinkle with the chopped arugula and serve.

Variation Use 70 g lean cooked ham, cut into fine strips, instead of the prosciutto, and extra small arugula leaves instead of the basil.

preparation time **15 mins**

cooking time **10 mins**

serves **4** (makes 8)

PER SERVING
269 calories
17 g protein
12 g total fat
5 g saturated fat
22 mg cholesterol
23 g total carbohydrate
2 g sugars
4 g fibre
611 mg sodium

Indian chicken and broccoli wrap

These mouthwatering Indian-style snacks are quick to make. They use whole-wheat pita wraps instead of the traditional Indian chapatis. A yogourt-based raita, containing cucumber and tomato, is the perfect accompaniment.

1 Preheat the broiler. Cut the chicken into bite-sized pieces, discarding any skin.

2 Heat the oil in a frying pan, add the broccoli, cashews, ginger and garlic, and cook for 5 minutes, stirring, until the broccoli is just tender.

3 Add the chicken, mango chutney and pepper to the broccoli mixture. Cook for a further 2 minutes, stirring, until the chicken is hot.

4 Meanwhile, place the pita wraps on the broiler rack. Cook for 2 minutes, turning once.

5 To make the raita, coarsely grate the cucumber and add to the yogourt with the remaining ingredients. Stir well to mix.

6 Place the chicken mixture on top of the pita wraps and roll them up loosely. Serve hot, with the raita on the side.

200 g cooked chicken breasts
2 tablespoons canola oil
250 g broccoli florets, finely chopped
¼ cup unsalted cashews, chopped
2 teaspoons grated fresh ginger
1 garlic clove, finely chopped
5 tablespoons mango chutney
pepper to taste
4 small whole-wheat pita wraps

CUCUMBER AND TOMATO RAITA

1 cucumber, cut into quarters
  lengthwise and seeded
350 g plain low-fat yogourt
1 tomato, very finely chopped
½ teaspoon ground coriander
½ teaspoon ground cumin
⅛ teaspoon cayenne pepper

preparation time **10 mins**
cooking time **10 mins**
serves **4**

PER SERVING

453 calories	
27 g protein	
19 g total fat	
3 g saturated fat	
52 mg cholesterol	
42 g total carbohydrate	
20 g sugars	
8 g fibre	
522 mg sodium	

HEART SUPERFOOD

Like cabbage and cauliflower, broccoli is packed with vitamins. It is an excellent source of the antioxidants beta carotene, and vitamins C and E. It also provides good amounts of the B vitamins niacin and B_6 and useful amounts of folate. All these vitamins protect and strengthen the heart and blood supply.

avocado and chicken club sandwich

This club sandwich packs in lots of interesting flavours and textures. Crispy prosciutto replaces the usual bacon, and mashed avocado the butter. Adding a few leaves to a sandwich is a cunning way to get children to eat their greens.

12 slices multi-grain bread

5 tablespoons low-fat mayonnaise

110 g iceberg lettuce, finely shredded

110 g cooked chicken breasts, skin removed, sliced

4 slices prosciutto, about 50 g in total, cut into strips

pepper to taste

1 avocado

1 tablespoon freshly squeezed lime juice

1 orange, peeled and chopped

1 bunch arugula or watercress, tough stalks discarded

⅓ cup alfalfa sprouts

2 teaspoons pumpkin seeds, toasted in a frying pan for 2 minutes without oil

1 Spread 4 slices of bread with half of the mayonnaise. Divide the shredded lettuce among the slices, then add the sliced chicken breasts.

2 Heat a nonstick frying pan and dry-fry the strips of prosciutto for 1–2 minutes or until crisp and curly. Pile on top of the chicken and season with pepper. Spread the remaining mayonnaise on another 4 slices of bread and put these, mayonnaise-side down, on the chicken and prosciutto.

3 Mash the avocado flesh with the lime juice. Divide among the sandwiches, spooning onto the uppermost layer of bread and spreading out roughly. Top with the chopped orange, arugula, alfalfa sprouts and pumpkin seeds. Place the final slices of bread on top. Press down gently, then cut each sandwich in half or into quarters before serving.

Variation For fruity chicken club sandwiches, replace the top deck of avocado, orange, arugula, alfalfa sprouts and pumpkin seeds on each sandwich with 1 tablespoon crunchy peanut butter, ½ sliced banana sprinkled with a little lemon juice, 2 fresh dates, skinned and chopped, and 1 teaspoon chopped parsley.

 30 **Fb**

preparation time **20 mins**

cooking time **2 mins**

serves **4**

PER SERVING

442 calories

20 g protein

21 g total fat
4 g saturated fat

32 mg cholesterol

43 g total carbohydrate
10 g sugars

6 g fibre

1085 mg sodium

HEALTH HINT

Avocados have a reputation for being a "fatty" fruit, but most of their fat is of the good, unsaturated type, making them a valuable source of essential fatty acids as well as vitamin E.

roasted vegetable baguettes

These Mediterranean-style "sandwiches" are generously filled with peppers, zucchinis and red onion, spiked with garlic and rosemary, and topped with a sprinkling of feta cheese. They make a satisfying brunch.

1 Preheat the broiler and cook the peppers, skin-side up, until the skins are blackened. Place the peppers in a plastic bag and set aside for 15 minutes.

2 Meanwhile, lightly toast the cut sides of the baguettes under the broiler. Remove from the broiler and set aside on a board.

3 Remove the broil rack and discard any crumbs from the broil pan. Place the onion, zucchini and garlic in the broil pan. Sprinkle with rosemary and drizzle with oil. Add pepper and cook for 8–10 minutes, turning the vegetables once, until browned.

4 Peel the skin off the peppers using a small sharp knife and cut them into thick slices. Arrange the pepper and zucchini mixture over the bottom halves of the toasted bread, spooning all the pan juices from the zucchinis over the top. Arrange side by side in the broiler rack.

5 Crumble the feta cheese over the vegetables and broil until the cheese is slightly browned. Top with the remaining bread halves. Cut the baguettes in half at an angle and serve immediately.

2 red peppers, quartered lengthwise and seeded

4 short baguettes, about 120 g each, halved lengthwise

1 red onion, cut into small wedges

2 large zucchinis, sliced diagonally

2 garlic cloves, chopped

3 sprigs fresh rosemary

1 tablespoon extra virgin olive oil

pepper to taste

100 g feta cheese

preparation time **15 mins**

cooking time **25 mins**

serves **4**

PER SERVING

534 calories

20 g protein

16 g total fat
5 g saturated fat

18 mg cholesterol

77 g total carbohydrate
12 g sugars

8 g fibre

1032 mg sodium

HEALTH HINT

Feta cheese is quite high in fat and salt, but because it has such a strong flavour, a little goes a long way.

soups,
starters
& snacks

hearty vegetable pesto soup

Fragrant basil pesto adds a taste of summer to this healthier version of a classic French soup. Aromatic vegetables add flavour and plenty of vitamins while keeping the fat in check. What a wonderful way to eat your vegetables!

500 g Italian tomatoes

1 onion, chopped

1 carrot, chopped

1 celery stalk, sliced

2 garlic cloves, finely chopped

1 yellow zucchini, or 3 baby squash, about 150 g in total, sliced

1 green zucchini, sliced

1¾ cups reduced-salt chicken stock

1¾ cups reduced-salt vegetable stock

1 cup loosely packed fresh basil leaves

3 tablespoons prepared basil pesto

1 Peel, seed and chop the Italian tomatoes.

2 Grease a large saucepan with nonstick cooking spray and set over medium-high heat. Sauté the onion, carrot, celery and garlic until soft, about 5 minutes. Add the tomatoes, yellow zucchini or squash, and the green zucchini. Sauté the vegetables until they are soft, about 8 minutes. Stir in the chicken stock and vegetable stock, and bring to a boil. Reduce the heat and simmer, uncovered, until the flavours have blended, about 20 minutes.

3 Place the basil and pesto in a food processor and pulse until the basil is chopped. Process until the pesto is thick and creamy.

4 Ladle the soup into bowls, top with the pesto and serve.

preparation time **25 mins**

cooking time **35 mins**

serves **4**

PER SERVING

114 calories

6 g protein

6 g total fat
1 g saturated fat

3 mg cholesterol

10 g total carbohydrate
9 g sugars

4 g fibre

891 mg sodium

COOK'S TIP

For vegetarian vegetable soup, substitute another 1¾ cups vegetable stock for the chicken stock. You can also vary the vegetables. Always start with sautéed onion, carrot, celery and garlic. In spring, add a handful of fresh green peas during the last 10 minutes. During summer, team the tomatoes with corn and green beans.

herbed chicken and potato soup

The simple, delicious flavours of this soup will make it popular with adults and children alike. Try it for lunch on the weekend, served with plenty of crusty bread and fresh fruit to follow.

C **Fb**

preparation time **20 mins**

cooking time **50 mins**

serves **4**

PER SERVING

250 calories

18 g protein

9 g total fat
2 g saturated fat

37 mg cholesterol

24 g total carbohydrate
10 g sugars

3 g fibre

837 mg sodium

HEART SUPERFOOD

Onions contain a phytochemical called allicin, which is believed to help reduce the risk of cancer and also of blood clots forming, thereby helping to prevent coronary heart disease.

1 Heat the oil in a large saucepan. Add the bacon, chicken and onions, and cook over low heat for 3 minutes. Increase the heat and cook for a further 5 minutes, stirring the ingredients occasionally and turning the chicken once, until the chicken is pale golden-brown in colour.

2 Add the potatoes and cook for a further 2 minutes, stirring constantly. Pour in the stock, then add the thyme and pepper. Bring to a boil. Reduce the heat, cover the pan, and leave to simmer for 30 minutes.

3 Using a slotted spoon, transfer the chicken to a plate. Remove and chop the meat and discard the bone, if necessary. Return the chicken meat to the soup. Stir in the milk and reheat the soup gently without boiling.

4 Ladle the soup into bowls, garnish with chopped parsley or parsley and thyme and serve.

Variations For a smooth result, you can purée the soup in a blender or food processor in step 3 after the chicken has been replaced. • For a winter vegetable soup use 800 g mixed diced leeks (use both the white and pale green parts), carrot and turnip instead of the onions and potatoes. Finely chop the green tops from the leeks, and add them to the soup with the milk at the end of cooking, for extra colour.

1 tablespoon extra virgin olive oil

2 strips bacon, trimmed of visible fat and finely chopped

1 chicken thigh (on the bone, if possible), about 140 g, skinned

2 onions, finely chopped

500 g potatoes, peeled and diced

3 cups reduced-salt chicken stock

leaves from 4 sprigs fresh thyme or ½ teaspoon dried thyme

pepper to taste

1¼ cups low-fat milk

chopped parsley, or a mixture of chopped parsley and fresh thyme, to garnish

chunky gazpacho with garlic croutons

This chilled soup is a delicious concoction of tomatoes, red and green peppers and cucumbers with a hint of garlic—all high in what's good for you and low in fat and calories. Ladle into cups as an entree or into bowls for a light dinner.

2 garlic cloves, peeled

4 slices crusty French bread (whole wheat if possible), about 2 cm thick

1 teaspoon pepper

$^1/_2$ cup coarsely chopped red onion

1 large can (796 ml) no-salt-added tomatoes

$^1/_4$ cup dry breadcrumbs

$^1/_4$ cup chopped parsley

4 tablespoons red wine vinegar

1 tablespoon olive oil

2 cucumbers, peeled and chopped

2 green peppers, chopped

2 red peppers, chopped

1 Preheat the oven to 350°F (180°C). Cut 1 garlic clove in half and rub the cut sides on the inside of a large bowl and on both sides of the bread slices. Tear the bread into 2 cm pieces. Place the bread in the large bowl and lightly coat with nonstick cooking spray. Sprinkle with $^1/_2$ teaspoon pepper. Toss to coat and transfer to a baking sheet. Bake the croutons in the oven until golden-brown, about 15 minutes. Allow to cool.

2 Pulse the onion and remaining garlic in a food processor or blender until finely chopped. Add half the tomatoes with all their juice, and purée. Add the breadcrumbs, parsley, vinegar, oil and remaining pepper. Process just until blended and pour into a large nonmetallic bowl.

3 Chop the remaining tomatoes. Stir them into the tomato mixture with half the chopped cucumbers and half the green and red peppers. Refrigerate until chilled, about 1 hour. Ladle the soup into bowls and top with the remaining cucumber, green and red peppers and croutons. Serve chilled.

preparation time **20 mins** plus 1 hour chilling time

cooking time **15 mins**

serves **4**

PER SERVING

181 calories

6 g protein

6 g total fat

1 g saturated fat

0 mg cholesterol

24 g total carbohydrate

13 g sugars

5 g fibre

181 mg sodium

COOK'S TIP

Acids in foods like tomatoes, citrus fruit, vinegar and even buttermilk can react with some metals, resulting in an undesirable metallic taste. Prepare acidic dishes such as this soup in glass or pottery bowls.

Mediterranean roasted vegetable soup

Roasting the onions, garlic, peppers, potatoes and zucchini caramelizes their natural sugars to bring out tantalizing sweetness. The pan juices, which contain minimal fat, are added to the soup so you won't lose a drop of flavour.

1 Preheat the oven to 450°F (230°C). Combine the olive oil and garlic in a roasting pan and roast until the oil begins to sizzle, about 5 minutes. Add the potatoes, peppers and rosemary, and toss to coat. Roast until the potatoes begin to colour and soften, about 15 minutes.

2 Add the yellow zucchini and the onion, and roast until the zucchini is tender, about 15 minutes.

3 In a medium saucepan, combine the carrot juice, tomatoes and tarragon and bring to a boil over medium heat. Spoon the roasted vegetables into the saucepan.

4 Pour a little water into the roasting pan and stir, making sure to scrape up any browned bits that cling to the pan. Pour the pan juices into the saucepan. Cook until heated through, about 2 minutes, then serve.

1 tablespoon olive oil

5 garlic cloves, peeled

350 g all-purpose potatoes, diced 1 cm thick

2 peppers (green and yellow), diced 1 cm thick

½ teaspoon fresh rosemary, finely chopped

1 yellow zucchini, halved lengthwise and cut crosswise into 1 cm pieces

1 large red onion, cut into 1 cm chunks

1½ cups carrot juice

370 g Italian tomatoes, diced

1 teaspoon fresh tarragon

preparation time **25 mins**
cooking time **40 mins**
serves **4**

PER SERVING

173 calories

7 g protein

5 g total fat
1 g saturated fat

0 mg cholesterol

25 g total carbohydrate
13 g sugars

7 g fibre

61 mg sodium

HEALTH HINT

By using deeply coloured vegetable ingredients like carrot juice and fresh or canned tomatoes as the basis for soups, you'll be getting a wide spectrum of nutrients and far less fat and sodium than from purchased chicken stock. And you'll also benefit from a number of potent, disease-fighting carotenoids, such as beta carotene and lycopene.

creamy chicken and corn soup

This hearty soup tastes really creamy, yet it doesn't contain any cream! Made with cooked chicken and fresh corn and potatoes, with a garnish of bacon, it's substantial enough for lunch, served with crusty whole-wheat bread.

3 fresh corncobs

2 tablespoons canola oil

1 onion, finely chopped

2 medium potatoes, peeled and diced

2 cups reduced-salt chicken stock

2 cups low-fat milk

250 g cooked chicken breasts, skinned and finely chopped

2 teaspoons chopped fresh tarragon

pepper to taste

2 strips smoked bacon, trimmed of visible fat, to garnish

fresh tarragon leaves to garnish

1 Remove the green husks and all the "silk" from the corncobs. Holding each cob upright on a chopping board, cut the kernels from the cob. (You should end up with about 1½ cups loose corn kernels.) Set the kernels aside.

2 Heat the canola oil in a large saucepan, add the onion and fry over medium heat until softened, but not browned. Add the potatoes and corn kernels to the pan and cook for a further 5 minutes, stirring frequently. Pour in the chicken stock and bring to a boil. Reduce the heat and simmer gently for 5 minutes or until the potatoes are just tender.

3 Stir in the milk, three-quarters of the chicken and the chopped tarragon. Season with the pepper. Cook, stirring, for a further 2–3 minutes.

4 Pour half of the mixture into a food processor or blender and blend to a coarse texture, not to a purée. Return the mixture to the pan. Add the rest of the chicken and stir to mix. Set the soup over a low heat to warm through.

5 Meanwhile, cook the bacon until it starts to brown. Drain on paper towel, then finely chop.

6 Ladle the chicken and corn soup into bowls, scatter on some bacon and a sprinkling of tarragon leaves, and serve.

Variation Instead of bacon, garnish the soup with croutons: cut 50 g crustless whole-wheat bread into small cubes and stir in a bowl with 1 tablespoon canola oil. Spread out on a baking sheet and bake in a preheated oven at 350°F (180°C) for 10 minutes or until golden. Toss the baked croutons with 1 teaspoon very finely chopped fresh tarragon, if desired. These baked croutons are far less fatty than croutons fried in oil. For garlic croutons, toss the bread cubes in 1 tablespoon olive oil mixed with a crushed garlic clove before baking them.

preparation time **15 mins**

cooking time **25 mins**

serves **4**

PER SERVING

398 calories
31 g protein
16 g total fat
3 g saturated fat
63 mg cholesterol
32 g total carbohydrate
13 g sugars
4 g fibre
735 mg sodium

HEALTH HINT

Corn is a useful source of dietary fibre (important for keeping the digestive system in good working order), and also offers potassium and folate.

Tuscan mixed bean soup

Tuscan cuisine focuses on fresh, healthy ingredients and uncomplicated cooking techniques to make traditionally delicious fare. These are dishes—like this colourful bean soup—that you can easily duplicate in your own kitchen.

1 tablespoon olive oil

2 onions, coarsely chopped

2 carrots, coarsely chopped

2 celery stalks, chopped

1¾ cups reduced-salt chicken stock

1 large can (796 ml) no-salt-added crushed tomatoes

½ cup chopped fresh basil

2 tablespoons chopped fresh oregano or 1 teaspoon dried oregano

1 can (540 ml) red kidney beans

1 can (540 ml) pinto beans

1 can (540 ml) chickpeas

½ cup freshly grated Parmesan cheese

1 Heat the oil in a large nonstick saucepan over medium-high heat. Sauté the onions, carrots and celery until soft, about 5 minutes. Add the chicken stock, tomatoes in purée, basil and oregano. Bring to a boil. Reduce the heat to medium-low, partially cover, and cook for 10 minutes.

2 Place the kidney and pinto beans and the chickpeas in a colander; rinse and drain. Stir them into the soup. Cook until the flavours develop, about 10 minutes. Remove from the heat.

3 Very coarsely purée about a quarter of the soup using a hand-held blender. Or transfer about 2 cups soup to a blender or food processor, very coarsely purée, and return to the pan. Serve 2 cups soup per person topped with 1 tablespoon of the freshly grated Parmesan cheese.

preparation time **25 mins**

cooking time **30 mins**

serves **6**

PER SERVING

250 calories

16 g protein

7 g total fat
2 g saturated fat

7 mg cholesterol

30 g total carbohydrate
10 g sugars

12 g fibre

848 mg sodium

HEALTH HINTS

Chunks of vegetables and plenty of beans make this soup rich in fibre. Beans are high in soluble fibre—the type that seems to control blood cholesterol in certain people by lowering LDL (the "bad" cholesterol). Carrots, celery and other vegetables contribute mostly insoluble fibre, which helps the intestines maintain regularity.

Remember, canned beans have salt added, so be sure to rinse them several times before adding them to the saucepan.

C Fb

preparation time **15 mins**
cooking time **30 mins**
serves **4**

PER SERVING

256 calories	
15 g protein	
9 g total fat	
3 g saturated fat	
56 mg cholesterol	
20 g total carbohydrate	
9 g sugars	
4 g fibre	
935 mg sodium	

HEALTH HINT

Tomatoes supply useful amounts of beta carotene and vitamin C, both of which have important antioxidant properties. The red colour of tomatoes comes from lycopene, another powerful antioxidant, which may help to reduce the risk of certain cancers if included in the diet regularly.

creamy tomato and crab soup

This tasty, hearty seafood soup is surprisingly quick and easy to make using fresh crab meat. The flaky crab meat goes well with the creamy texture lent by the potatoes, and the anchovies give it a bit of zing.

1 Heat the margarine and oil in a large saucepan. Add the onion and potatoes and cook over medium heat, stirring, for 5 minutes or until the onion is softened.

2 Stir in the tomatoes and chopped anchovies, then add the stock, wine and tomato paste. Season with pepper. Bring to a boil, then cover and simmer for 15 minutes, stirring occasionally.

3 Add about three-quarters of the crab meat to the pan and stir in the milk. Cover again and simmer gently for a further 10 minutes.

4 Ladle the soup into soup bowls and swirl the sour cream over the top. Garnish with the remaining crab meat, strips of anchovy and a sprinkling of paprika. Serve hot.

Variation For a smooth texture, at the end of step 3 purée the soup in a blender or food processor. Stir in an extra ¾ cup stock or low-fat milk, or a mixture of the two, and heat through.

1 tablespoon reduced-salt margarine

2 teaspoons extra virgin olive oil

1 large onion, finely chopped

400 g potatoes, peeled and finely diced

350 g ripe tomatoes, skinned, seeded and diced

2 anchovy fillets, drained and chopped

2⅓ cups fish stock (preferably reduced-salt)

¾ cup dry white wine

1 tablespoon tomato paste

pepper to taste

200 g ready-prepared, fresh crab meat

⅔ cup low-fat milk

4 tablespoons reduced-fat sour cream to garnish

2 anchovy fillets, drained and cut into thin strips, to garnish

paprika to garnish

old-fashioned chicken noodle soup

Packed with flavour, mixing pasta with chicken and a bounty of just-tender vegetables, it is easy to see why this soup is traditionally eaten as a restorative. Serve it as an entree and enjoy the leftover chicken in sandwiches the next day.

120 g vermicelli or thin spaghetti, broken into 5 cm pieces

1 carrot, halved lengthwise and thinly sliced

1 celery stalk, thinly sliced

50 g small broccoli florets

1 can (341 ml) corn kernels, drained

pepper to taste

2 tablespoons finely chopped fresh parsley

2 teaspoons fresh thyme leaves

CHICKEN BROTH

1 chicken, about 1.5 kg, skinned and jointed, or 4 chicken quarters, skinned

2 onions, halved, the inner layer of skin left on

3 carrots, chopped

3 celery stalks, chopped

1 bouquet garni

4 black peppercorns

1 For the broth, place the chicken in a large pan. Add the onions, carrots and celery. Pour in 8 cups water to cover the ingredients. Bring to a boil, skimming the surface constantly.

2 Reduce the heat to low as soon as the liquid boils. Add the bouquet garni and peppercorns. Partially cover the pan and simmer for 1 hour, skimming as necessary. After about 30–40 minutes remove the chicken if the juices run clear when the joints are pierced with the point of a knife. Set aside.

3 Line a colander with damp cheesecloth, place it over a bowl and strain the broth. Discard the vegetables and seasonings. Return 6 cups of the broth to the rinsed-out pan. Skim off any fat on the surface. Cool and freeze the leftover broth for stock. When the chicken is cool, remove the meat and discard the bones. Cut 220 g meat into bite-sized pieces for use in the soup. Reserve the remaining chicken for sandwiches.

4 Bring the broth to a boil; reduce the heat so the broth is simmering. Add the vermicelli and carrot, and simmer for 4 minutes. Add the celery, broccoli and corn, and cook for 5 minutes or until the pasta and vegetables are just tender.

5 Stir in the chicken with pepper to taste and heat through. Sprinkle in the parsley and thyme, and serve the soup at once.

C   GI

preparation time **45 mins**

cooking time **1¼ hours**

serves **4**

PER SERVING

281 calories

22 g protein

7 g total fat
2 g saturated fat

73 mg cholesterol

31 g total carbohydrate
4 g sugars

6 g fibre

195 mg sodium

HEALTH HINT

Chicken is a good source of protein and provides many of the B vitamins, particularly thiamin and niacin. Both the dark and white chicken meat can be added to the soup. The dark meat contains twice as much iron and zinc as the white meat.

hot and spicy black bean dip

Update your party menu with a chili-laced bean dip that's practically fat-free and an excellent source of fibre. The dip can also be spooned onto plates and served as a light lunch, accompanied by warm whole-wheat pita bread.

1 In a small saucepan of boiling water, cook the garlic for 2 minutes to blanch. Drain and transfer the garlic to a large bowl. Add the beans and mash with a potato masher.

2 Stir in the vinegar, lemon juice and cumin until the ingredients are well combined.

3 Fold in the coriander, green onions and jalapeño chili peppers and serve. (This recipe can be made ahead and refrigerated. Bring the dip to room temperature before serving.)

Variations This recipe is ideal for doubling or tripling. You'll need a really big mixing bowl, but if you don't have one, you can stir it up in batches.
• If you have time, cook dried black beans from scratch (use 1¼ cups dried beans for a single batch of the dip). Soak the beans overnight in water to cover, drain off the soaking water, then cover with fresh water and cook for 45 minutes to 1 hour, or until they are tender. Prepare the dip.

5 garlic cloves, peeled

1 can (540 ml) black beans, rinsed and drained (see the variation if using dried beans)

2 tablespoons white wine vinegar

1 tablespoon freshly squeezed lemon juice

2 teaspoons ground cumin

⅔ cup chopped fresh coriander

4 green onions, thinly sliced

2 pickled jalapeño chili peppers, finely chopped

preparation time **15 mins**

cooking time **5 mins**

serves **8**

PER SERVING

52 calories

3 g protein

0.4 g total fat
0.1 g saturated fat

0 mg cholesterol

9 g total carbohydrate
1 g sugars

3 g fibre

23 mg sodium

HEALTH HINT

No oil, no sour cream, no cream cheese—there's simply no added fat in this recipe, and the powerful seasonings mean that you'll never miss it. Canned beans are a handy pantry staple. They are an excellent and inexpensive source of protein and fibre, and contain little fat.

sundried tomato and basil crostini

Little bites of bliss, bursting with all the flavours of the Mediterranean—here, sundried tomatoes are marinated with a blend of Italian herbs. These snacks are so delicious, your guests will never guess how healthy they really are.

16 sundried tomatoes (not oil-packed)
½ cup fat-free Italian salad dressing
⅓ loaf Vienna bread, about 180 g
6 large fresh basil leaves

1 Place the tomatoes in a medium bowl. Add 6 tablespoons of the Italian dressing and toss to coat evenly. Marinate at room temperature for 30 minutes. Cut the bread diagonally into 8 slices, about 1 cm thick.

2 Stack the basil leaves and tightly roll them up lengthwise. Cut them crosswise into very thin slices to make "chiffonade."

3 Meanwhile, preheat the oven to 350°F (180°C). Arrange the slices of bread on a baking sheet and brush both sides with the remaining dressing. Bake the crostini until they are light golden, about 3 minutes on each side. Divide the tomatoes evenly among the bread slices. Bake until they are heated through, about 4 minutes. Sprinkle with basil and keep warm. Serve 2 crostini per person.

preparation time **15 mins** plus 30 mins marinating

cooking time **10 mins**

serves **4** (makes 8)

PER SERVING

201 calories

6 g protein

2 g total fat
0 g saturated fat

0 mg cholesterol

38 g total carbohydrate
11 g sugars

4 g fibre

632 mg sodium

COOK'S TIP

Triple this recipe for a quick hors d'oeuvre for your next party. Use 48 sundried tomatoes, 1½ cups salad dressing, 1 large loaf Vienna bread or 2 smaller loaves (550 g in total), and 18 basil leaves. Prepare the recipe as above, making 24 crostini.

Fb

preparation time **35 mins**

cooking time **40 mins**

serves **6**

PER SERVING

158 calories

5 g protein

6 g total fat

0 g saturated fat

2 mg cholesterol

20 g total carbohydrate

11 g sugars

4 g fibre

62 mg sodium

HEALTH HINT

Cooking carrots increases their nutritional value—it breaks down the tough cell walls so that the body can more readily absorb the beta carotene on offer and convert it to vitamin A. Sweet potatoes are another good source of beta carotene.

spiced vegetable wedges with tangy mustard dip

Lightly crushed coriander seeds and a hint of cinnamon accentuate the flavours of the vegetables, baked in wedges and served with a tangy mustard and yogourt dip. This is a terrific way to add more vegetables to your diet.

1 Preheat the oven to 425°F (220°C). Cut the carrots and parsnips into wedges. Place them in a saucepan and pour in enough water to just cover them. Bring to a boil; reduce the heat slightly and partially cover the pan. Cook for 2 minutes.

2 Meanwhile, mix together the lime juice, oil, coriander, cinnamon and pepper in a roasting pan. Cut the sweet potatoes across in half, then into thick wedges, about the same size as the carrot and parsnip. Add the sweet potatoes to the pan and coat in the spice mixture, then push them to one side of the pan.

3 Drain the carrots and parsnips and add them to the roasting pan. Use a spoon and fork to turn the hot vegetables and coat them with the spice mixture. Place the roasting pan in the oven and bake for 40 minutes, stirring and turning the vegetables twice, until they are well browned in places and just tender.

4 To make the dip, mix together the mustard, sugar and lime rind, then stir in the yogourt and dill. Transfer the dip to a serving bowl, cover and set aside.

5 Remove the vegetable wedges from the oven and leave them to cool slightly. Garnish the mustard dip with a little extra chopped dill, and serve with the vegetables.

2 large carrots

2 parsnips

juice of 1 lime

2 tablespoons canola oil

2 tablespoons lightly crushed coriander seeds

½ teaspoon ground cinnamon

pepper to taste

600 g sweet potatoes, peeled

TANGY MUSTARD DIP

2 teaspoons whole-grain mustard

1 teaspoon caster (superfine) sugar

grated rind of 1 lime

200 g plain low-fat yogourt

4 tablespoons chopped fresh dill, plus extra to garnish

vegetable chips with spicy peanut dip

 Oven-baked chips are not only healthier than those that are fried, their flavour is fresher and more concentrated, too. Here, thin slices of beet and potato are baked in a hot oven to make dippers for a spicy Asian peanut dip.

2 medium potatoes, about 300 g in total, washed

3 medium beets, about 350 g in total, washed

2 tablespoons canola oil

SPICY PEANUT DIP

2 teaspoons canola oil

1 large shallot, finely chopped

1 garlic clove, crushed

½ teaspoon ground cumin

½ teaspoon ground coriander

¼ cup crunchy peanut butter

1 teaspoon reduced-salt soy sauce

1 tablespoon clear honey

1 tablespoon freshly squeezed lemon juice

1 To make the dip, heat the oil in a small pan over medium heat, and fry the shallot and garlic for 3–4 minutes.

2 Stir in the cumin and coriander and cook for a few more seconds, then add the peanut butter, soy sauce, honey and 5 tablespoons water. Stir over low heat until the ingredients are combined. Remove from the heat and mix in the lemon juice. Spoon into a small bowl, cover and set aside.

3 Preheat the oven to 425°F (220°C). Cut the potatoes and beets into very thin (2 mm) slices, using the fine slicing blade in a food processor, or slice as thinly as possible with a knife.

4 Place the potato and beet slices in 2 separate bowls and add 1 tablespoon canola oil to each bowl. Toss the vegetable slices until they are coated lightly with oil, then spread them out in a single layer on 3 large nonstick baking sheets. Bake for 35 minutes, turning the vegetables frequently and moving the position of the baking sheets each time you turn the vegetables, until the potatoes are crisp and golden and the beets are firm but slightly moist. Keep a close eye on the vegetable chips to make sure they do not burn. Transfer to a wire rack to cool.

5 To serve, place the bowl of peanut dip on a large serving platter and pile the cooled vegetable chips around it.

 Fb

preparation time **15 mins**

cooking time **45 mins**

serves **4**

PER SERVING

288 calories

7 g protein

18 g total fat
2 g saturated fat

0 mg cholesterol

25 g total carbohydrate
14 g sugars

5 g fibre

150 mg sodium

HEALTH HINT

The beet, which was originally grown for its spinach-like leaves rather than the now more familiar dark red, swollen root, is related to the sugar beet. It has a sugar content similar to an apple. Beets are a good source of folate, a B vitamin essential for healthy blood.

crudités with three dips

Few foods are healthier than raw vegetables, so serve them with tempting low-fat dips for a starter. Or, for a light lunch, this recipe serves four. You can also offer fruit and whole-wheat pita bread for dipping.

preparation time **25 mins** plus 30 mins soaking

serves **8**

PER SERVING

110 calories	
8 g protein	
4 g total fat	
1 g saturated fat	
12 mg cholesterol	
9 g total carbohydrate	
6 g sugars	
2 g fibre	
93 mg sodium	

HEALTH HINT

Dairy products such as yogourt and cottage cheese are valuable sources of calcium.

1 To make the pesto-yogourt dip, use a blender or food processor to purée the basil, garlic and pine nuts to a paste. Work in the yogourt a spoonful at a time, until thoroughly combined. Add pepper to season. Transfer to a bowl, cover and chill until required.

2 To make the fresh herb dip, stir all the ingredients together in a bowl until well blended. Cover tightly and chill until required.

3 For the Italian-style tomato dip, place the sundried tomatoes in a heatproof bowl and pour over boiling water to cover them. Leave to soak for about 30 minutes or until the tomatoes are plump and tender. Drain the tomatoes well, then pat them dry and finely chop them.

4 Purée the cottage cheese with the yogourt in a food processor or blender. Alternatively, press the cheese through a sieve and stir in the yogourt. Transfer to a bowl and stir in the tomatoes. Cover and chill until required.

5 Just before serving the Italian-style tomato dip, finely shred the basil and stir in with pepper.

6 Serve the bowls of dip on a large platter with the vegetable crudités arranged around them.

450 g mixed vegetable crudités: baby carrots, zucchini sticks, baby corn (blanched in boiling water for 1 min), green beans (blanched 1 min), red and yellow pepper strips and broccoli florets

PESTO-YOGOURT DIP

1 cup firmly packed fresh basil leaves

1 garlic clove, crushed

1 tablespoon pine nuts

250 g plain low-fat yogourt

pepper to taste

FRESH HERB DIP

170 g reduced-fat ricotta or cream cheese

1 green onion, finely chopped

2 tablespoons finely chopped parsley

1 tablespoon finely snipped chives

1 teaspoon tarragon vinegar

ITALIAN-STYLE TOMATO DIP

50 g sundried tomatoes (not oil-packed)

80 g reduced-fat cottage cheese

80 g plain low-fat yogourt

½ cup firmly packed fresh basil leaves

pepper to taste

sesame shrimp and crab toast

This crispy toast can be served as a starter or as a good savoury snack to hand around with drinks. Traditionally the toast is deep-fried in oil, but in this healthy version it is baked in a hot oven until crisp and golden.

1 Preheat the oven to 400°F (200°C). For the topping, place the shrimp, flaked crab meat, green onions, garlic, red pepper, lemon rind, cayenne pepper and cream into a bowl and mix all the ingredients together well to make a spreadable paste. Season with pepper and set the mixture aside until ready to cook. (If you want to prepare the mixture ahead, it can be kept in the refrigerator for 4 hours.)

2 Beat together the cream and egg until smooth. Dip the slices of multi-grain bread in the mixture to coat both sides well, then place the bread on a greased baking sheet. Spread the shrimp and crab topping evenly over the bread, spreading right up to the edges.

3 Lightly brush the remaining egg and cream mixture over the surface of the shrimp and crab topping and sprinkle evenly with the sesame seeds.

4 Bake the toast for 20–25 minutes or until crisp and golden-brown. Cut each slice of toast into 8 small triangles and serve immediately, while still hot, garnished with shredded green onions.

Variation For five-spice shrimp and water chestnut toast, omit the crab meat and use 170 g shrimp instead of 80 g. Season the mixture with ¼ teaspoon five-spice powder instead of the cayenne pepper and lemon rind. Instead of the red pepper, stir in 6 water chestnuts, very finely chopped, and 4 teaspoons chopped fresh coriander.

1 tablespoon reduced-fat cream
1 large egg
2 large slices multi-grain bread
2 teaspoons sesame seeds
pepper to taste
shredded green onions to garnish

SHRIMP AND CRAB TOPPING
80 g peeled raw shrimp, very finely chopped
80 g fresh crab meat, flaked
2 green onions, thinly sliced
1 large garlic clove, crushed
½ small red pepper, seeded and diced
½ teaspoon finely grated lemon rind
⅛ teaspoon cayenne pepper
1 tablespoon reduced-fat cream
pepper to taste

preparation time **15 mins**
cooking time **25 mins**
serves **4**

PER SERVING

140 calories

12 g protein

5 g total fat
2 g saturated fat

119 mg cholesterol

11 g total carbohydrate
2 g sugars

2 g fibre

288 mg sodium

HEALTH HINT

Crab meat is low in saturated fat and in calories and has many nutrition benefits for heart-conscious people. It gives you omega-3 fats and is rich in B vitamins and many minerals, particularly potassium, zinc, iodine and phosphorus. An entree-size portion of crab (100 g) has only 13 calories.

rice croquettes with mozzarella

These rice croquettes are moulded around nuggets of mozzarella and rolled in breadcrumbs before cooking. Traditionally croquettes are deep-fried, but these are oven-baked for a modern streamlined version that is much healthier.

1 tablespoon extra virgin olive oil

1 small onion, finely chopped

1 cup arborio (risotto) rice

4 tablespoons dry vermouth

2⅓ cups hot reduced-salt vegetable stock

pepper to taste

1 egg, beaten

⅓ cup freshly grated Parmesan cheese

⅔ cup fine white breadcrumbs, made from bread 1–2 days old

50 g mozzarella cheese, cut into 8 cubes

100 g baby spinach to serve

lemon wedges to serve

1 Heat the oil in a saucepan, add the onion and cook until softened, 5 minutes. Add the rice and stir. Stir in the vermouth and boil until it has almost evaporated. Add a ladleful of stock and simmer, stirring, until it is almost all absorbed. Continue adding stock, a ladleful at a time, allowing it to be almost absorbed before adding the next, stirring frequently, about 15–20 minutes. The risotto is ready when the rice is tender but the grains are still firm, and the overall texture is creamy.

2 Remove from heat and season with pepper. Stir in the egg and Parmesan cheese, then leave to cool. Preheat the oven to 400°F (200°C). Heat a lightly oiled ovenproof dish in the oven. Mix the breadcrumbs with some pepper on a large plate. Spoon the risotto into 8 mounds on a board. Press a cube of mozzarella into the centre of each mound, then press the risotto over the cheese to enclose it. With your hands, mould each mound into a neat egg-shaped croquette. Roll the croquettes in the seasoned breadcrumbs until completely coated. Place in the hot ovenproof dish and bake for 30–40 minutes, turning halfway through, until golden-brown.

3 Make a heap of spinach on 4 plates and top each one with 2 croquettes. Serve immediately, with lemon wedges.

preparation time **15 mins** plus cooling

cooking time **1¼ hours**

serves **4** (makes 8)

PER SERVING

391 calories

13 g protein

12 g total fat
4 g saturated fat

68 mg cholesterol

52 g total carbohydrate
4 g sugars

2 g fibre

867 mg sodium

HEALTH HINT

Raw spinach is a good source of beta carotene and provides vitamins C and E, all of which are antioxidants that help to protect against heart disease, strokes and cancer.

chicken nuggets with mustard dip

This healthy version of the popular deep-fried takeout snack will soon become a favourite. Serve the nuggets hot, with oven-baked potatoes and fresh vegetables, or cold for a picnic or a packed lunch.

1 To make the mustard dip, mix together the yogourt, mustard, chives and pepper to taste. Spoon into a small serving bowl. Cover and chill until required.

2 Meanwhile, slit open each chicken breast horizontally, then cut lengthwise into thin strips. Place the flour in a large plastic bag, add the chicken strips and shake the bag until all the strips are coated in flour.

3 Place the breadcrumbs, garlic, mustard and paprika in a large bowl, and mix together until well blended. Tip the mixture onto a large plate. Break the eggs onto a deep plate and lightly beat with a fork.

4 Remove the chicken strips, one at a time, from the bag of flour, shaking off any excess, and dip first into the beaten egg and then into the breadcrumb mixture, pressing the breadcrumbs evenly over them. Arrange the nuggets on a large nonstick baking sheet and chill for about 30 minutes.

5 Preheat the oven to 400°F (200°C). Bake the chicken nuggets for around 30–40 minutes or until they are golden-brown in colour and crisp in texture. Serve hot or cold, with the mustard dip and with lemon or lime wedges.

550 g chicken breasts
2 tablespoons all-purpose flour
2½ cups fresh whole-wheat breadcrumbs
1 garlic clove, crushed
8 tablespoons whole-grain mustard
1 tablespoon paprika
2 eggs
lemon or lime wedges to serve

MUSTARD DIP
⅔ cup plain low-fat yogourt
1 tablespoon whole-grain mustard
1 tablespoon snipped fresh chives
pepper to taste

preparation time **25 mins** plus 30 mins chilling
cooking time **40 mins**
serves **4**

PER SERVING

438 calories

43 g protein

14 g total fat
4 g saturated fat

207 mg cholesterol

34 g total carbohydrate
5 g sugars

3 g fibre

691 mg sodium

HEALTH HINT

Here we have based a dip on low-fat yogourt instead of the usual sour cream to cut the fat and calories. A little mustard, fresh chopped herbs and pepper to taste helps liven the flavour.

avocado and shrimp cups

Here, lettuce-lined bowls are filled with shrimp and avocado, mixed with spiced new potatoes and topped with yogourt for a real hot and cold taste explosion. Serve for lunch with whole-wheat or multi-grain bread.

600 g new potatoes, washed and diced

2 tablespoons canola oil

1 small red onion, thinly sliced

1 garlic clove, crushed

1 large mild red chili, seeded and finely chopped

1 teaspoon coriander seeds, roughly crushed

1 teaspoon cumin seeds, roughly crushed

1 large avocado

400 g peeled cooked shrimp

juice of 2 limes

pepper to taste

8 tablespoons plain low-fat acidophilus yogourt

4 tablespoons chopped fresh coriander

8 round lettuce leaves

1 Cook the potatoes in a saucepan of boiling water for 8 minutes or until just tender. Drain and rinse under cold running water. Dry in a clean dish towel.

2 Heat the oil in a frying pan, add the onion and fry for 5 minutes or until softened and lightly browned. Add the garlic, chili and crushed coriander and cumin seeds, and cook for 1 more minute, stirring. Stir in the potatoes and fry over a high heat for 3 minutes. Remove from the heat and leave to cool.

3 Peel the avocado, remove the pit and cut the flesh into small chunks. Add to the potatoes together with the shrimp and lime juice. Season with pepper and toss gently.

4 Mix together the yogourt and coriander and season with pepper. Arrange 2 lettuce leaves in each of 4 bowls. Spoon the salad into them and top with the coriander yogourt.

Variation For an avocado, potato and tofu salad, replace the shrimp with 250 g plain tofu, drained and cubed. Add the tofu in step 2.

preparation time **20 mins** plus cooling

cooking time **20 mins**

serves **4**

PER SERVING

425 calories
29 g protein
24 g total fat
4 g saturated fat
190 mg cholesterol
22 g total carbohydrate
3 g sugars
5 g fibre
441 mg sodium

HEALTH HINT

Acidophilus yogourts are made using probiotic bacteria called *Lactobacillus acidophilus* and *Bifidobacterium* (bifidus), and they have a milder, slightly creamier taste than ordinary yogourts. Probiotic yogourts are believed to be more effective at keeping a healthy balance of bacteria in the gut than other yogourts. All types of yogourt are a good source of calcium, phosphorus, riboflavin and vitamin B_{12}.

preparation time **40 mins** plus 2 hours marinating

cooking time **30 mins**

serves **4**

PER SERVING

325 calories

28 g protein

21 g total fat
4 g saturated fat

71 mg cholesterol

6 g total carbohydrate
4 g sugars

3 g fibre

678 mg sodium

HEART SUPERFOOD

Like most other nuts, peanuts are high in fat, although much of the fat they contain is of the unsaturated variety. New research suggests that diets that contain a daily intake of peanuts, peanut butter or peanut oil may help to lower total cholesterol, particularly harmful LDL cholesterol, and thus help to protect against heart disease.

spicy chicken satay

Moist, gingery cubes of chicken and crunchy vegetables are cooked on skewers and served with peanut sauce. Wedges of lime are included so the hot juice can be squeezed over the cooked chicken just before eating.

1 To make the marinade, mix the ginger, soy sauce, lime juice and oil together in a bowl. Add the chicken and toss to coat. Cover with plastic wrap and leave to marinate in the refrigerator for at least 2 hours, turning once or twice.

2 Soak 8 wooden skewers in cold water for at least 30 minutes.

3 Meanwhile, to make the peanut sauce, heat the oil in a small saucepan, add the onion and cook over medium heat, stirring, for 3 minutes. Add the peanuts and cook for 3–5 minutes or until both the nuts and onion are lightly browned, stirring occasionally. Add the garlic, curry paste, soy sauce, sugar and ⅔ cup water. Bring to a boil. Stir in the coconut cream. Simmer gently for 5 minutes or until thickened, stirring occasionally. Purée the sauce in a blender or food processor to make a thick cream. Return to the saucepan and set aside.

4 Preheat the broiler. Lift the chicken out of the marinade; reserve the marinade. Thread the chicken, lime wedges and vegetables onto the soaked skewers. Arrange the skewers on the broiler rack and brush with the marinade. Place under the broiler, close to the heat, and cook, turning once or twice, until the ingredients are browned and the chicken is cooked thoroughly—test by cutting one of the chicken pieces in half with a knife; there should be no hint of pink.

5 While the satay is cooking, reheat the sauce. Arrange the satay on 4 serving plates, garnish with sprigs of coriander and serve with the sauce.

350 g chicken breasts, cut into 2 cm cubes

1 lime, cut into 8 wedges

8 cherry tomatoes

1 yellow pepper, seeded and cut into chunks

1 zucchini, thickly sliced

sprigs of fresh coriander to garnish

MARINADE

2 cm piece fresh ginger, peeled and finely chopped

2 tablespoons reduced-salt soy sauce

juice of ½ lime

1 tablespoon canola oil

PEANUT SAUCE

2 teaspoons canola oil

1 small onion, finely chopped

⅓ cup unsalted peanuts, finely chopped

1 garlic clove, chopped

1 teaspoon prepared Thai green curry paste

1 tablespoon reduced-salt soy sauce

½ teaspoon caster (superfine) sugar

2 tablespoons reduced-fat coconut cream

dim sum with dipping sauce

These Chinese dumplings have a chicken filling, which is lighter than the traditional pork mixture. Wonton wrappers, sold in most supermarkets, can be used. Serve these dim sum as the starter for a multi-course Chinese meal.

1 can (199 ml) water chestnuts, drained and chopped

4 green onions, thinly sliced

2 tablespoons chopped fresh coriander

1 tablespoon reduced-salt soy sauce

1 tablespoon sesame oil

350 g ground chicken

1 teaspoon caster (superfine) sugar

1 tablespoon finely chopped fresh ginger

5 garlic cloves, finely chopped

30 g fresh shiitake mushrooms, chopped

1 tablespoon cornstarch, plus extra for dusting

cayenne pepper to taste

48 wonton wrappers

150 g bok choy

DIPPING SAUCE

hoisin sauce, chopped green onions, chopped fresh coriander, reduced-salt soy sauce and/or sesame oil

1 Mix together the water chestnuts, green onions, coriander, soy sauce and sesame oil. Add the chicken, sugar, ginger, garlic and mushrooms. Stir in the cornstarch and the cayenne pepper and mix well. Cook a small spoonful of the chicken mixture in a frying pan, then taste it to check the seasoning.

2 Dust a plate with cornstarch. Place about 1 teaspoon of filling on the middle of a wonton wrapper. Dampen the wrapper slightly just around the filling. Gather up the wrapper, pinching it around the filling to form a cup, open at the top and with "frilly" edges. Set aside on the plate, and fill the remaining wrappers.

3 Line a multi-layered steamer with the bok choy or spinach. Stand the dim sum on the leaves and steam over rapidly boiling water for about 8–10 minutes. Serve the dumplings hot with the bok choy, and with the ingredients for the dipping sauce in individual bowls so that diners can mix them together to make a sauce to their own taste.

preparation time **45 mins**

cooking time **50 mins**

serves **6**

PER SERVING

340 calories

18 g protein

13 g total fat

3 g saturated fat

47 mg cholesterol

38 g total carbohydrate

5 g sugars

3 g fibre

503 mg sodium

HEALTH HINT

Garlic, onions, leeks and chives contain allicin, which has antifungal and antibiotic properties. Garlic also contains other compounds that have been shown in animal studies to inactivate carcinogens and suppress the growth of tumours.

pork pot-sticker dumplings with crisp and spicy peanut salad

These fragrant Chinese-style pasta purses are made with wonton wrappers. They are part fried, then simmered in stock and served on a bed of green leaves with a spicy salad of peanuts and crunchy vegetables.

1 Mix the pork, water chestnuts, green onions, ginger, hoisin sauce and soy sauce in a bowl, using your hands. Divide the mixture into 20 equal portions.

2 Brush a wonton wrapper with beaten egg and place a portion of the pork mixture in the centre. Gather up the wrapper around the pork and squeeze it together at the top to seal in the filling and form an old-fashioned moneybag shape. Repeat with the remaining pork and wonton wrappers.

3 Heat the oil in a large frying pan. Stand the dumplings in the pan, in one layer, cover and cook them very gently for 5 minutes or until they are lightly browned on the base.

4 Pour in enough hot stock to come halfway up the sides of the dumplings, then cover the pan again and simmer gently for 10 minutes or until the wonton wrappers are cooked.

5 Meanwhile, to make the salad, stir the cucumber, carrot, shallots and coriander together. Gradually add the sweet chili sauce, tasting the mixture to ensure that it is not too spicy for you, then add the peanuts and pepper to season.

6 To serve, arrange the lettuce leaves on 4 large plates and pile 5 drained dumplings on top of each. Spoon some of the spicy peanut salad around and garnish with coriander sprigs. Serve any remaining salad separately.

250 g lean ground pork
¼ can (199 ml) water chestnuts, drained and finely chopped
3 green onions, finely chopped
1 tablespoon finely grated fresh ginger
2 tablespoons hoisin sauce
1 tablespoon reduced-salt soy sauce
20 wonton wrappers
1 egg, beaten
2 tablespoons canola oil
1¼ cups hot reduced-salt chicken stock

SPICY PEANUT SALAD
7 cm piece cucumber, seeded and finely diced
1 large carrot, finely diced
2 shallots, finely chopped
2 4 tablespoons chopped fresh coriander
2 tablespoons sweet chili sauce
5 tablespoons finely chopped unsalted peanuts
pepper to taste
4–8 crisp green lettuce leaves to serve
sprigs of fresh coriander to garnish

preparation time **25 mins**
cooking time **15 mins**
serves **4**

PER SERVING

424 calories

22 g protein

22 g total fat
4 g saturated fat

91 mg cholesterol

34 g total carbohydrate
11 g sugars

4 g fibre

853 mg sodium

COOK'S TIP

Instead of frying and then simmering the dumplings, they can be steamed as for the dim sum with dipping sauce (see opposite page).

roast salmon strips with potato salad

This elegant entree is what the French would call a "salade composée"—a salad where the elements are arranged separately. In this healthy example, salmon shares the spotlight with a light potato salad and a healthy helping of greens.

370 g salmon fillet (in one piece)
750 g small red potatoes, unpeeled
3 shallots, finely chopped
1/3 cup white wine vinegar
2 tablespoons Dijon mustard
1/2 teaspoon pepper or to taste
1/2 cup finely chopped fresh dill
2 cups radishes, cut into thin matchstick strips
250 g mixed salad greens

1 Preheat the oven to 450°F (230°C). Place the salmon skin-side down in a roasting pan. Roast until it is just cooked through, about 10–15 minutes. Let it cool to room temperature. Remove skin.

2 Meanwhile, in a large saucepan of boiling water, cook the potatoes until they are just tender, about 20 minutes. Drain the potatoes and set aside. When cool enough to handle, slice the potatoes crosswise.

3 Combine the shallots, vinegar, mustard and pepper in a large bowl. Add the warm potatoes, tossing to combine. Just before serving, add the dill and radishes, and toss well to combine. Slice the salmon on the diagonal into 8 pieces. Arrange the potato salad, salmon and mixed salad greens on a serving platter and serve.

preparation time **30 mins**
cooking time **25 mins**
serves **4**

PER SERVING

285 calories

25 g protein

8 g total fat
2 g saturated fat

50 mg cholesterol

28 g total carbohydrate
5 g sugars

6 g fibre

166 mg sodium

COOK'S TIP

You can prepare both the fish and the potato salad a day ahead of time and refrigerate, but be sure to allow time for them both to return to room temperature before serving.

salmon cakes with creamy tomato-garlic sauce

Give those fatty beef burgers a miss and try these heart-healthy, thick, juicy salmon "burgers" instead. And while you're at it, leave the ketchup in the fridge and slather the salmon patties with a homemade tomato-garlic sauce.

1 To make the sauce, cook the sundried tomatoes and garlic in a small saucepan of boiling water for 3 minutes. Drain, reserving $1/3$ cup of the cooking liquid. Transfer the tomatoes and garlic to a food processor. Add the reserved cooking liquid, yogourt and hot chili sauce and purée until smooth.

2 Meanwhile, cook the potato and garlic in a medium saucepan of boiling water until tender, about 7 minutes. Drain and transfer to a large bowl. With a potato masher, mash the potato and garlic.

3 Stir in the salmon, 2 tablespoons breadcrumbs, the dill and the capers. Shape the salmon mixture into 8 cakes.

4 Heat the oil in a large nonstick frying pan over medium heat. Coat the salmon cakes in the remaining breadcrumbs. Add to the frying pan and sauté until golden-brown, about 3 minutes per side. Serve with the tomato-garlic sauce.

1 large baking potato, thinly sliced

2 garlic cloves, peeled

1 can (418 g) pink salmon, drained

2 tablespoons plus $1/2$ cup dried breadcrumbs

$1/2$ cup finely chopped fresh dill

1 tablespoon capers, thoroughly rinsed and drained

1 tablespoon olive oil

TOMATO-GARLIC SAUCE

$1/4$ cup sundried tomatoes (not oil-packed)

2 garlic cloves, peeled

100 g plain low-fat yogourt

$1/2$ teaspoon hot chili sauce

preparation time **15 mins**

cooking time **20 mins**

serves **4**

PER SERVING

320 calories

27 g protein

12 g total fat
3 g saturated fat

74 mg cholesterol

25 g total carbohydrate
6 g sugars

4 g fibre

751 mg sodium

HEART SUPERFOOD

Why is canned salmon so healthy? First, salmon is rich with omega-3 fatty acids—highly nutritious oils that keep the blood "flowing freely." In addition, canned salmon contains a useful amount of calcium, which helps lower blood pressure. The calcium comes from the salmon bones, which are softened and made edible in the canning process.

pasta, rice
& grains

fresh tomato sauce

Vine-ripened or full-flavoured summer tomatoes are best for this recipe, but you can also use canned tomatoes.

2 tablespoons extra virgin olive oil

1 large onion, finely chopped

1 garlic clove, chopped

1 kg tomatoes, skinned, seeded and chopped

2/3 cup red wine or vegetable stock (reduced-salt if possible)

2 tablespoons chopped fresh basil or 1 teaspoon dried basil

1/8 teaspoon sugar

pepper to taste

8–10 sprigs fresh basil, shredded, to garnish (optional)

5 tablespoons freshly grated Parmesan cheese or 5 heaping tablespoons Parmesan cheese shavings to serve (optional)

1 Heat the oil in a large saucepan. Add the onion and garlic, and cook gently, stirring occasionally, for 5 minutes or until softened but not browned.

2 Add the tomatoes, wine or stock and basil. Cook over medium heat for 20–30 minutes or until the sauce is thick.

3 Purée the sauce in a blender or food processor until smooth, then pass it through a fine sieve if a particularly smooth result is required.

4 Add the sugar to balance the acidity of the tomatoes. Stir in pepper to season and reheat the sauce.

5 Use the sauce as required. Or, if desired, pour it over freshly cooked pasta, toss well and top with shredded basil and freshly grated or shaved Parmesan cheese.

preparation time **10 mins**

cooking time **35 mins**

serves **4** (makes 2 1/3 cups)

PER SERVING

133 calories

3 g protein

9 g total fat

1 g saturated fat

0 mg cholesterol

7 g total carbohydrate

6 g sugars

3 g fibre

22 mg sodium

béchamel sauce

This classic white sauce is used in a range of dishes, such as lasagna. Many ingredients can be added to vary the flavour.

2 1/3 cups low-fat milk

1 onion or 2 shallots, halved

1 bay leaf

6 black peppercorns

1/8 teaspoon grated nutmeg or 1 blade of mace

4 tablespoons reduced-salt margarine

2/3 cup all-purpose flour

pepper to taste

1 Pour the milk into a heavy-based saucepan and add the onion or shallots, bay leaf, peppercorns and nutmeg or mace. Bring just to a boil over medium heat, then remove from the heat, cover and set aside to infuse for 10 minutes. Strain the flavoured milk into a large bowl.

2 Melt the margarine in the rinsed-out pan. Stir in the flour and cook gently, stirring occasionally, for 1 minute. Do not allow the flour to brown.

3 Remove the pan from the heat and gradually pour in the milk, stirring or whisking constantly. Return the pan to the heat and bring to a boil, still stirring or whisking.

4 Reduce the heat and simmer the sauce gently for 2 minutes, stirring occasionally, until it is smooth and thick.

5 Taste and add pepper. Use the sauce immediately.

preparation time **5 mins** plus 10 mins infusing

cooking time **5 mins**

serves **4** (makes 2 1/3 cups)

PER SERVING

237 calories

9 g protein

13 g total fat

2 g saturated fat

6 mg cholesterol

22 g total carbohydrate

11 g sugars

1 g fibre

156 mg sodium

preparation time **10 mins**
plus 30 mins infusing

cooking time **2 mins**

serves **4** (makes ²/₃ cup)

PER SERVING

206 calories

0 g protein

23 g total fat
3 g saturated fat

0 mg cholesterol

1 g total carbohydrate
0 g sugars

1 g fibre

4 mg sodium

garlic and herb dressing

Pasta is superb with this simple dressing. The secret is to warm the garlic with bay leaves in the oil, to mellow the garlic flavour slightly. Then the dressing is left to stand so that the flavour of the garlic can infuse the oil.

1 Crease the bay leaves in half and place them in a small saucepan with the garlic. Add about 1 tablespoon olive oil and heat gently for 2 minutes or until the oil just begins to sizzle around the garlic. Remove from the heat.

2 Stir in the lemon rind, then pour in the remaining oil. Set aside to infuse for at least 30 minutes.

3 Remove the bay leaves and add the herbs. Toss the dressing over hot pasta and serve.

2 fresh bay leaves
4 garlic cloves, thinly sliced
6 tablespoons extra virgin olive oil
grated rind of 1 lemon
5 tablespoons snipped fresh chives
5 tablespoons chopped fresh parsley
5 tablespoons chopped fresh
  tarragon, sage, marjoram
  or dill, or a mixture of
  fresh herbs

30

preparation time **10 mins**

serves **4** (makes ²/₃ cup)

PER SERVING

312 calories

4 g protein

33 g total fat
5 g saturated fat

7 mg cholesterol

1 g total carbohydrate
0 g sugars

1 g fibre

103 mg sodium

pesto sauce

A little homemade pesto sauce goes a long way. Toss this sauce into piping hot pasta just before eating. Store any leftover pesto in a screwtop jar in the refrigerator (cover the surface of the pesto with a little extra olive oil).

1 Place the garlic in a food processor or blender. Add the pine nuts and Parmesan cheese, and process until the ingredients are finely chopped and thoroughly combined.

2 Add the basil, including all the soft stalks. Process until the basil is chopped and the mixture begins to clump together.

3 Add the olive oil and process until combined. The sauce should have a fine, slightly grainy texture. Serve with pasta.

2 garlic cloves, peeled
¼ cup pine nuts
⅓ cup freshly grated Parmesan cheese
1 medium bunch fresh basil
6 tablespoons extra virgin olive oil

fusilli and meatballs

Unlike traditional recipes, these meatballs are low in fat, yet they're full of the terrific taste you crave. Long curls of pasta add a fun twist. For a casual dinner with friends, you can just double or triple the recipe.

1 large onion, chopped
2 garlic cloves, finely chopped
1 large can (796 ml) whole tomatoes
1 large can (796 ml) Italian tomatoes
¼ cup chopped fresh basil
1 tablespoon fresh oregano or
    1 teaspoon dried oregano
2 slices firm-textured whole-wheat
    bread
500 g lean ground beef
1 large egg
2 tablespoons low-fat milk
pepper to taste
370 g long fusilli (spiral pasta)

1 Coat a large saucepan with nonstick cooking spray and place over medium-high heat. Sauté the onion and garlic until soft, about 5 minutes. Transfer 2 tablespoons of the onion mixture to a large bowl.

2 Process the whole and Italian tomatoes in a food processor until fairly smooth. Add to the saucepan. Bring to a boil over medium-high heat. Reduce the heat to medium-low. Cover and simmer, stirring often, 30 minutes. Add the basil and oregano during the last 15 minutes.

3 Process the bread until crumbs form. Add the crumbs, beef, egg, milk and pepper to the onion mixture and mix until blended. Shape into eighteen 2 cm meatballs. Coat a frying pan with nonstick cooking spray and place over medium-high heat. Cook the meatballs in batches until they are browned, about 8 minutes. Drain on paper towel. Add the meatballs to the sauce. Cover and cook, stirring occasionally, 20 minutes.

4 Meanwhile, cook the pasta according to the package directions. Drain and toss with 1½ cups of the sauce in a large bowl. Spoon 1 cup of sauce over the pasta. Serve the meatballs accompanied by the remaining sauce.

preparation time **30 mins**
cooking time
1 hour 20 mins
serves **6**

PER SERVING

386 calories

28 g protein

8 g total fat
3 g saturated fat

85 mg cholesterol

51 g total carbohydrate
10 g sugars

7 g fibre

163 mg sodium

HEALTH HINT

By making the meatballs with very lean ground beef, you can enjoy this satisfying bowl of pasta without feeling any guilt.

herbed eggplant lasagna

Eggplants make delicious lasagna, but traditional methods usually involve slicing and frying them in copious quantities of oil. Here, they are diced and simmered with flavouring ingredients to make a rich, zesty sauce.

Fb GI

preparation time **30 mins** plus 10 mins standing

cooking time **1¼ hours**

serves **4**

PER SERVING

566 calories

39 g protein

16 g total fat
4 g saturated fat

73 mg cholesterol

68 g total carbohydrate
23 g sugars

15 g fibre

296 mg sodium

HEALTH HINT

Eggplants do not have a strong flavour, but absorb other flavours in a dish well. They add "bulk" for very few calories.

COOK'S TIP

Puréed cottage cheese makes a creamy base for a delicious low-fat lasagna topping.

1 Heat the oil in a large saucepan. Add the fennel and bay leaf, and cook for a few seconds, pressing the bay leaf with the back of a spoon to bring out its aroma. Add the onion, garlic, celery, carrot, mushrooms, marjoram and sage. Cook, stirring frequently, for 10 minutes until the vegetables soften slightly.

2 Stir in the eggplant mixture and lemon rind, mixing well. Continue to cook for 5 minutes, stirring frequently. Pour in the tomatoes with their juice and add pepper. Bring to a boil, then reduce the heat and simmer the eggplant mixture for 15 minutes. Preheat the oven to 350°F (180°C).

3 While the sauce is simmering, cook the lasagna in boiling water for 3–5 minutes, or according to the package instructions, until al dente. Drain well and lay out the pieces on a clean dish towel, in a single layer, to dry.

4 Purée the cottage cheese with the flour and egg in a food processor or blender until smooth. Add the milk and process again briefly. Season to taste with nutmeg and pepper.

5 Pour half the eggplant mixture into a large rectangular or square ovenproof dish. Discard the bay leaf. Cover with half the lasagna, then add the remaining eggplant mixture and top with the rest of the lasagna, overlapping the pieces neatly.

6 Pour the cottage cheese mixture over the lasagna to cover it completely. Sprinkle the Parmesan cheese evenly over the top. Bake the lasagna for about 45 minutes or until the topping is set and deep golden.

7 Leave the lasagna to stand for 10 minutes before serving. This allows time for the pasta and sauce to cool and set slightly.

2 tablespoons extra virgin olive oil

1 tablespoon fennel seeds

1 bay leaf

1 large onion, chopped

1 garlic clove, crushed

1 celery stalk, diced

1 carrot, diced

100 g mushrooms, roughly chopped

4 tablespoons chopped fresh marjoram or 1 tablespoon dried oregano

6 fresh sage leaves, shredded, or 1 tablespoon dried sage

2 large eggplants, diced 1 cm thick

grated rind of 1 lemon

1 large can (796 ml) diced tomatoes

pepper to taste

12 sheets fresh lasagna, about 250 g in total

450 g reduced-fat cottage cheese

2 tablespoons all-purpose flour

1 egg

⅓ cup low-fat milk

⅛ teaspoon freshly grated nutmeg

pepper to taste

2 tablespoons freshly grated Parmesan cheese

mushroom ravioli in herb jus

Store-bought stuffed pasta just does not taste anything like silken-textured homemade pasta with a freshly prepared savoury filling. This is not a convenience meal—making pasta does take time—but it is well worth it!

4 tablespoons extra virgin olive oil

4 shallots, chopped

1 garlic clove, chopped

450 g mushrooms, finely chopped

4 tablespoons brandy

pepper to taste

30 g dried porcini mushrooms, soaked, drained and finely chopped

1¼ cups fresh whole-wheat breadcrumbs

50 g Parmesan cheese, freshly grated

2 eggs

2 tablespoons chopped fresh parsley or basil

1 teaspoon chopped fresh marjoram or ¼ teaspoon dried marjoram

2 tablespoons all-purpose flour

250 g snow peas or sugar snap peas

2 tablespoons tiny tender sprigs fresh thyme to garnish

1 tablespoon extra virgin olive oil to serve (optional)

PASTA

4¼ cups all-purpose flour

4 eggs, beaten

1 tablespoon extra virgin olive oil

HERB JUS

3 cups reduced-salt chicken or vegetable stock

¾ cup dry white wine

1 garlic clove, chopped

1 tablespoon fresh thyme leaves or ¼ teaspoon dried thyme

4 zucchinis, thinly sliced or coarsely diced

1 Heat the olive oil in a large saucepan. Add the shallots and cook for a few seconds, then add the garlic and the mushrooms. Cook over high heat, stirring, to brown the mushrooms, then reduce the heat and cook for 10 minutes or until the mixture has reduced in volume.

2 Pour in the brandy and cook, stirring, until it has evaporated. Remove from the heat and add pepper.

3 Stir in the porcini mushrooms, breadcrumbs, Parmesan cheese, eggs, parsley and marjoram. The ingredients should form a moist paste. Place in the refrigerator while you make the pasta.

4 To make the pasta, sift the flour onto a work surface, make a well in the centre and add the eggs and oil.

5 Using your hands, gradually mix the flour into the eggs and oil, until the mixture begins to form a firm dough. If necessary, add a few drops of water.

6 Knead the dough for 10 minutes or until smooth and elastic. The dough should still be firm. Add a little extra flour if the dough becomes too sticky. Wrap the dough tightly in plastic wrap and set aside to rest for 30 minutes.

7 Cut the pasta dough into quarters and roll out each separately. If using a pasta machine to roll the dough, use the second-thinnest setting. Otherwise, roll it out by hand on an unfloured surface. Cut each rolled-out quarter into 2 strips, each about 10 x 50 cm.

8 Lay a pasta strip on the work surface. Dot the filling on the dough in small mounds (about 1 teaspoon each), about 5 cm apart. Ensure that there is enough room between the mounds of filling for the covering of dough to stick to the base.

9 Brush the dough around each mound with a little water. Top with a second strip of pasta and press it down firmly around the filling to seal. Cut between the mounds of filling with a fluted pastry wheel or sharp knife.

10 Carefully pull the ravioli apart and toss with the flour. Place in a single layer on a plate in the fridge. Repeat with the remaining dough and filling.

11 To make the herb jus, combine the stock, wine and garlic in a saucepan. Bring to a boil and cook over high heat for

preparation time **1 hour** plus 30 mins standing

cooking time **40 mins**

serves **6**

PER SERVING

643 calories	
28 g protein	
25 g total fat	
6 g saturated fat	
224 mg cholesterol	
70 g total carbohydrate	
6 g sugars	
8 g fibre	
603 mg sodium	

HEALTH HINT

Mushrooms are low in fat and calories, and they also provide useful amounts of copper as well as some of the B vitamins.

5–10 minutes or until the liquid is well flavoured. Add the thyme and zucchinis, and continue cooking over medium-high heat for 5–10 minutes or until the zucchinis are quite tender but not mushy, and the liquid has intensified in flavour and evaporated slightly.

12 Meanwhile, cook the ravioli in boiling water for 4–5 minutes or until they rise to the surface. Add the snow or sugar snap peas for the final 30–60 seconds of cooking. Drain well.

13 Serve the ravioli and snow peas in shallow soup bowls with the zucchinis and herb and garlic jus ladled over. Sprinkle thyme over the top and drizzle with the 1 tablespoon olive oil, if using. Serve immediately.

Variations Store-bought wonton wrappers can be used instead of homemade pasta dough to make ravioli. • Alternatively, you can buy fresh lasagna and roll it out slightly thinner, if necessary, then use it to make the ravioli.

mushroom and cheese macaroni

 Introduce vegetables to old favourites for healthy family meals. This well-loved pasta dish is delicious with mushrooms, peas and red pepper added. Using a small amount of powerful blue vein cheese adds flavour, but not too much fat.

220 g macaroni or rigatoni
170 g frozen peas
2 tablespoons sunflower oil
1 red pepper, seeded and chopped
220 g mushrooms, quartered if large
¼ cup all-purpose flour
2⅓ cups low-fat milk
1 tablespoon Dijon mustard
50 g blue vein cheese, chopped
pepper to taste
30 g 25% reduced-fat Cheddar
    cheese, grated
⅔ cup fresh whole-wheat breadcrumbs

1 Preheat the oven to 425°F (220°C). Cook the pasta in boiling water for 10–12 minutes, or according to the package instructions, until almost al dente. Add the peas for the final 2 minutes of cooking. Drain the pasta and peas well.

2 Heat the oil in a heavy-based saucepan and cook the red pepper for 1–2 minutes. Add the mushrooms and cook for 2–3 minutes or until softened, stirring occasionally.

3 Stir in the flour, then gradually stir in the milk and bring to a boil, stirring. Simmer until thickened.

4 Add the mustard and blue vein cheese with pepper to season, and stir until the cheese has melted. Add the pasta and peas and mix thoroughly. Pour the mixture into an ovenproof dish.

5 Mix the Cheddar cheese with the breadcrumbs and sprinkle this over the pasta mixture. Bake for 10–15 minutes or until lightly browned and bubbling hot. Serve immediately.

preparation time **10 mins**
cooking time **40 mins**
serves **4**

PER SERVING

410 calories

22 g protein

17 g total fat
5 g saturated fat

25 mg cholesterol

43 g total carbohydrate
13 g sugars

6 g fibre

404 mg sodium

HEALTH HINT

Frozen vegetables often contain more vitamin C than fresh ones. For example, frozen peas retain 60–70 per cent of their vitamin content after freezing and maintain this level throughout storage.

squash, ricotta and sage gnocchi

There are numerous versions of gnocchi. Here a flour-based dough of ricotta cheese and mashed squash, flavoured with sage and Parmesan cheese, is used. A colourful roasted red pepper and onion sauce completes the dish.

preparation time **30 mins** plus 1–2 hours drying

cooking time **1¼ hours**

serves **4**

PER SERVING

386 calories

19 g protein

15 g total fat
6 g saturated fat

87 mg cholesterol

44 g total carbohydrate
8 g sugars

5 g fibre

244 mg sodium

HEALTH HINT

Like other cheeses, ricotta is a good source of calcium. In addition, it offers good quantities of phosphorus, another mineral involved in ensuring that bones and teeth are healthy. Phosphorus is also important in the release of energy from food.

1 Preheat the oven to 400°F (200°C). Spread the pepper and onion halves, cut-side down, on a baking sheet. Place the squash wedges, skin-side up, on another baking sheet. Bake the peppers and onion for 30 35 minutes, and the squash for 45–55 minutes, or until all the vegetables are tender.

2 Transfer the peppers and onions to a blender or food processor and add the oil. Blend until almost smooth. Season with pepper. Pour into a saucepan and set aside.

3 Leave the squash until cool enough to handle, then scrape the flesh from the skin into a bowl. Mash until smooth. Beat in the ricotta cheese, egg, chopped sage and Parmesan cheese, then gradually work in the flour to make a soft dough.

4 Flour a work surface. Divide the dough into quarters and, with floured hands, roll each piece into a long, 2 cm thick rope. Cut into 2 cm lengths. Press the back of a fork into each piece of dough to make a pattern. Leave the gnocchi at room temperature to dry for 1–2 hours.

5 Bring a large saucepan of water to a boil. Drop in the gnocchi, 10–12 at a time, and poach for 2–3 minutes or until they bob up to the surface. Remove with a slotted spoon and drain well on paper towel. Set aside and keep warm until all the gnocchi are cooked. Meanwhile, gently warm the roasted pepper sauce over low heat. Spoon the sauce over the gnocchi, garnish with sage leaves and serve at once.

2 red peppers, halved and seeded

1 onion, halved

500 g squash, cut into wedges and seeded

1 tablespoon extra virgin olive oil

pepper to taste

250 g reduced-fat ricotta cheese

1 egg, beaten

4 tablespoons chopped fresh sage

30 g Parmesan cheese, freshly grated

2 cups all-purpose flour, plus extra for rolling

fresh sage leaves to garnish

linguine with tomato sauce

This quick and easy sauce is bursting with tomatoes and olive oil—foods that will keep your heart pumping strong.

750 g Italian tomatoes, seeded and chopped
²⁄₃ cup chopped fresh basil
¼ cup extra virgin olive oil
¼ cup chopped Italian parsley
2 tablespoons chopped fresh mint
2 teaspoons grated orange rind
3 garlic cloves, finely chopped
pepper to taste
370 g linguine
¼ cup freshly grated Parmesan cheese to serve

1 Mix the tomatoes, basil, oil, parsley, mint, orange rind, garlic and pepper in a bowl. Let the mixture stand for between 30 minutes and 2 hours at room temperature.

2 Cook the pasta according to the package directions. Drain the pasta well and place in a large bowl. Top with the sauce, sprinkle with the Parmesan cheese and serve.

preparation time **20 mins** plus standing
cooking time **15 mins**
serves **4**

PER SERVING

424 calories

12 g protein

17 g total fat
3 g saturated fat

5 mg cholesterol

55 g total carbohydrate
3 g sugars

6 g fibre

94 mg sodium

angel hair pasta with basil and walnut pesto

This pesto recipe adds the extra health boost of spinach and the peppery surprise of arugula, in true heart-healthy style.

2 cups fresh basil leaves
2 cups trimmed fresh spinach
1 cup trimmed arugula
¹⁄₃ cup walnut pieces
4 tablespoons grated Parmesan cheese
3 garlic cloves, peeled
1 tablespoon olive oil
370 g angel hair pasta or spaghettini
fresh basil sprigs to garnish
½ lemon to serve

1 Place the basil, spinach and arugula in a colander. Wash the leaves well under cold running water. Shake to dry. Transfer the leaves to a food processor.

2 Add the walnuts, Parmesan cheese and garlic and process until finely chopped. With the machine still running, slowly drizzle the oil through the feed tube, processing until the pesto is thick.

3 Meanwhile, cook the pasta according to the package directions; drain. Toss the pasta with the pesto in a large serving bowl until evenly coated. Garnish with the basil sprigs, squeeze the lemon juice over the pasta and serve.

preparation time **15 mins**
cooking time **10 mins**
serves **4**

PER SERVING

400 calories

13 g protein

14 g total fat
2 g saturated fat

5 mg cholesterol

54 g total carbohydrate
1 g sugars

6 g fibre

90 mg sodium

HEALTH HINT

This dish provides a heavy dose of thiamine, essential in converting glucose into energy.

spaghetti with puttanesca sauce

Puttanesca is an Italian sauce that's hearty, spicy and rich in flavour. This version keeps in the traditional capers, anchovies and olives, but just uses fewer of them to keep down the level of fat.

1 Cook the spaghetti in boiling water for 10–12 minutes, or according to the package instructions. Drain and keep hot. Meanwhile, crush the olives with the side of a large knife; remove the pits and finely chop.

2 Heat the oil in a large nonstick frying pan over medium heat. Sauté the garlic until golden, 3 minutes. Stir in the tomatoes, capers, anchovies and chili powder. Cook, stirring, until the sauce thickens slightly, 10 minutes. Stir in the olives.

3 Add the spaghetti to the sauce in the frying pan and toss to coat well. Sprinkle with the parsley and serve.

370 g spaghetti

4 black olives

1 tablespoon olive oil

2 garlic cloves, finely chopped

1 large can (796 ml) crushed tomatoes

1 tablespoon capers, drained and rinsed

2 anchovies, finely chopped, or 1 teaspoon anchovy paste

¼ teaspoon chili powder

1 tablespoon finely chopped parsley to garnish

preparation time **10 mins**
cooking time **15 mins**
serves **4**

PER SERVING

341 calories

11 g protein

6 g total fat
1 g saturated fat

2 mg cholesterol

60 g total carbohydrate
8 g sugars

7 g fibre

204 mg sodium

COOK'S TIP

To maximize the flavour of olives and minimize the fat, opt for a full-bodied imported variety—a small amount delivers big taste. Look for black-purple kalamatas from Greece, wrinkled black gaetas from Italy or small black niçoise olives from France.

pasta and chicken salad with basil

Quick to prepare, this salad makes an ideal midweek dinner and won't spoil if someone is late home. Tossing the pasta with lemon juice and white wine not only adds flavour but also means that the quantity of oil can be reduced.

300 g pasta shells

100 g snow peas

4 tablespoons extra virgin olive oil

finely shredded rind and juice
    of 1 lemon

5 tablespoons dry white wine

pepper to taste

400 g chicken breasts, cut into bite-
    sized chunks

2 garlic cloves, thinly sliced

200 g small Italian tomatoes, halved,
    or 3 medium Italian tomatoes,
    each cut into 6 wedges

50 g pitted black olives

1 small bunch fresh basil

1 Drop the pasta into a large saucepan of boiling water. When the water returns to a boil, cook for 10–12 minutes, or according to the package instructions, until al dente. Add the snow peas for the final minute of cooking. Drain, rinse with cold water and drain again well.

2 Mix 2$\frac{1}{2}$ tablespoons of the oil with the lemon rind and juice and the wine in a large salad bowl. Season with pepper. Add the pasta and snow peas, and toss to coat with the dressing. Set aside to cool slightly.

3 Meanwhile, heat the remaining 1$\frac{1}{2}$ tablespoons of oil in a large frying pan. Add the chicken and garlic, and stir-fry over high heat for 5–6 minutes or until the chicken is lightly browned and thoroughly cooked. Add to the pasta.

4 Scatter the tomatoes and olives over the top. Sprinkle with the basil leaves, tearing larger ones into pieces. Toss the salad together and serve while the chicken is still warm.

Fb GI

preparation time **15 mins**

cooking time **20 mins**

serves **4**

PER SERVING

533 calories

34 g protein

22 g total fat

4 g saturated fat

81 mg cholesterol

48 g total carbohydrate

5 g sugars

5 g fibre

174 mg sodium

HEALTH HINT

Pasta, when cooked al dente, has a low GI (Glycemic Index), so it is digested and absorbed slowly—you stay full for longer. The lemon juice in the dressing increases the acidity, which also works to delay digestion.

Asian-style chicken and pasta salad

Pasta bows taste deliciously different when combined with an exotic dressing of fish sauce, fresh red chili and rice vinegar in a moist chicken salad. Fresh crunchy vegetables complete this well-balanced main-course dish.

1 Place the chicken breasts in a large shallow pan and pour over enough water to cover them. Add the lemon or lime slices and the rice wine or sherry, and heat until just simmering. Reduce the heat and poach the chicken for 20 minutes or until cooked through. Remove from the heat and cover the pan, then leave the chicken to cool completely in the cooking liquid.

2 Meanwhile, cook the pasta in boiling water for about 10–12 minutes, or according to the package instructions, until al dente. Drain, rinse under cold running water and drain again. Set the pasta aside until cool.

3 Place the carrot, red pepper, celery and cucumber in a large salad bowl. To make the dressing, mix together the fish sauce and sugar, stirring until the sugar dissolves, then add the vinegar, soy sauce, chili and garlic. Pour the dressing over the raw salad vegetables.

4 Drain the cooled chicken and pat dry on paper towel, then cut into bite-sized pieces. Stir the chicken and pasta into the dressed vegetables. Cover and leave to marinate in the refrigerator for about 1 hour. Bring the salad to room temperature before serving.

450 g chicken breasts

2 lemon or lime slices

1 tablespoon rice wine (sake or mirin) or dry sherry

300 g farfalle (pasta bows)

1 large carrot, cut into matchstick strips

1 red pepper, seeded and cut into matchstick strips

2 celery stalks, cut into matchstick strips

½ large cucumber, halved, seeded and cut into matchstick strips

DRESSING

2 tablespoons fish sauce

1 teaspoon caster (superfine) sugar

1 tablespoon rice vinegar, cider vinegar or white wine vinegar

1 tablespoon reduced-salt soy sauce

1 small fresh red chili, seeded and finely chopped

1 large garlic clove, crushed

preparation time **20 mins** plus cooling, standing and marinating

cooking time **30 mins**

serves **4**

PER SERVING

393 calories

32 g protein

7 g total fat
2 g saturated fat

75 mg cholesterol

47 g total carbohydrate
5 g sugars

5 g fibre

1200 mg sodium

HEALTH HINT

The combination of raw carrots, red pepper and celery makes this salad an excellent source of vitamins, particularly vitamin C.

spaghetti bolognese

Here's a new lower-fat version of a pasta classic, a full-flavoured meat sauce tossed with strands of spaghetti and served with Parmesan cheese. There's less beef than in traditional recipes, but low-fat chicken livers enrich the sauce.

2 tablespoons extra virgin olive oil

1 large onion, finely chopped

1 large carrot, finely chopped

2 celery stalks, finely chopped

2 garlic cloves, crushed

8 sundried tomatoes (not oil-packed), finely chopped

250 g extra-lean ground beef

120 g chicken livers, finely chopped

½ cup red wine

1 can (540 ml) diced tomatoes

½ cup reduced-salt beef stock

1 teaspoon fresh thyme or marjoram or ½ teaspoon dried thyme or marjoram

4 tablespoons chopped fresh parsley

pepper to taste

350 g spaghetti

3 tablespoons Parmesan cheese, freshly grated

1 Heat the oil in a large saucepan, add the onion, carrot, celery, garlic and sundried tomatoes, and fry for 5–10 minutes, stirring frequently, until the vegetables start to brown.

2 Add the ground beef and chicken livers and fry, stirring, until the meat is browned. Pour in the wine, the tomatoes with their juice and the beef stock. Stir in the herbs and pepper to season. Cover the pan and simmer for 30 minutes, stirring occasionally.

3 Meanwhile, cook the spaghetti in boiling water for 10–12 minutes, or according to the package instructions, until al dente.

4 Drain the spaghetti and mix it with the meat sauce, tossing until the strands are well coated. Sprinkle with Parmesan cheese and serve at once.

  Fb GI

preparation time **20 mins**

cooking time **45 mins**

serves **4**

PER SERVING

551 calories

34 g protein

18 g total fat
5 g saturated fat

228 mg cholesterol

60 g total carbohydrate
9 g sugars

8 g fibre

328 mg sodium

HEALTH HINT

Chicken livers are a good source of B vitamins, vitamin A, zinc and copper. They are also one of the richest sources of iron.

spaghetti carbonara with roasted tomato salad

 This version of an all-time favourite makes use of low-fat dairy products and dry-cured ham instead of bacon to make a healthier dish with no compromise on flavour. To complete the meal, serve with a roasted tomato salad.

preparation time **20 mins**

cooking time **15 mins**

serves **4**

PER SERVING

501 calories

25 g protein

18 g total fat

8 g saturated fat

203 mg cholesterol

59 g total carbohydrate

9 g sugars

9 g fibre

704 mg sodium

HEALTH HINT

Pasta, when cooked al dente, scores healthily low on the Glycemic Index, which means that it breaks down slowly into glucose in the body, providing long-lasting energy.

COOK'S TIP

Serving an interesting salad as a major part of a meal is a good way to avoid over-indulging in fatty foods.

1 Preheat the oven to 425°F (220°C). To make the salad, place the tomatoes in a shallow ovenproof dish, cut-sides up. Sprinkle with the garlic and basil. Season with pepper and drizzle the olive oil over. Roast for 10 minutes.

2 Mix the salad greens in a serving dish. Add the onion, cucumber and fennel. When the tomatoes are done, spoon them, with all their hot juices, over the greens.

3 While the tomatoes are still roasting, cook the spaghetti in boiling water for 10–12 minutes, or according to the package instructions, until al dente.

4 Meanwhile, dry-fry the slices of prosciutto in a very hot, heavy-based frying pan for 2–3 minutes or until just crisp. Remove and drain on paper towel, then crumble or snip into small pieces. Set aside. Beat the eggs with the cream, then mix in the ricotta, half of the Parmesan cheese and a little pepper.

5 Drain the pasta. Return the empty pan to the heat and pour in the egg mixture. Heat for 1 minute over low heat, stirring constantly, then put the drained pasta back into the pan. Toss the spaghetti with the creamy egg to coat the strands with the mixture. The heat of the pan and the hot pasta will lightly set the eggs to make a creamy sauce. Serve immediately, sprinkled with the remaining Parmesan cheese and the prosciutto, and accompanied by the roasted tomato salad.

350 g spaghetti

8 slices prosciutto, about 100 g in total, trimmed of visible fat

3 eggs

⅓ cup reduced-fat cream

4 tablespoons reduced-fat ricotta cheese

5 tablespoons freshly grated Parmesan cheese

pepper to taste

ROASTED TOMATO SALAD

450 g cherry tomatoes or baby Italian tomatoes, halved

2 garlic cloves, very thinly sliced

8 large sprigs fresh basil, shredded

pepper to taste

2 teaspoons extra virgin olive oil

salad greens, such as oakleaf lettuce, arugula, baby spinach

1 red onion, thinly sliced

½ cucumber, thinly sliced

1 small bulb fennel, halved and thinly sliced

stir-fried beef with fine noodles

Tangy tamarind and lemongrass infuse a Thai-inspired sauce for tender strips of beef and fine rice noodles. With snow peas and baby corn adding all-important vegetable balance, this is a quick and easy dish that is a meal in itself.

1 In a small bowl, combine the tamarind paste and boiling water and leave to soak for 10 minutes, stirring frequently to break down the paste. Mix the resulting tamarind liquid with the soy sauce, sesame oil and rice wine or sherry.

2 While the tamarind is soaking, soak the rice noodles in boiling water for 4 minutes, or according to the package instructions. Then drain, rinse under cold running water and set aside to drain thoroughly.

3 Heat the sunflower oil in a wok or very large frying pan and stir-fry the beef over a high heat for about 3 minutes or until cooked. Use a slotted spoon to remove the beef from the wok and set it aside.

4 Add the onion, lemongrass, chili and garlic to the wok and stir-fry over a high heat for 1 minute. Add the snow peas, baby corn and mushrooms, and continue stir frying for 2 minutes.

5 Return the beef to the wok. Add the tamarind liquid and the noodles and stir for about 1 minute to heat through. Serve immediately, while still hot.

Variations You can use strips of chicken breast instead of beef. • Other vegetables that work well in the stir-fry include strips of red or green pepper, sliced canned water chestnuts, chopped or shredded green onions and bean sprouts.

1 teaspoon tamarind paste
4 tablespoons boiling water
2 tablespoons reduced-salt soy sauce
2 teaspoons sesame oil
1 tablespoon rice wine (sake or mirin) or sherry
100 g fine rice noodles
1 tablespoon sunflower oil
220 g lean steak, cut into strips
1 small onion, cut into wedges
2 teaspoons chopped lemongrass
1 fresh red chili, seeded and chopped
2 large garlic cloves, crushed
80 g snow peas, halved diagonally
6 baby corn, sliced
100 g fresh shiitake, chestnut or button mushrooms, sliced

30 Fb

preparation time **20 mins**
cooking time **10 mins**
serves **2**

PER SERVING

489 calories

29 g protein

21 g total fat
4 g saturated fat

53 mg cholesterol

45 g total carbohydrate
4 g sugars

4 g fibre

920 mg sodium

HEALTH HINT

Weight for weight, chilies are richer in vitamin C than citrus fruits, such as oranges. However, you would have to eat substantially more chilies than you are likely, or would want, to eat!

chicken and ricotta cannelloni

Cannelloni are often filled with rich beef or veal mixtures, but this lighter version uses chicken with fresh vegetables. The cannelloni can be assembled early in the day, and left in the refrigerator until you are ready to bake them.

300 g ground chicken

50 g red pepper, seeded and finely diced

½ small leek, finely chopped

50 g frozen peas

250 g reduced-fat ricotta cheese

50 g mascarpone cheese

1 egg

5 tablespoons finely chopped fresh herbs, such as parsley, chives or basil, or a mixture

pepper to taste

24 x 7.5 cm instant cannelloni tubes, about 185 g in total

SAUCE

4 cups low-fat milk

½ onion, studded with 4 cloves

1 bay leaf

⅛ teaspoon freshly grated nutmeg

pepper to taste

½ cup all-purpose flour

TOPPING

½ cup fine fresh whole-wheat breadcrumbs

¼ cup Parmesan cheese, freshly grated

1 To make the sauce, pour the milk into a heavy-based pan. Add the onion, bay leaf, nutmeg and pepper. Bring to a boil, remove from the heat, cover and set aside to cool.

2 Meanwhile, in a frying pan over medium-high heat, cook the chicken until white and crumbly. Set aside to cool slightly.

3 Place the diced red pepper, leek and frozen peas in a heatproof bowl, pour in enough boiling water to cover them and leave for 30 seconds. Drain the vegetables well.

4 Beat the ricotta, mascarpone and egg together, then mix in the chicken, the drained vegetables, herbs and pepper.

5 Using a slotted spoon, remove and discard the flavourings from the cool milk. Whisking constantly, sprinkle the flour into the milk. When incorporated, return the pan to medium heat and bring the sauce to a boil, whisking. Reduce the heat and simmer gently, whisking frequently, for about 3 minutes.

6 Preheat the oven to 400°F (200°C). Spread a layer of sauce on the bottom of a 30 x 20 cm (13 x 9 in.) ovenproof dish. Use a teaspoon to fill the cannelloni with the chicken mixture. Arrange in a single layer on the sauce in the dish. Spoon the remaining sauce over. For the topping, mix together the breadcrumbs and Parmesan and sprinkle over the cannelloni. Bake for 35–40 minutes or until the topping is golden and the sauce bubbling. Leave to stand for 10 minutes before serving.

preparation time **35 mins**

cooking time **55 mins**

serves **6**

PER SERVING

447 calories

32 g protein

17 g total fat
9 g saturated fat

120 mg cholesterol

43 g total carbohydrate
13 g sugars

3 g fibre

372 mg sodium

COOK'S TIP

Adding vegetables to cannelloni fillings will "stretch" a small quantity of protein food, such as chicken. Frozen vegetables are better than canned vegetables as they retain more vitamins. However, when fresh or frozen vegetables are not available, use canned vegetables to contribute fibre, flavour and bulk.

rice with wild mushrooms and cheese

C Fb

preparation time **20 mins** plus 20 mins standing

cooking time **50 mins**

serves **6**

PER SERVING

245 calories	
9 g protein	
5 g total fat	
2 g saturated fat	
7 mg cholesterol	
40 g total carbohydrate	
5 g sugars	
4 g fibre	
92 mg sodium	

HEALTH HINT

Sundried tomatoes are fat- and cholesterol-free (as long as they are not oil-packed). The dried tomatoes supply the same amount of lycopene (which has been linked to reducing the risk of prostate cancer) found in one large Italian tomato.

A sturdy standby, rice can be flavoured in myriad ways. Brown rice, with its toasty taste and healthy fibre, is delicious with added wild mushrooms, sundried tomatoes and tasty cheese, and a little goes a long way.

1 Place the porcini mushrooms in a small bowl and pour 1½ cups hot water over them. Place the sundried tomatoes in another small bowl and pour the remaining 1 cup hot water over them. Let both stand until softened, about 20 minutes.

2 Scoop the mushrooms out of the soaking liquid and finely chop them. Strain the soaking liquid through a fine-meshed sieve into a bowl. Strain the sundried tomato soaking liquid into the same bowl and set aside. Coarsely chop the tomatoes.

3 Preheat the oven to 350°F (180°C). Heat the olive oil and 4 tablespoons of the mushroom-tomato soaking liquid in a medium saucepan over medium heat. Add the onion and garlic to the pan and cook until the onion is golden, about 7 minutes.

4 Add the rice, stirring to coat. Add the mushrooms, tomatoes, remaining soaking liquid, sage and pepper to the pan and bring to a boil. Transfer the rice mixture to a 20 cm (8 in.) square glass baking dish. Cover with foil, transfer to the oven, and bake until the rice is tender and the liquid has been absorbed, about 40 minutes. Sprinkle the hot rice with the Cheddar and Parmesan cheeses and serve.

⅓ cup dried porcini mushrooms
2½ cups hot water
⅓ cup sundried tomatoes (not oil-packed)
1 teaspoon olive oil
1 large onion, finely chopped
3 cloves garlic, finely chopped
1 cup brown rice
½ teaspoon chopped fresh sage
pepper to taste
⅓ cup grated 25% reduced-fat Cheddar cheese
2 tablespoons freshly grated Parmesan cheese

chicken biryani with cucumber raita

A biryani consists of curried meat, poultry, fish or vegetables combined with basmati rice to make a complete meal. Here chicken curry is layered with the rice and baked, then served with a fresh cucumber raita.

1 tablespoon sunflower oil

1 large onion, chopped

450 g chicken thighs, diced

10 g fresh ginger, finely chopped

1 small red or green chili, seeded and finely chopped

seeds from 10 cardamom pods, lightly crushed

1 tablespoon ground cumin

1 tablespoon ground coriander

6 cloves

1 cinnamon stick

2 bay leaves

½ teaspoon crushed black peppercorns

1 can (540 ml) chopped tomatoes

1¼ cups reduced-salt chicken stock

⅓ cup sultanas

1 cup basmati rice, rinsed

½ teaspoon turmeric

⅓ cup toasted flaked almonds to garnish

CUCUMBER RAITA

200 g plain low-fat yogourt

½ large cucumber, coarsely grated and squeezed dry

2 tablespoons chopped fresh mint

pepper to taste

1 Heat the oil in a large frying pan, add the onion and cook gently for 5 minutes or until softened. Add the chicken and cook over medium heat for 5 minutes until browned all over.

2 Stir in the ginger, chili, cardamom, cumin, coriander, cloves, cinnamon stick, bay leaves and peppercorns. Cook for 1 minute, stirring all the time to ensure the spices do not burn.

3 Add the tomatoes, the stock and sultanas. Bring to a boil, reduce the heat, cover and cook for 45 minutes.

4 Meanwhile, preheat the oven to 325°F (160°C). Place the rice in a saucepan, add 2⅓ cups water and the turmeric, and bring to a boil. Cover and simmer very gently for about 7 minutes or until the rice is almost tender. Drain off any excess water.

5 Layer the chicken curry and rice in a casserole dish. Cover and cook in the oven for 25 minutes, checking after 20 minutes and adding a little more stock if needed (there should be enough liquid for the rice to complete cooking).

6 Meanwhile, make the raita. Stir together the yogourt, cucumber and mint. Season with pepper.

7 When the biryani is ready, stir it well, then scatter the toasted almonds on top. Serve with the raita.

preparation time **20 mins**

cooking time
1 hour 20 mins

serves **4**

PER SERVING

611 calories

36 g protein

24 g total fat
4 g saturated fat

128 mg cholesterol

63 g total carbohydrate
20 g sugars

5 g fibre

368 mg sodium

HEALTH HINT

Eaten without the skin, chicken is low in fat and the fat it does contain is mostly unsaturated.

C Fb GI

preparation time **20 mins**
plus 1 hour marinating

cooking time **20 mins**

serves **4**

PER SERVING

404 calories	
17 g protein	
7 g total fat	
1 g saturated fat	
63 mg cholesterol	
64 g total carbohydrate	
18 g sugars	
5 g fibre	
642 mg sodium	

HEART SUPERFOOD

Tofu plays a very important part in a heart-healthy diet. Soy protein lowers the level of artery-clogging LDL ("bad") cholesterol without reducing the beneficial HDL ("good") cholesterol in the body.

fried rice with tofu and vegetables

 Soy foods can lower cholesterol levels and reduce the risk of heart disease. If you've been looking for a tasty tofu recipe, your search is over. Here, tofu is marinated in a sweet and savoury sauce and stir-fried with plenty of vegetables.

1 Place the wine or stock, 1 tablespoon soy sauce, the honey and 1 teaspoon ginger in a sealable plastic bag. Add the tofu, push out the excess air, close and shake gently to coat. Marinate in the refrigerator for 1 hour, turning occasionally.

2 Cook the rice according to the package directions; keep warm. Lightly coat a wok or large deep frying pan with nonstick cooking spray and place over high heat until hot.

3 Stir-fry the garlic and remaining ginger until fragrant, about 1 minute. Add the mixed vegetables, half the green onions, the rice, the remaining soy sauce and pepper. Stir-fry until the mixed vegetables are heated through, about 4 minutes. Push the ingredients to one side of the wok and pour in the egg. Cook until almost set, cutting the egg into strips with a spatula.

4 Pour the marinade into a small saucepan. Boil over high heat for 2 minutes. Add the tofu and marinade to the wok. Stir-fry until the tofu is heated through, about 4 minutes. Sprinkle with the remaining green onions and serve.

1 cup dry white wine or reduced-salt chicken stock

¼ cup reduced-salt soy sauce

2 tablespoons clear honey

1 tablespoon peeled, grated fresh ginger

370 g extra-firm tofu, diced 1 cm thick

1 cup long-grain white rice

2 garlic cloves, finely chopped

1 package (500 g) frozen mixed Asian vegetables, slightly thawed

5 green onions, cut into 5 cm pieces

pepper to taste

1 large egg, lightly beaten

green coriander rice

Toasting the rice, then cooking with a herb and vegetable paste before adding stock and simmering, develops and enriches the flavour of this dish. The rice makes a great accompaniment to grilled or roast chicken.

1 large green pepper, quartered
   and seeded
1 onion, quartered
1 garlic clove, crushed
⅓ cup fresh coriander
⅓ cup Italian parsley
2 teaspoons reduced-salt margarine
2 teaspoons extra virgin olive oil
1 cup long-grain white rice
2⅓ cups boiling reduced-salt
   chicken stock
pepper to taste
sprigs fresh coriander to garnish

1 Place the pepper, onion, garlic, coriander and parsley in a food processor and blend to a very finely chopped paste. Alternatively, very finely chop them all together with a knife.

2 Heat the margarine and olive oil in a saucepan, add the rice and fry gently for 2–3 minutes until the grains are translucent.

3 Remove from the heat and stir in the herb paste. Return to the heat and cook for 2 minutes, stirring constantly. Pour in the stock, and season with pepper. Bring to a boil, then reduce the heat, cover and cook gently for 10–15 minutes or until the rice is tender and the stock is absorbed.

4 Remove from the heat and leave to stand, with the pan still covered, for 3–4 minutes. Then fork through to separate the grains. Serve hot, garnished with the coriander sprigs.

preparation time **20 mins**
plus standing
cooking time **20 mins**
serves **4**

PER SERVING

69 calories

2 g protein

1 g total fat
0 g saturated fat

0 mg cholesterol

12 g total carbohydrate
1 g sugars

1 g fibre

108 mg sodium

HEALTH HINT

Green peppers are an excellent source of vitamin C, important for maintaining the body's immune system. Even though some of the vitamin C is destroyed during cooking, useful amounts still remain.

risotto primavera

Yes, you can make creamy risotto the way they do in Italian restaurants! This recipe makes a delightful starter or main meal. Vegetables add vitamins A and C, and a small amount of Parmesan adds calcium, protein and a lot of flavour.

1 Bring the stock to a boil in a medium saucepan. Reduce the heat to maintain a simmer.

2 Meanwhile, melt the margarine in a large heavy saucepan over medium heat. Sauté the onion until barely soft, about 3 minutes. Add the rice and 6 strips of red pepper and sauté until the rice is opaque, about 2 minutes. Add the wine and stir until it is absorbed, about 3 minutes. Gradually add 2½ cups stock, about ½ cup at a time, stirring until the liquid is absorbed after each addition—about 10 minutes in total.

3 Stir in the asparagus, the remaining pepper, and ½ cup stock. Cook, stirring constantly, until the stock is absorbed. Repeat with the zucchini, peas and another ½ cup stock.

4 Continue cooking—stirring constantly and adding the remaining stock ½ cup at a time—about 15 minutes more, or until the rice is creamy and tender but firm. Remove from the heat and stir in the Parmesan cheese and pepper. Serve hot.

5 cups reduced-salt chicken stock
1 tablespoon reduced-salt margarine
1 medium onion, chopped
1¼ cups arborio (risotto) rice
1 large red pepper, cut into thin strips
½ cup dry white wine
250 g asparagus, trimmed and sliced
1 small yellow zucchini, chopped
½ cup fresh or frozen green peas
½ cup freshly grated Parmesan cheese
pepper to taste

preparation time **20 mins**
cooking time **40 mins**
serves **4**

PER SERVING

388 calories

17 g protein

7 g total fat
3 g saturated fat

10 mg cholesterol

61 g total carbohydrate
8 g sugars

4 g fibre

940 mg sodium

COOK'S TIP

Risotto isn't difficult to make, but it does need constant attention. Stirring the rice continuously, while adding the stock gradually, helps the rice absorb the hot stock. This causes the rice grains to release starch, yielding a very creamy dish.

rice with shrimp and dill dressing

In this good-looking salad, quickly seared tiger shrimp are served on a mixture of aromatic basmati and wild rice, crunchy broccoli, snow peas and yellow pepper tossed in a fresh dill and lime juice dressing.

250 g mixed basmati and wild rice, well rinsed

thinly pared rind and juice of 1 lime

4 tablespoons sunflower oil

2 teaspoons sesame oil

1 tablespoon reduced-salt soy sauce

pepper to taste

120 g broccoli, broken into small florets

120 g snow peas, halved lengthwise

400 g raw tiger shrimp, peeled but tails left on

1 small yellow pepper, seeded and thinly sliced

70 g green onions, sliced

5 tablespoons coarsely chopped fresh dill

1 Cook the rice with the lime rind in a saucepan of boiling water for 20 minutes, or according to the package instructions, until tender. Drain the rice and put it into a wide salad bowl. Discard the lime rind.

2 Whisk together 1 tablespoon of the lime juice, 2½ tablespoons of the sunflower oil, the sesame oil, soy sauce and pepper in a small bowl. Drizzle this dressing over the rice and stir to mix. Spread out the rice in the bowl and leave to cool.

3 Meanwhile, place the broccoli in a steamer basket set over a pan of boiling water and steam for 4 minutes. Add the snow peas and steam for 2 minutes or until the vegetables are tender but still crisp. Place the vegetables into a colander and refresh under cold running water.

4 Heat the remaining sunflower oil in a large frying pan. Add the shrimp and cook over high heat for 1–2 minutes on each side until pink and cooked through. Remove from the heat and sprinkle with the remaining lime juice.

5 Add the broccoli, snow peas, yellow pepper, onions and 4 tablespoons of the dill to the rice and stir gently to mix. Pile the shrimp on top, scatter over the rest of the dill and serve.

 Fb GI

preparation time **20 mins** plus cooling

cooking time **20 mins**

serves **4**

PER SERVING

461 calories

20 g protein

18 g total fat
2 g saturated fat

93 mg cholesterol

54 g total carbohydrate
3 g sugars

3 g fibre

425 mg sodium

HEART SUPERFOOD

Shrimp are low in fat and calories. They supply omega-3 fatty acids, which help stabilize the electrical pulse of the heart and keep the blood free of clots. They also provide good amounts of copper, phosphorus, iodine and the antioxidant selenium, plus small amounts of iron.

seafood paella

No trip to Spain would be complete without sampling its famous rice dish, paella. The ingredients vary from region to region, but this recipe uses white fish fillets, squid and mussels. Serve with crusty whole-wheat bread.

Fb

preparation time **20 mins**
cooking time **45 mins**
serves **4**

PER SERVING

604 calories

49 g protein

15 g total fat
3 g saturated fat

317 mg cholesterol

66 g total carbohydrate
9 g sugars

6 g fibre

1433 mg sodium

COOK'S TIP

Using the stock obtained by boiling the head, skin and bones from any white fish not only adds flavour to a dish but also some nutrients. Any vitamins and minerals that leach out into the water will make a nutritious contribution to the dish.

1 Place the saffron threads in a heavy-based saucepan over medium heat and stir until they begin to give off an aroma. Add the stock and bring to a boil. Remove the pan from the heat, cover and set aside to infuse.

2 Slice the squid into thin strips. Set aside.

3 Heat 1 tablespoon of the oil in a frying pan. Add the fish pieces and quickly fry on all sides until lightly browned. Remove and set aside. Add the remaining oil to the pan. Add the garlic, onion and paprika and cook over medium heat for 2 minutes, stirring occasionally. Stir in the red pepper and cook for about 3 minutes or until softened but not brown.

4 Stir in the rice so all the grains are well coated with oil. Bring the saffron-infused stock to simmering point and add half of it to the rice. Stir, then bring to a boil. Reduce the heat to low and simmer for 5 minutes or until the liquid is almost all absorbed.

5 Add the rice mixture to the stock remaining in the large pan. Gently stir in the tomatoes with their juice, the peas and fish pieces. Arrange the mussels on the top. Simmer for about 5 minutes. Very gently stir in the squid, then simmer for a further 15 minutes or until the rice is tender and all the liquid has been absorbed. Season with pepper.

6 Remove the pan from the heat, cover and leave to stand for 5 minutes. Discard any mussels that have not opened. Sprinkle the top of the paella with the parsley and serve.

¼ teaspoon saffron threads

4 cups fish stock (reduced-salt if possible)

400 g squid, cleaned and prepared

2 tablespoons extra virgin olive oil

200 g fish fillet, such as sole, snapper or perch, cut into bite-sized pieces

2 large garlic cloves, crushed

1 large onion, finely chopped

½ teaspoon paprika

2 large red peppers, seeded and chopped

1¼ cups long-grain white rice

½ of 1 can (540 ml) diced tomatoes

150 g frozen peas

12 mussels, washed and beards removed

pepper to taste

4 tablespoons finely chopped parsley to garnish

herbed polenta with Gorgonzola

Broiled slices of polenta topped with a creamy, melting mixture of Gorgonzola and ricotta cheeses is a delicious dish, ideal for a tempting starter. It is served hot with a garnish of salad greens.

3 cups reduced-salt vegetable stock
170 g instant polenta
2 tablespoons chopped fresh
   Italian parsley
1 tablespoon chopped fresh
   oregano or marjoram
pepper to taste
50 g Gorgonzola cheese
50 g reduced-fat ricotta cheese
1 tablespoon extra virgin olive oil
salad greens to garnish

1 Bring the stock to a boil in a medium-sized saucepan. Add the polenta in a steady stream, stirring constantly, and cook for about 5 minutes, or according to the package instructions, until the mixture has thickened and is pulling away from the sides of the saucepan.

2 Stir in the parsley and oregano or marjoram, and season with pepper. Pour the polenta onto a greased baking sheet and spread out to make a rectangle about 20 x 18 cm and 1 cm thick. Leave in a cool place to set for about 1 hour.

3 Preheat the broiler. In a bowl, mash the Gorgonzola with the ricotta cheese and set aside. Brush the top of the polenta lightly with the oil, then cut into 12 rectangles, each about 5 x 6 cm. Place on the rack of the broiler pan, oiled-side up, and broil until the tops are lightly browned.

4 Turn the polenta slices over and top with the Gorgonzola mixture. Continue to broil until the cheese has melted and is beginning to brown. Serve at once, garnished with salad greens.

Variations You can substitute other herbs such as rosemary, basil or sage for the oregano or marjoram. • For grilled polenta with sautéed leeks and herbs, make the polenta mixture without the herbs. Melt 3 tablespoons margarine in a pan, add 2 finely chopped leeks and 2 crushed garlic cloves, and cook over medium heat for about 10 minutes or until soft, stirring occasionally. Stir in 4 tablespoons dry sherry and simmer briefly, then stir in 2–4 tablespoons chopped fresh mixed herbs and season to taste with pepper. Broil the polenta slices until the tops are lightly browned on each side, then top with the hot leek mixture and serve.

preparation time **15 mins**
plus 1 hour cooling

cooking time **25 mins**

serves **4**

PER SERVING

264 calories

8 g protein

11 g total fat
4 g saturated fat

18 mg cholesterol

33 g total carbohydrate
5 g sugars

2 g fibre

937 mg sodium

HEALTH HINTS

Like wheat and other grains, corn (from which polenta is made) is rich in starchy carbohydrate and low in fat.

Gorgonzola is a semi-hard, blue-veined cheese with a rich, full flavour, while ricotta is much milder, and lower in fat. Mixing the two cheeses together helps to keep the total fat content of this dish healthy.

Cajun-spiced barley

Barley is one of the crops that farmers love, due to its short growing season and hardy nature. We should love this nutty, wholesome grain too, since it is so good for us. Serve it with extra-lean, beef sausages or lamb kebabs.

1 cup pearl barley

2 tablespoons extra virgin olive oil

4 green onions, the white and green parts chopped separately

2 celery stalks, chopped

1 onion, chopped

1 green pepper, seeded and chopped

1 large mild green chili, seeded and finely chopped

2 garlic cloves, finely chopped

½ teaspoon ground cumin

¼ teaspoon dried thyme

¼ teaspoon cracked black peppercorns

⅛ teaspoon cayenne pepper

2 cups reduced-salt vegetable stock

2 tablespoons freshly squeezed lemon juice

lemon wedges to serve

1 Heat a heavy-based frying pan over medium heat. Add the pearl barley and toast, stirring constantly, for about 4 minutes or until the grains just start to brown and smell fragrant. Remove from the heat immediately, transfer to a shallow bowl and set aside.

2 Heat the oil in a heavy-based saucepan over medium heat. Add the white parts of the green onions, the celery, onion and green pepper, and sauté for about 5 minutes or until slightly softened, stirring occasionally.

3 Stir in the chili, garlic, cumin, thyme, peppercorns and cayenne pepper. Sauté for a further 5 minutes, stirring well.

4 Add the barley and stock. Bring to a boil, then cover, reduce the heat and simmer for 30–40 minutes or until the barley is tender and the liquid has been absorbed.

5 Stir in the lemon juice. Scatter over the green onion tops and serve with the lemon wedges.

preparation time **15 mins**

cooking time **55 mins**

serves **4**

PER SERVING

209 calories

4 g protein

11 g total fat

2 g saturated fat

0 mg cholesterol

23 g total carbohydrate

5 g sugars

5 g fibre

547 mg sodium

HEART SUPERFOOD

Like oats, barley is rich in soluble fibre, the type of fibre that can bind the end-products of cholesterol metabolism and sweep them out of the body. When the outer bran and germ are removed to make pearl barley, there is some loss of vitamins, particularly thiamine.

apricot lamb with shredded cabbage

Based on the Moroccan way of stewing meat with fruit, here lamb is marinated with mushrooms and herbs, then cooked slowly with dried apricots. Shredded cabbage and fresh mint enliven the couscous accompaniment.

Fb

preparation time **15 mins** plus 12 hours marinating

cooking time **2½ hours**

serves **4**

PER SERVING

486 calories

36 g protein

12 g total fat

5 g saturated fat

81 mg cholesterol

51 g total carbohydrate

28 g sugars

13 g fibre

1023 mg sodium

HEALTH HINT

Combining cabbage and mint with couscous adds flavour and beneficial nutrients to the satisfying carbohydrate.

1 Place the lamb in a bowl with the mushrooms and onion. Tie the bay leaves and thyme together into a bouquet garni and add to the bowl with the garlic, carrots, celery and nutmeg. Pour over the ale and stir to mix, then cover and leave to marinate in the refrigerator for 12 hours.

2 Preheat the oven to 325°F (160°C). Transfer the lamb, mushrooms and flavouring ingredients to a large casserole and pour the marinade over. Add the tomatoes and the stock. Cover and cook in the oven for 2 hours.

3 Discard the bouquet garni from the casserole. Stir in the apricots and pepper and return the casserole to the oven to cook for a further 30 minutes.

4 Just before the casserole is ready, prepare the couscous. Bring the stock to a boil in a large saucepan. Add the cabbage and bring back to a boil, then remove from the heat and immediately add the couscous and mint. Stir once, then cover the pan and leave, off the heat, for about 5 minutes or until the couscous has absorbed all the stock. Use a fork to fluff up the couscous.

5 Divide the couscous among 4 bowls and ladle the lamb casserole over the top. Scatter over the chopped parsley and serve immediately while hot.

450 g lean boneless lamb, cut into chunks

350 g mushrooms, sliced

1 onion, thinly sliced

2 bay leaves

2 sprigs fresh thyme

2 garlic cloves, crushed

2 carrots, sliced

2 celery stalks, sliced

¼ teaspoon freshly grated nutmeg

2 cups strong brown ale

1 can (540 ml) diced tomatoes

⅔ cup reduced-salt lamb or chicken stock

150 g dried apricots, halved

pepper to taste

2 tablespoons chopped parsley to garnish

MINT COUSCOUS

3 cups reduced-salt vegetable stock

450 g green cabbage, such as Savoy, finely shredded

350 g couscous

⅓ cup chopped fresh mint

fish &

seafood

Japanese sushi rolls

Japanese food tends to be low in fat, and these stylish sushi rolls are no exception. Now that the ingredients are available in grocery stores, it is easy to make them yourself. You must use sushi rice, which is sticky when cooked.

2 cups sushi rice

1 tablespoon caster (superfine) sugar

4 tablespoons rice wine vinegar

2 green onions, very finely chopped

30 g piece of cucumber, seeded and finely chopped

110 g smoked salmon

4 sheets of sushi nori, about 10 g in total

2 teaspoons wasabi paste

gari (pickled ginger) to garnish

reduced-salt soy sauce to serve

1 Cook the sushi rice in a saucepan of boiling water according to the package instructions.

2 Meanwhile, place the sugar and vinegar in a small pan and heat gently until the sugar dissolves. When the rice is cooked, drizzle the mixture over it, then add the green onions and cucumber, and mix. Cover with a dish towel and leave to cool.

3 Divide the sushi rice into 4 equal portions. Cut the salmon into strips about 1 cm wide. Place a sheet of nori, shiny-side down, on a bamboo mat, or a sheet of parchment paper on a board. Spread a portion of rice over the nori, pressing it down evenly and leaving a 1 cm space at the top and bottom. Place a quarter of the salmon along the middle of the layer of rice, then spread the salmon with ½ teaspoon of the wasabi paste.

4 With the help of the bamboo mat or paper, roll up the nori, rice and salmon into a neat tube. Roll tightly to ensure that the rice sticks together and holds the filling in place. Make 3 more rolls in the same way.

5 Using a wet knife, cut each roll across into 8 slices and stand them upright on a serving plate. Rinse the knife between cuts. Garnish with pieces of gari and offer a small dish of reduced-salt soy sauce for dipping.

preparation time **20 mins** plus cooling

cooking time **20 mins**

makes **32 sushi rolls**

PER SUSHI ROLL

109 calories

3 g protein

0 g total fat

0 g saturated fat

2 mg cholesterol

23 g total carbohydrate

1 g sugars

0 g fibre

187 mg sodium

HEALTH HINT

Like other foods from the sea, nori—a dark brownish seaweed—is a good source of iodine, essential for the healthy functioning of the thyroid gland. It also provides some calcium, potassium and beta carotene, which is converted to vitamin A in the body.

tuna Provençale on a baguette

Flavoursome, savoury and full of heart-smart nutrients, this sandwich is sure to become a favourite. The special today: a variation of the classic "pan bagnat," a baguette bursting with tuna, olives and garden-fresh veggies.

1 Mix the tomatoes and olives in a medium bowl, and then let stand until juicy, about 15 minutes.

2 Meanwhile, cut the baguette almost in half lengthwise (do not slice completely through). Open the baguette like a book, being careful not to separate the bread. Pull out about ½ cup of the soft bready centre with your hands. Using ½ tablespoon oil, brush the cut sides of the bread. Then spread on the tomato mixture and any juices that have collected in the bowl.

3 Cut the onion in half through the stem end, then cut it crosswise into thin semicircles. Cut the pepper in half, and then cut it crosswise into thin semicircles. Layer the onion, green pepper and tuna over the tomato mixture. Whisk the vinegar, garlic and remaining oil in a small bowl. Drizzle over the tuna.

4 Wrap the stuffed baguette tightly in plastic wrap. Weigh it down with a heavy frying pan and let it stand at room temperature until the ingredients have soaked into the bread, 30 minutes. Cut it diagonally into 4 equal pieces before serving.

2 large tomatoes, peeled and chopped

5 black olives (not oil-packed), pitted and finely chopped

1 baguette (whole wheat if possible), about 60 cm long

2 tablespoons extra virgin olive oil

1 large onion

1 large green pepper

2 cans (170 g) tuna in water, drained

2 tablespoons white wine vinegar

2 garlic cloves, finely chopped

preparation time **20 mins** plus 30 mins standing

serves **4**

PER SERVING

374 calories	
27 g protein	
11 g total fat	
2 g saturated fat	
40 mg cholesterol	
40 g total carbohydrate	
8 g sugars	
5 g fibre	
475 mg sodium	

HEALTH HINT

Canned, water-packed tuna provides more of the heart-protecting omega-3 fatty acids than tuna packed in oil. Why? These fatty acids dissolve in the vegetable oil used to pack the tuna and are generally drained off, not eaten.

pasta and tuna salad with zucchini and sundried tomato pesto

The dressing for this simple, colourful salad has a sweet-sour flavour, which perfectly complements the lightly cooked zucchinis, tuna, tomatoes and pasta. Serve the salad cool, but not chilled, or try it while it is still warm.

1 Cook the pasta twists in boiling water for approximately 10–12 minutes, or according to the package instructions, until they are just al dente. Drain the pasta well, rinse well with cold water and then drain again very thoroughly.

2 While the pasta is cooking, heat half the olive oil in a medium saucepan. Add the onion and garlic, and fry for 3 minutes, stirring frequently, until the onion and garlic are softened. Add the remaining olive oil and the zucchinis and cook, stirring occasionally, for 3 minutes.

3 Add the sugar, the sundried tomato pesto, white or red wine vinegar and capers to the onion and zucchini mixture. Heat for a few seconds, stirring until all the ingredients have combined to form a dressing.

4 Stir in the tomatoes, then transfer the mixture to a large mixing bowl and set aside to cool.

5 Add the drained pasta to the bowl, then gently mix in the tuna and black olives. Divide the salad among 4 plates or transfer to a large serving bowl. Serve garnished with some Italian parsley leaves.

Variations To increase the fibre content of this dish and make a more substantial meal, you can add 1 can (540 ml) pinto beans, drained, with the pasta. • Omit the tuna for a vegetarian dish. • Canned anchovies can also be used instead of tuna. Drain the oil from 1 small can (50 g) and use it instead of the olive oil for cooking the ingredients in step 2. • You can also use 220 g baby yellow squash instead of zucchinis. Trim their tops and bases, then slice them in half.

250 g pasta twists or spirals, such as fusilli or rotini, or other shapes

2 tablespoons extra virgin olive oil

1 onion, chopped

1 garlic clove, chopped

2 zucchinis, thinly sliced

2 teaspoons caster (superfine) sugar

2 tablespoons sundried tomato pesto

1 tablespoon white or red wine vinegar

2 tablespoons capers

6 tomatoes, skinned, halved and cut into thin wedges

1 can (170 g) tuna in water, drained and roughly flaked

6 black olives (not oil-packed), pitted and halved

fresh Italian parsley to garnish

preparation time **15 mins** plus cooling

cooking time **15 mins**

serves **4**

PER SERVING

377 calories

18 g protein

13 g total fat
2 g saturated fat

18 mg cholesterol

47 g total carbohydrate
11 g sugars

7 g fibre

253 mg sodium

HEALTH HINTS

Using tuna canned in water, rather than in oil, keeps the fat and salt content of the dish somewhat lower.

Tomatoes and zucchinis together ensure that this simple salad provides an excellent supply of vitamin C.

tropical salmon salad

Conjure up the colours and flavours of a tropical island with this unusual warm salad. The rich flavour of salmon is perfectly balanced by the gentle acidity of orange and the sweetness of mango and papaya.

8 cardamom pods, crushed

1 teaspoon cumin seeds

finely grated rind and juice of 1 lime

juice of 1 large orange

1 tablespoon reduced-salt soy sauce

1 tablespoon clear honey

pepper to taste

4 pieces of skinless salmon fillet, about 100 g each

150 g mixed colourful salad leaves, such as radicchio, red coral or red oakleaf lettuce

1 mango, peeled and diced 1 cm thick

1 papaya, peeled, seeded and diced 1 cm thick

1 orange, peeled and segmented

1 Heat a small frying pan. Remove the seeds from the cardamom pods and add them to the hot pan together with the cumin seeds. Toast for just a few seconds to release the aromas, then tip the cardamom and cumin seeds into a nonmetallic dish.

2 Add the lime rind and juice, orange juice, soy sauce and honey to the seeds, and season with pepper. Place the pieces of salmon fillet in the dish. Turn them over to coat both sides. Cover and leave to marinate for about 30 minutes.

3 Preheat the broiler. Lift the salmon out of the marinade and broil on one side only; the salmon fillets should still be slightly translucent in the centre. Meanwhile, pour the marinade into a small saucepan and bring just to a boil.

4 Arrange the salad leaves in the middle of 4 plates. Scatter the mango and papaya cubes and orange segments over and around the salad. Place the cooked salmon pieces on top of the salad and pieces of fruit and spoon over the warm marinade. Serve immediately.

preparation time **20 mins** plus 30 mins marinating

cooking time **10 mins**

serves **4**

PER SERVING

256 calories

23 g protein

8 g total fat
2 g saturated fat

54 mg cholesterol

25 g total carbohydrate
24 g sugars

4 g fibre

249 mg sodium

HEART SUPERFOOD

Salmon is not only valuable for its omega-3 fatty acids, it is a useful source of potassium, which helps to regulate fluid balance and prevent high blood pressure.

French tuna and bell pepper salad

This colourful salad is full of varied flavours and textures. Chunks of tuna, wedges of potato, crisp beans and tangy tomatoes make for a quick and easy summery meal. Serve with crusty whole-wheat baguettes.

1 Place the potatoes in a saucepan and cover with boiling water. Cook over medium heat for 10 minutes. Add the green beans and cook for a further 5 minutes or until the potatoes are tender and the beans are just cooked. Drain well and set aside to cool.

2 Place the quail eggs, if using, into a saucepan with cold water to cover and bring to a boil. Reduce the heat and cook at a low simmer for 3 minutes. Rinse well in cold water. Peel the eggs carefully and place in cold water.

3 Toss the salad greens with the parsley, chives and red onion in a large shallow bowl.

4 To make the dressing, mix the tapenade with the garlic, olive oil, red wine vinegar and balsamic vinegar, and season with pepper. Pour two-thirds of the dressing over the salad greens and toss well to mix.

5 Halve the potatoes and arrange them on top of the salad greens with the green beans, radishes, tuna, tomatoes, peppers and olives. Halve the eggs and add them to the salad. Pour over the remaining dressing, garnish with basil leaves and serve.

400 g new potatoes
50 g fine green beans
2 quail eggs (optional)
220 g mixed salad greens
1 tablespoon chopped parsley
1 tablespoon snipped fresh chives
1 small red onion, thinly sliced
1 tablespoon tapenade (black olive paste)
2 garlic cloves, chopped
2 tablespoons extra virgin olive oil
1 tablespoon red wine vinegar
1 teaspoon balsamic vinegar
pepper to taste
10–15 radishes, thinly sliced
1 can (170 g) tuna in water, drained
100 g cherry tomatoes
1 each of red, yellow and green pepper, seeded and thinly sliced
8 black olives
fresh basil leaves to garnish

C Fb

preparation time **20 mins**
cooking time **20 mins**
serves **4**

PER SERVING

254 calories

15 g protein

12 g total fat
2 g saturated fat

22 mg cholesterol

21 g total carbohydrate
8 g sugars

5 g fibre

189 mg sodium

HEALTH HINT

Radishes are a useful source of vitamin C and are very low in calories. The radish has a very hot flavour due to an enzyme in the skin that reacts with another substance to form a mustard-like oil.

smoked trout and pasta salad

Tempt your family with this delicious heart-healthy pasta salad. It makes an ideal midweek meal served with crusty whole-wheat bread. If you wait until the last minute to add the arugula, it won't spoil if anyone's late home.

1 red pepper, seeded and quartered

1 yellow pepper, seeded and quartered

280 g penne rigati (ridged penne) or other pasta shapes

280 g smoked trout fillets

1 orange

1 large avocado

2 green onions, sliced

2 tablespoons capers, well drained

1½ cups arugula

DRESSING

5 tablespoons plain low-fat yogourt

2 teaspoons lemon juice

1 teaspoon Dijon mustard

2 tablespoons chopped fresh dill

½ teaspoon caster (superfine) sugar

pepper to taste

1 Preheat the broiler. Place the peppers on the broiler rack, skin-side up, and broil until the skins are blistered and blackened. Remove from the broiler and place in a plastic bag. Seal and set aside to cool.

2 Meanwhile, bring a large pan of water to a boil and add the pasta. Cook for 10–12 minutes, or according to the package instructions, until al dente. Drain, rinse with cold water and drain well again. Transfer the pasta into a large salad bowl.

3 Flake the trout fillets into bite-sized pieces, discarding the skin and any bones. Cut all the skin and pith from the orange and cut out the segments from between the membranes. Halve the segments. Halve, pit and peel the avocado, and cut into small chunks. Mix together the dressing ingredients and season with pepper.

4 Peel the peppers and cut into strips. Add the peppers to the pasta together with the trout, orange, avocado, green onions and capers. Add the dressing and toss gently but thoroughly. Just before serving, toss in the arugula.

Fb **GI**

preparation time **20 mins**

cooking time **15 mins**

serves **4**

PER SERVING

474 calories

28 g protein

18 g total fat
4 g saturated fat

51 mg cholesterol

49 g total carbohydrate
9 g sugars

6 g fibre

134 mg sodium

HEALTH HINT

Smoked trout is usually prepared from rainbow trout and, like its fresh counterpart, is an excellent source of many vitamins, minerals and healthy omega-3 fatty acids.

Thai fish cakes with dipping sauce

 These delicious fish cakes are flavoured with lemongrass and coriander, and spiced with Thai red curry paste. They're served with a tangy lime and honey dipping sauce, and a lettuce, cucumber and mint salad.

C Fb

preparation time **40 mins**
plus 1 hour chilling

cooking time **30 mins**

serves **8**

PER SERVING

234 calories

15 g protein

10 g total fat
2 g saturated fat

91 mg cholesterol

21 g total carbohydrate
7 g sugars

3 g fibre

238 mg sodium

HEART SUPERFOOD

Research suggests that garlic may help to reduce high blood cholesterol levels and inhibit blood clotting, thereby reducing the risk of heart disease and strokes.

1 Boil the potatoes in a saucepan with enough water to cover for 15–20 minutes or until tender. Drain well, then mash.

2 Meanwhile, place the fish in a shallow pan with enough cold water to cover and add half the lime juice. Bring to a boil, reduce the heat to low and simmer for 1 minute. Remove from the heat, cover pan and leave to cool for 4 minutes. Drain the fish and flake the flesh with a fork, discarding skin and bones.

3 Mix together the potatoes and fish with a fork, adding the lemongrass, curry paste, green onions, garlic, coriander, ginger and the remaining lime juice.

4 Place the flour onto one plate, the eggs onto a second plate and the breadcrumbs onto a third plate. Take about 1 tablespoon of the fish mixture and shape into a fish cake. Turn first in the flour, then dip into the egg and, finally, coat with crumbs. Shape and coat the remaining fish cakes in the same way, making 24 altogether. Chill the fish cakes for 1 hour.

5 Heat half the oil in a nonstick frying pan. Add half the fish cakes and cook over medium heat for about 3 minutes on each side or until golden. Remove and keep warm while you cook the rest of the fish cakes, using the remaining oil.

6 For the dipping sauce, place all of the ingredients in a small pan and heat gently for 1 minute. Do not boil. Mix together the lettuce, cucumber and mint for the salad. Arrange the fish cakes on individual plates with the salad and serve each with a tiny dish of the dipping sauce.

350 g potatoes, peeled
   and cut into chunks

350 g white fish fillets

juice of 1 lime

1 thin lemongrass stalk, thinly
   sliced and lightly crushed

2 teaspoons Thai red curry paste

3 green onions, thinly sliced

3 garlic cloves, chopped

4 tablespoons chopped
   fresh coriander

1 teaspoon chopped fresh ginger

1/3 cup all-purpose flour

2 eggs, lightly beaten

1 cup fresh whole-wheat
   breadcrumbs

2 tablespoons extra virgin
   olive oil

LIME AND HONEY DIPPING SAUCE

juice of 3 limes

2 tablespoons clear honey

1 teaspoon chopped fresh ginger

2 teaspoons reduced-salt soy sauce

3/4 teaspoon Thai red curry paste

1 large mild red chili, seeded
   and thinly sliced

CUCUMBER AND MINT SALAD

1 iceberg lettuce, finely shredded

1/2 cucumber, diced

3/4 cup mint leaves, finely shredded

crumbed fish with parsley and lemon

Gremolata is an Italian mixture of parsley, lemon rind and garlic. This recipe uses the gremolata with breadcrumbs to make a tasty topping for fish, which is baked with tomatoes and zucchini and served with saffron mashed potatoes.

2 lemons
²/₃ cup fresh whole-wheat breadcrumbs
¼ cup chopped parsley
2 garlic cloves, crushed
pepper to taste
4 chunky pieces of skinless white fish fillet, about 130 g each
2 teaspoons whole-grain mustard
3 Italian tomatoes, quartered
1 large zucchini, thinly sliced diagonally
1 tablespoon extra virgin olive oil

SAFFRON MASHED POTATOES

1 kg potatoes, peeled and cut into chunks
1 teaspoon saffron threads
¼ cup low-fat milk
pepper to taste

1 Preheat the oven to 400°F (200°C). Finely grate the rind and squeeze the juice from 1 of the lemons. Mix the rind with the breadcrumbs, parsley and garlic, and season with pepper.

2 Place the fish fillets in a lightly oiled, large ovenproof dish. Spread the mustard evenly over the top of the fish, then sprinkle over the lemon juice. Arrange the tomatoes and zucchini around the fish. Cut the remaining lemon into 4 wedges and put these into the dish, too.

3 Spoon the breadcrumb mixture over the fish and press down lightly. Drizzle with the olive oil. Bake the fish for 25 minutes or until it flakes easily and the topping is crisp.

4 Meanwhile, to make the saffron mashed potatoes, place the potatoes in a saucepan, cover with boiling water and add the saffron. Cook the potatoes for 15–20 minutes or until tender. Drain the potatoes and mash with the milk. Season with pepper. Serve the fish with the saffron mashed potatoes, tomatoes and zucchini.

Variations For a special occasion, bake the fish fillets in individual ovenproof dishes. Slice the tomatoes, and replace the zucchini with one red or yellow pepper, seeded and chopped. Place a piece of fish in each dish and arrange the sliced tomatoes on top. Scatter over the pepper and then the breadcrumb mixture, and bake for 20 minutes. Garnish with wedges of lemon. • If you want to make an oaty topping, you can replace a third of the breadcrumbs with rolled oats. You can also replace the lemon rind with orange rind and add some snipped fresh chives to the breadcrumb topping.

preparation time **20 mins**
cooking time **25 mins**
serves **4**

PER SERVING

451 calories

42 g protein

14 g total fat
4 g saturated fat

125 mg cholesterol

38 g total carbohydrate
5 g sugars

7 g fibre

254 mg sodium

HEALTH HINT

Tomatoes are full of healthy compounds, like vitamin C and carotenoids, which act as antioxidants and may protect against heart disease and cancer. When you cook tomatoes, the antioxidant lycopene becomes more readily available to the body; a small amount of oil, as in this recipe, is thought to help its absorption by the body.

Indian-style fish parcels

 Fish fillets are flavoured with chili, ginger, mint and coconut milk, then wrapped in parcels and baked in the oven. Zucchinis tossed with mustard and sesame seeds and mint new potatoes are served alongside.

1 kg small new potatoes, washed
4 white fish fillets, about 150 g each
pepper to taste
2 cm piece fresh ginger, finely chopped
½ red onion, finely chopped
1 large mild red chili, seeded and finely chopped
4 tablespoons chopped fresh mint
4 tablespoons reduced-fat coconut milk
2 zucchinis, diced
1 tablespoon sesame seeds
2 teaspoons yellow mustard seeds
2 teaspoons reduced-salt soy sauce

1 Preheat the oven to 350°F (180°C). Place the potatoes in a medium-sized saucepan, cover with boiling water and simmer for about 15 minutes or until tender.

2 Meanwhile, cut out 4 large pieces of parchment paper or foil, each large enough to enclose a fish fillet. Place a fillet on each piece of paper or foil and season with pepper.

3 Mix together the ginger, onion, chili, half of the mint and the coconut milk, and spread over the fish. Fold over the paper or foil and pleat or twist the ends to seal. Place the parcels on a large baking sheet and bake for 10–12 minutes or until the fish flakes easily (open a parcel to check).

4 When the potatoes and fish are almost ready, steam the zucchinis in a steamer basket set above the potatoes for 4 minutes. Heat a frying pan, add the sesame and mustard seeds, cover and fry over medium heat for 2–3 minutes or until lightly toasted, shaking the pan frequently.

5 Remove the pan from the heat. Add the soy sauce to the seeds and quickly stir, then re-cover the pan and set aside until the seeds stop "popping." Stir the zucchinis into the seed mixture.

6 Drain the potatoes and toss with the remaining chopped mint. Arrange the fish parcels on serving plates and serve with the zucchinis and the new potatoes.

preparation time **15 mins**
cooking time **25 mins**
serves **4**

PER SERVING

404 calories
45 g protein
9 g total fat
4 g saturated fat
115 mg cholesterol
35 g total carbohydrate
3 g sugars
8 g fibre
275 mg sodium

COOK'S TIP

Baking the fish in a parcel captures all the flavour and nutrients, and the fish stays deliciously moist.

baked trout with cucumber sauce

 Orange and lemon slices add great flavour to this simple recipe for baked fish, and a cucumber and yogourt sauce provides a refreshing contrast. New potatoes are roasted in the oven with the fish.

Fb

preparation time **20 mins**
cooking time **35 mins**
serves **4**

PER SERVING

440 calories

48 g protein

13 g total fat
3 g saturated fat

115 mg cholesterol

32 g total carbohydrate
8 g sugars

6 g fibre

147 mg sodium

HEALTH TIP

Like other oily fish, trout is rich in beneficial omega-3 fatty acids. It is also valuable for its high protein content and B vitamins, especially niacin and vitamin B_{12}.

1 Preheat the oven to 400°F (200°C) and put 2 baking sheets in the oven to heat. Place the potatoes in a large saucepan and pour over enough boiling water to cover them. Bring back to a boil, then simmer for 5 minutes. Drain and return to the pan.

2 Drizzle the oil over the potatoes and toss them quickly to coat. Spread them out on one of the hot baking sheets and roast for 10 minutes. Turn the potatoes over and roast for another 10 minutes, then turn them again and roast for a further 5 minutes or until crisp and tender.

3 Meanwhile, tuck the sprigs of tarragon inside the trout with some pepper. Cut out 4 squares of foil, each large enough to wrap up a fish. Cut the orange and lemon slices in half. Divide half the orange and lemon slices among the foil squares, lay the fish on top and cover with the remaining fruit slices. Sprinkle 1 tablespoon orange juice over each fish. Wrap up the foil to enclose the fish completely, twisting the ends to seal. Place the parcels on the second hot baking sheet and bake for 20 minutes.

4 While the fish and potatoes are cooking, make the cucumber sauce. Grate the cucumber, place it in a sieve and press to squeeze out any liquid. Mix together the cucumber, yogourt and mint, and season with pepper.

5 Arrange the fish, orange and lemon slices and roasted potatoes on individual warm plates. Add a garnish of baby arugula and serve with the cucumber sauce.

750 g new potatoes, washed and quartered lengthwise

1 tablespoon extra virgin olive oil

4 sprigs fresh tarragon

4 small whole trout, about 300 g each, cleaned

pepper to taste

1 orange, cut into 8 slices

1 lemon, cut into 8 slices

4 tablespoons orange juice

1/2 cup baby arugula leaves to garnish

CUCUMBER SAUCE

200 g cucumber

150 g plain low-fat yogourt

2 tablespoons chopped fresh mint

pepper to taste

grilled swordfish steaks with tomato and pepper salsa

Fish steaks make ideal fast food, and serving them with a vibrant salsa, rice and a mixed-leaf salad transforms plain cooked fish into an exciting dish. Use a ridged cast-iron grill pan to produce attractive markings on the fish.

4 swordfish or other fish steaks, about 150 g each

4 tablespoons extra virgin olive oil

juice of 1 small orange

1 garlic clove, crushed

pepper to taste

1 orange, cut into wedges, to garnish

TOMATO AND PEPPER SALSA

200 g Italian tomatoes, diced

½ red pepper, seeded and diced

½ red onion, finely chopped

juice of 1 small orange

15 g fresh basil, chopped

1 tablespoon balsamic vinegar

1 teaspoon caster (superfine) sugar

pepper to taste

1 To prepare the fish steaks, place them in a shallow non-metallic dish. Mix together the extra virgin olive oil, the orange juice, garlic and a little pepper to season, and spoon this mixture over the fish steaks.

2 To make the salsa, combine the tomatoes, red pepper, onion, orange juice, basil, balsamic vinegar and sugar, and season with pepper. Spoon into a serving bowl.

3 Heat a lightly oiled, ridged cast-iron grill pan (to give the fish the attractive striped markings on the flesh) or a heavy-based frying pan over a high heat. Place the fish steaks in the grill pan or in the frying pan and cook for approximately 2–3 minutes on each side, basting from time to time with the oil mixture, until the fish flakes easily.

4 Place the fish steaks on individual warm serving plates and grind over some additional black pepper. Garnish the fish with wedges of orange and serve with the salsa.

Variations For a tomato and olive salsa, combine the diced tomatoes with ½ diced cucumber, 4 chopped green onions, 50 g chopped pitted green or black olives and ½ cup chopped fresh basil. Or use 1 tablespoon well-drained and rinsed capers instead of olives. • In summer, instead of being cooked indoors, the fish can be cooked outdoors on a barbecue. Place the steaks on a sheet of foil to prevent the delicate flesh from slipping through the barbecue.

30 **C**

preparation time **15 mins**

cooking time **10 mins**

serves **4**

PER SERVING

399 calories

40 g protein

22 g total fat

4 g saturated fat

75 mg cholesterol

9 g total carbohydrate

9 g sugars

2 g fibre

181 mg sodium

HEALTH HINT

Peppers are an excellent source of vitamin C and beta carotene, but the beta carotene content varies depending on the colour of the pepper. Green peppers contain around 265 mcg carotene per 100 g, while red peppers contain approximately 3,840 mcg for the same weight.

fish with spicy green lentils

Dark green Puy lentils, grown in the south of France, have a unique, peppery flavour that is enhanced by chili. They do not disintegrate during cooking and their texture is a perfect complement to the flakiness of fresh fish.

2 tablespoons extra virgin olive oil

1 onion, chopped

2 celery stalks, chopped

2 leeks, chopped

1–2 large mild red chilies, seeded and finely chopped

170 g Puy-style (dark green) lentils, rinsed and drained

3 cups reduced-salt vegetable stock

1 sprig fresh thyme

1 bay leaf

juice of 1 lemon

⅛ teaspoon cayenne pepper

4 pieces of skinless white fish fillet or 4 fish steaks, about 150 g each

pepper to taste

lemon wedges to serve

1 Heat 1 tablespoon of the olive oil in a saucepan, add the onion, celery, leeks and chilies, and cook gently for 2 minutes. Stir in the lentils. Add the vegetable stock, thyme and bay leaf and bring to a boil. Lower the heat and simmer for about 20 minutes or until the lentils are tender. If at the end of this time the lentils have not absorbed all the stock, drain them (you can use the excess stock to make a soup).

2 Ten minutes before the lentils are ready, preheat the broiler. Mix together the remaining 1 tablespoon oil, the lemon juice and cayenne pepper. Place the fish in the broiler pan, skin-side up, season with pepper and brush with the oil mixture. Broil until the fish flakes easily. There is no need to turn the fish over.

3 Spread the lentils in a warmed serving dish and arrange the pieces of fish on top. Serve immediately, with lemon wedges.

preparation time **15 mins**

cooking time **30 mins**

serves **4**

PER SERVING

372 calories

44 g protein

14 g total fat
3 g saturated fat

115 mg cholesterol

16 g total carbohydrate
7 g sugars

5 g fibre

970 mg sodium

HEALTH HINT

Lentils, which are small seeds from a variety of leguminous plants, are classified as pulses, but unlike other pulses they do not need to be soaked before cooking. Lentils are a good source of protein, starch, dietary fibre and B vitamins. Iron absorption from lentils is poor, but vitamin C-rich foods, such as the lemon juice in this recipe, can improve this process considerably.

seafood and mushroom pie

A simple fish pie can be transformed into a feast by the addition of shrimp and mushrooms. Serve with a colourful medley of steamed vegetables, such as snow or sugar snap peas, carrots and baby corn.

Fb

preparation time **15 mins**
cooking time **45 mins**
serves **4**

PER SERVING

424 calories

42 g protein

9 g total fat
3 g saturated fat

130 mg cholesterol

44 g total carbohydrate
11 g sugars

4 g fibre

310 mg sodium

HEALTH HINT

Plain yogourt is often used as an alternative to cream. This has the advantage of helping to lower the fat content of a recipe. In addition, yogourt provides more calcium than cream.

1 Preheat the oven to 350°F (180°C). Place the potatoes in a saucepan, cover with boiling water and cook for 15–20 minutes or until tender. When the potatoes are done, drain them well and mash with the yogourt. Set aside and keep hot.

2 Meanwhile, melt the margarine in a flameproof casserole dish, add the onion and cook gently for 5 minutes or until soft. Place the fish on top, pour over 1¾ cups of the milk and add the bay leaves and parsley. Cover and poach in the oven for 15 minutes or until the fish flakes easily.

3 Cook the pasta in a saucepan of boiling water for 10 minutes, or according to the package instructions, until just al dente. Drain and set aside.

4 Place the cornstarch and mustard in a saucepan, add the remaining milk and mix to a smooth paste. Strain the poaching milk from the fish into the saucepan, reserving the onion, and add nutmeg. Bring to a boil, stirring constantly. Reduce the heat and simmer for 5 minutes or until thick.

5 Flake the fish, discarding the skin and any bones. Stir the fish, reserved onion, shrimp, mushrooms, drained pasta shells and chopped parsley into the sauce, and season with pepper. Return the mixture to the casserole dish. Spoon the mashed potatoes over the fish mixture, spreading the potato evenly, right to the edge of the dish. Fork up the surface. Bake for about 20 minutes or until bubbling and browned. Serve hot.

550 g potatoes, peeled and cut into chunks
5 tablespoons Greek-style yogourt
1 tablespoon reduced-salt margarine
1 small onion, sliced
400 g white fish fillets
2 cups low-fat milk
2 bay leaves
4 sprigs parsley
80 g small pasta shells
4 tablespoons cornstarch
½ teaspoon mustard powder
freshly grated nutmeg to taste
120 g cooked peeled shrimp
80 g mushrooms, thinly sliced
4 tablespoons chopped parsley
pepper to taste

Asian-style fish with noodles

A whole fish cooked with ginger, garlic and green onions is a traditional centrepiece in a Chinese meal. Here it is served with a mixture of noodles and bean sprouts to make a very special dish.

1 Preheat the oven to 400°F (200°C). Brush a large sheet of thick foil with the oil and place the fish on top. Place the lime slices inside the fish and scatter over the green onions, carrot, ginger and garlic. Drizzle over the soy sauce and sesame oil, and sprinkle over the coriander leaves. Bring the ends of the foil together and fold and twist to seal in the fish. Place on a baking sheet. Bake for 30–35 minutes or until the fish flakes easily (open the parcel to check).

2 Meanwhile, place the noodles in a saucepan of boiling water, return to a boil and simmer for 3 minutes. Or cook them according to the package instructions. Drain well. Heat the oil in a wok, add the red onions and garlic, and cook over a high heat for 30 seconds. Add the bean sprouts and cook for 1 minute or until they begin to soften. Add the noodles together with the soy sauce. Cook over high heat for 2–3 minutes, stirring and tossing well.

3 Remove the fish from the oven, unwrap and transfer to a hot serving platter. Garnish with coriander leaves and lime halves. Serve the fish cut into slices, with the noodles.

Variation For Mediterranean-style baked snapper, use 4 fillets, about 150 g each, and place on 4 oiled pieces of foil. Mix together 4 tomatoes, seeded and diced, 40 g pitted black olives, quartered, 2 tablespoons drained capers, roughly chopped, 1 tablespoon chopped parsley, 2 tablespoons extra virgin olive oil and some pepper. Divide the mixture among the fish and wrap in the foil. Bake for 15 minutes. Meanwhile, make a salad by mixing together 1 bulb fennel (finely grated), 1 large zucchini (sliced), and 2 red onions, cut into thin wedges. Toss with 2 tablespoons lemon juice, 1 tablespoon extra virgin olive oil, and pepper to taste. Serve the fish with the salad and boiled new potatoes.

1 teaspoon sunflower oil

1 whole snapper, about 800 g, cleaned and scaled

1 lime, cut into 4 slices

6 green onions, cut into fine shreds

1 carrot, cut into fine matchsticks

2 cm piece fresh ginger, cut into fine matchsticks

2 garlic cloves, thinly sliced

2 tablespoons reduced-salt soy sauce

1 teaspoon sesame oil

1 tablespoon fresh coriander leaves, plus extra leaves to garnish

lime halves to serve

NOODLES

250 g fine Chinese egg noodles

1 tablespoon sunflower oil

2 small red onions, cut into very thin wedges

1 garlic clove, thinly sliced

300 g bean sprouts

4 tablespoons reduced-salt soy sauce

preparation time **15 mins**

cooking time **35 mins**

serves **4**

PER SERVING

569 calories
58 g protein
12 g total fat
2 g saturated fat
129 mg cholesterol
55 g total carbohydrate
3 g sugars
7 g fibre
1123 mg sodium

HEALTH HINTS

Sunflower is one of the most popular oils, having a mild flavour. It is a good source of vitamin E, which is a powerful antioxidant that protects cell membranes from damage by free radicals.

Eggs add flavour and colour to noodles and only a tiny amount of fat. Egg noodles are also an excellent source of starchy carbohydrate.

steamed fish with ginger and sesame

Steaming is unbeatable when it comes to heart-healthy cooking: there's no need for added fat, and flavour and nutrients are locked in. Serve this fish with grilled pepper and a pilaf of wild and brown rice for a satisfying meal.

2 tablespoons grated fresh ginger

3 garlic cloves, finely chopped

½ teaspoon grated lime rind

½ cup chopped fresh coriander

4 flathead or other fish fillets, about 150 g each

pepper to taste

2½ teaspoons sesame oil

2 tablespoons fresh lime juice

1 teaspoon cornstarch blended with 1 tablespoon water

1 Combine the ginger, garlic, lime rind and half the coriander in a small bowl. Place the fish fillets skin-side up on a work surface and sprinkle with pepper and the coriander mixture. Fold the fish fillets in half. Drizzle the sesame oil over the folded fish and place the fish on a heatproof plate.

2 Place a cake rack in a frying pan large enough to hold the plate of fish and add enough water to come just below the cake rack. Cover the pan and bring the water to a simmer.

3 Carefully place the plate of fish on the rack over the simmering water. Cover and steam until cooked, about 5 minutes. With a slotted spoon, transfer the fish to a platter; keep warm.

4 Pour the cooking liquids on the plate used for steaming into a small saucepan. Add the lime juice and ½ cup water and bring to a boil. Stir in the cornstarch mixture and cook, stirring, until the sauce is slightly thickened, about 1 minute. Stir in the remaining coriander. Serve the fish accompanied with the sauce.

preparation time **10 mins**

cooking time **10 mins**

serves **4**

PER SERVING

208 calories

39 g protein

5 g total fat
1 g saturated fat

117 mg cholesterol

1 g total carbohydrate
0.3 g sugars

1 g fibre

139 mg sodium

HEALTH HINT

The oil extracted from sesame seeds is high in polyunsaturated fatty acids, which can help to prevent heart disease.

teriyaki swordfish kebabs

Teriyaki is a popular cooking style in Japan. The teriyaki marinade for fish or meat is made with soy sauce, rice wine and sugar and can be bought ready made from most grocery stores. It is intense, so you only need to use a little.

Fb GI

preparation time **25 mins** plus 30 mins soaking of the skewers

cooking time **10 mins**

serves **4**

PER SERVING

663 calories

49 g protein

15 g total fat
3 g saturated fat

69 mg cholesterol

79 g total carbohydrate
20 g sugars

7 g fibre

1026 mg sodium

HEALTH HINT

Swordfish is an excellent source of vitamin B_{12}, which apart from its role in the formation of red blood cells is involved in maintaining a healthy nervous system, as it helps to form the protective sheath around nerves.

1 If using wooden skewers, soak them in cold water for at least 30 minutes. Preheat the broiler.

2 Cut the swordfish into 24 bite-sized pieces. Mix together the marinade ingredients in a bowl, add the fish and toss to coat. Thread the fish onto 8 skewers, alternating the cubes with the red onions, pepper and limes.

3 Broil the kebabs until the fish is just cooked but still very slightly translucent in the centre and all the ingredients are golden-brown. Turn the kebabs halfway through the cooking and baste with the remaining marinade.

4 While the kebabs are cooking, prepare the noodles. Place the noodles in a saucepan of boiling water, bring back to a boil and simmer for 3 minutes. Or cook the noodles according to the package instructions. Drain well. Heat the oil in a wok over a high heat and cook the garlic and ginger for 30 seconds. Add the snow peas and green onions and stir-fry for 1 minute. Add the noodles with the sweet chili and soy sauces, and stir and toss together for 1–2 minutes.

5 Spoon the noodle mixture onto warm plates and top with the fish kebabs. Garnish with the chopped coriander and serve.

550 g thick swordfish steaks

4 small red onions, quartered

1 large yellow pepper, seeded and cut into 16 cubes

2 limes, each cut into 8 slices

2 tablespoons chopped fresh coriander to garnish

MARINADE

4 tablespoons teriyaki marinade

1 tablespoon clear honey

1 teaspoon sesame oil

1 garlic clove, crushed

SWEET CHILI NOODLES

250 g fine Chinese egg noodles

1 tablespoon sunflower oil

2 garlic cloves, sliced

1 tablespoon finely chopped fresh ginger

120 g snow peas, sliced

6 green onions, shredded

4 tablespoons sweet chili sauce

2 tablespoons reduced-salt soy sauce

Thai green fish curry

This Thai green curry is wonderfully fragrant and is prepared with a homemade curry paste. Serve it with rice and a side dish of Chinese cabbage or broccoli florets stir-fried with garlic and a little salt-reduced soy sauce.

2 tablespoons sunflower oil

2⅓ cups fish stock (reduced-salt if possible)

2 tablespoons fish sauce (optional)

2 tablespoons sugar

300 g new potatoes, halved

1 red pepper, seeded and cut into strips

500 g white fish fillets, sliced across into medallions

110 g small snow or sugar snap peas

⅓ cup reduced-fat coconut milk

juice of 1 lime

1 tablespoon chopped fresh coriander to garnish

GREEN CURRY PASTE

2 tablespoons finely grated fresh galangal

2 teaspoons finely chopped lemongrass

4 lime leaves, shredded

½ cup finely chopped fresh coriander

6 shallots, very finely chopped

4 garlic cloves, crushed

1 teaspoon ground coriander

1 teaspoon ground cumin

1 small red chili, seeded and finely chopped

finely grated rind of 1 lime

1 Mix together all the ingredients for the green curry paste and stir in ½ cup water. (If you have a food processor, you can save chopping time by using the machine to blend all of the paste ingredients with the water until smooth.)

2 Heat the oil in a nonstick pan. Add the curry paste and fry for 5 minutes, stirring frequently, until the water has evaporated and the shallots have softened and are starting to colour.

3 Pour the fish stock and fish sauce, if using, into the pan and stir in the sugar, potatoes and red pepper. Bring to a boil, then cover and cook for about 10 minutes or until the potatoes are almost tender.

4 Add the fish, snow or sugar snap peas and coconut milk, then cover again and cook gently for 5 minutes or until the fish flakes easily. Remove from the heat, stir in the lime juice and scatter over the coriander to garnish. Serve hot.

Variation To make a speedy Thai shrimp curry, fry the shallots and garlic in the sunflower oil until softened, then pour in the fish stock, fish sauce, if using, and sugar. Add 2–4 tablespoons ready-made green curry paste from a jar (compare brands to find the one with the lowest fat) and stir well. Simmer for 10 minutes. Add the snow or sugar snap peas and cook for 3 minutes, then add 200 g peeled raw shrimp. Cook for 1–2 minutes or until the shrimp turn pink. Add the lime juice and 5 tablespoons chopped fresh basil and serve.

preparation time **25 mins**

cooking time **20 mins**

serves **4**

PER SERVING

378 calories

34 g protein

16 g total fat

4 g saturated fat

77 mg cholesterol

24 g total carbohydrate

12 g sugars

4 g fibre

552 mg sodium

HEALTH HINT

Shallots tend to be milder and more subtle in flavour than onions. Like onions, they contain some vitamin C and B vitamins.

COOK'S TIP

Galangal is a rhizome, similar to ginger, with a hot peppery flavour. It is usually available at grocery stores.

seafood lasagna

Packed with seafood and vegetables, this lasagna is a superb vitamin-rich, nutritious meal. Choose vegetables that are fresh and in season, including fresh peas, asparagus, beans, broccoli and sautéed mushrooms.

preparation time **45 mins**

cooking time
1 hour 10 mins

serves **6**

PER SERVING

618 calories

43 g protein

23 g total fat
8 g saturated fat

237 mg cholesterol

58 g total carbohydrate
9 g sugars

10 g fibre

658 mg sodium

HEART SUPERFOOD

Oily fish, such as salmon, is rich in omega-3 fatty acids, which are a type of polyunsaturated fat believed to help protect against coronary heart disease and strokes.

1 Preheat the oven to 350°F (180°C). Heat 2 tablespoons of oil in a saucepan. Add the fennel, onion and half the garlic. Cook for 5 minutes until the onion softens, then add the parsley, fennel seeds, Italian herbs and chili. Cook for 1–2 minutes. Add the squid and salmon, and cook for 1 minute; stir in the shrimp and mixed seafood. Cook for 30 seconds, then use a slotted spoon to transfer the seafood to a bowl and set aside.

2 Add the wine, stock, lemon rind, bay leaves and carrot to the juices remaining in the pan. Boil for 5 minutes, or until the liquid is reduced to about ½ cup. Stir in the tomatoes and cook over high heat for 3–4 minutes or until the sauce has reduced. Add the beans and remaining garlic. Cover and cook for 10 minutes. Add the zucchini. Cover and cook for 5 minutes; add the asparagus and peas. Cook, covered, for 5 minutes.

3 Grease a deep 30 x 20 cm (13 x 9 in.) ovenproof dish with a little oil. Place two-thirds of the vegetables in the dish, lifting them out of the sauce with a slotted spoon. Discard the bay leaves. Top with a layer of lasagna, overlapping the sheets slightly. Add the seafood and a second layer of lasagna. Pour on the remaining vegetables and sauce. Top with the remaining lasagna.

4 Mix the ricotta with the eggs and Parmesan cheese. Season with a little nutmeg, pepper and cayenne. Pour this evenly over the top of the lasagna and drizzle with the remaining olive oil.

5 Bake for 30 minutes, or until the lasagna is heated through and the top is speckled golden-brown. Serve immediately.

4 tablespoons extra virgin olive oil
1 small bulb fennel, diced
1 onion, chopped
4 garlic cloves, coarsely chopped
2 tablespoons chopped fresh parsley
¼–½ teaspoon fennel seeds
½ teaspoon dried mixed Italian herbs
⅛ teaspoon crushed dried chilies
120 g prepared squid
120 g salmon fillet, cut into chunks
120 g raw shrimp, peeled
120 g mixed seafood
⅔ cup dry white wine
⅔ cup fish stock (reduced-salt)
grated rind of ½ lemon
2 bay leaves
1 carrot, roughly chopped
1 kg tomatoes, diced
5 green beans, sliced
1 zucchini, sliced or diced
250 g asparagus spears
1 cup shelled fresh peas
400 g instant lasagna
250 g reduced-fat ricotta cheese
2 eggs, lightly beaten
½ cup Parmesan cheese, freshly grated
freshly grated nutmeg to taste
pepper and cayenne pepper to taste

salmon with tarragon mayonnaise

Fresh salmon is readily available all year round. This deliciously healthy dish can be served warm or cold, with a green leaf salad tossed with snow peas or green beans, and some crusty whole-wheat bread.

4 salmon steaks or fillets,
about 120 g each

²⁄₃ cup dry white wine

1–2 bay leaves

strip of pared lemon rind

pepper to taste

250 g couscous

4 tomatoes, roughly chopped

3 green onions, chopped

1 cup arugula, roughly chopped

1 tablespoon extra virgin olive oil

juice of 1 lemon

TARRAGON MAYONNAISE

5 tablespoons low-fat mayonnaise

150 g plain low-fat yogourt

finely grated rind of 1 lemon

2 tablespoons chopped fresh tarragon

pepper to taste

1 Place the salmon in a deep-sided nonstick frying pan. Pour over the wine and add the bay leaves, lemon rind and pepper. Bring to a boil, then reduce the heat, cover and poach the salmon for 5–6 minutes or until just cooked—it should still be very slightly translucent in the centre.

2 Meanwhile, for the tarragon mayonnaise stir together the mayonnaise, yogourt, grated lemon rind and tarragon. Season with pepper and spoon the mixture into a serving bowl.

3 When the salmon is cooked, drain off most of the cooking liquid into a measuring cup and add enough boiling water to make 1½ cups. Cover the pan with a lid to keep the salmon warm, off the heat.

4 Pour the diluted fish stock over the couscous in a bowl and leave for 3–4 minutes for the liquid to be absorbed. Fluff up the couscous with a fork and stir in the chopped tomatoes, green onions and arugula. Drizzle over the olive oil and lemon juice, and stir to blend everything together. Season with more pepper.

5 Serve the warm salmon with the couscous salad and the tarragon mayonnaise.

Variation If you like the aniseed flavour of Pernod, poach the salmon in ⅓ cup water or stock mixed with 5 tablespoons Pernod or pastis. The Pernod flavour works well with the tarragon in the mayonnaise. Light sour cream and Greek-style yogourt can all be used for making the sauce in place of the yogourt and mayonnaise.

30 **C** **Fb**

preparation time **20 mins**

cooking time **10 mins**

serves **4**

PER SERVING

352 calories

29 g protein

14 g total fat
2 g saturated fat

62 mg cholesterol

24 g total carbohydrate
11 g sugars

3 g fibre

321 mg sodium

HEALTH HINT

Combining mayonnaise with plain low-fat yogourt makes a lighter sauce that is lower in calories and fat than mayonnaise alone.

COOK'S TIP

Couscous, made from semolina, is the staple food in many north African countries. Buy it at the grocery store.

spaghettini marinara

Cooked in a delicious wine-enriched tomato sauce, a nutritious mix of seafood makes an elegant partner for the thin spaghettini. Prepare a leafy mixed side salad to go with this dinner party main course.

2 tablespoons extra virgin olive oil

1 onion, chopped

2–3 garlic cloves, chopped

2 tablespoons chopped fresh parsley

1 cup dry white wine

1 can (540 ml) diced tomatoes

⅛ teaspoon crushed dried chilies

¼ teaspoon sugar

⅛ teaspoon saffron threads

pepper to taste

8 mussels, washed and beards removed

2 squid, cleaned, then tentacles
   cut into bite-sized pieces and
   bodies cut into rings

300 g raw tiger or king shrimp, peeled

400 g spaghettini (thin spaghetti)

sprigs fresh oregano or marjoram
   to garnish

1 Heat the oil in a large saucepan, add the onion and sauté for 5–7 minutes or until softened but not browned. Add the garlic and parsley and cook for a further 1 minute.

2 Pour in the wine and bring to a boil. Regulate the heat so that the wine boils steadily, and cook for about 15 minutes or until the wine has almost all evaporated.

3 Stir in the tomatoes, the crushed chilies, sugar and saffron. Reduce the heat and cook gently for 15 minutes. Season to taste with pepper.

4 Add the mussels. Cover and cook over medium heat for 5 minutes or until the mussels start to open. Add the squid and shrimp, and cook for a further 3–4 minutes or until the shrimp turn pink. Remove from the heat. Discard any mussels that have not opened, then cover the pan to retain the heat.

5 Meanwhile, cook the spaghettini in boiling water for 10 minutes, or according to the package instructions, until al dente. Drain and return to the empty pan. Add some of the tomato sauce and toss the pasta until coated. Serve the pasta with the remaining tomato sauce and seafood piled on top, garnished with small sprigs of fresh oregano or marjoram.

 Fb **GI**

preparation time **25 mins**

cooking time **50 mins**

serves **4**

PER SERVING

494 calories

30 g protein

11 g total fat
2 g saturated fat

170 mg cholesterol

64 g total carbohydrate
6 g sugars

6 g fibre

500 mg sodium

HEALTH HINT

Pasta and seafood make a delicious dish that is both special and nutritious: it is high in starchy carbohydrate and low in fat. Wine and tomatoes make a sauce that is far lower in fat than the usual cream-based dressings.

lobster salad with lime dressing

A lobster makes a luxurious salad for two people. The lobster meat is here served on a bed of peppery salad greens, shredded snow peas, grapes and new potatoes cooked in their skins, all tossed in a lime-spiked dressing.

1 Place the potatoes in a saucepan and cover with boiling water. Cook for about 15 minutes or until just tender. Drain and leave to cool, then cut the potatoes in half.

2 While the potatoes are cooling, mix together the mayonnaise, yogourt and lime rind, and season with pepper. Set aside.

3 Pull and twist off the lobster claws and set aside. With a sharp knife, cut the body in half lengthwise, from tail end through the head. Remove the meat from the body/tail shell and the claws. Chop all the meat into chunks. (The meat from the spindly legs can also be removed with tweezers, but this takes a lot of effort for the small amount of meat inside them.)

4 Toss the potatoes with the shallots, snow peas, grapes, watercress and lime dressing. Arrange the arugula on large plates and add the watercress and potato salad. Scatter the lobster meat on top and serve.

Variation For a lightly curried lime and honey dressing, mix together 2 tablespoons peanut oil with 1 tablespoon lemon juice, ½ teaspoon curry paste and ½ teaspoon clear honey.

250 g small red new potatoes, washed
2 tablespoons low-fat mayonnaise
2 tablespoons Greek-style yogourt
finely grated rind of ½ lime
pepper to taste
1 cooked lobster, about 500 g
2 small shallots, thinly sliced
90 g snow peas, shredded
90 g seedless red grapes
90 g seedless green grapes
1 cup watercress
2 cups arugula to serve

preparation time **35 mins**
cooking time **15 mins**
serves **2**

PER SERVING

272 calories

21 g protein

3 g total fat
1 g saturated fat

74 mg cholesterol

40 g total carbohydrate
22 g sugars

6 g fibre

502 mg sodium

HEALTH HINT

Some varieties of grape are cultivated for wine, others for drying to become raisins and sultanas, and others for just eating. The nutrient content of different coloured grapes is very similar. Of all fruits, grapes have one of the highest sugar contents—mainly as glucose and fructose—and they are a good source of potassium.

shrimp, melon and mango salad

This salad combines shrimp with colourful, juicy fruit tossed in a light dressing flavoured with fresh mint and honey.

400 g cooked peeled shrimp
1 mango
350 g honeydew melon, diced
8 cherry tomatoes, halved
1½ cups arugula
¼ cucumber, sliced
fresh mint leaves to garnish

MINT AND HONEY DRESSING
2 tablespoons extra virgin olive oil
juice of 1 lemon
1 tablespoon clear honey
2 tablespoons chopped
    fresh mint
pepper to taste

1 To make the dressing, whisk together all the dressing ingredients in a large bowl and season with pepper. Add the shrimp to the dressing, cover and leave to marinate in the refrigerator for about 30 minutes to 1 hour.

2 Halve the mango lengthwise, cutting down around each side of the pit. Cut the flesh on each half in a criss-cross fashion to make cubes, then cut the cubes away from the skin.

3 Remove the shrimp from the refrigerator. Add the mango, melon and tomatoes and gently stir together. Arrange the arugula and cucumber slices around the edge of a shallow serving dish, and spoon the shrimp salad into the centre. Garnish with mint leaves and serve.

preparation time **20 mins**
plus 30 mins marinating
serves **4**

PER SERVING

264 calories

23 g protein

11 g total fat
2 g saturated fat

188 mg cholesterol

18 g total carbohydrate
18 g sugars

3 g fibre

448 mg sodium

barbecued shrimp with mustard sauce

Next time you have a barbecue, treat yourself to a little luxury—skewers of juicy shrimp in an exotically spiced marinade.

3 tablespoons Dijon mustard
2 tablespoons fresh lemon juice
2 teaspoons ground coriander
2 teaspoons ground cumin
½ teaspoon pepper
24 large raw shrimp, peeled
    and deveined

1 To make the mustard dipping sauce, stir together the mustard, lemon juice, ½ teaspoon coriander, ½ teaspoon cumin and ¼ teaspoon pepper in a small bowl. Set aside.

2 Combine the remaining 1½ teaspoons coriander, 1½ teaspoons cumin and ¼ teaspoon pepper in a large bowl. Add the shrimp, tossing to coat.

3 Preheat the barbecue. Thread the shrimp onto four long skewers. Place the shrimp on the barbecue and cook until opaque throughout, about 1 minute per side. Serve at room temperature or chilled, with the mustard dipping sauce.

preparation time **10 mins**
cooking time **2 mins**
serves **4**

PER SERVING

111 calories

23 g protein

2 g total fat
0.3 g saturated fat

180 mg cholesterol

1 g total carbohydrate
0.5 g sugars

0.3 g fibre

563 mg sodium

preparation time **20 mins**
cooking time **20 mins**
serves **4**

PER SERVING

394 calories

21 g protein

21 g total fat
3 g saturated fat

22 mg cholesterol

32 g total carbohydrate
5 g sugars

10 g fibre

757 mg sodium

HEALTH HINT

Buckwheat contains
useful amounts of
beta carotene and
vitamins from the
B group. It is low in fat
and rich in starchy
carbohydrate. It is
not related to wheat
so can be eaten by those
with wheat intolerance.

scallops with noodles and ginger

 This salad is based on soba—Japanese buckwheat noodles. They are tossed with bean sprouts, bok choy, fresh coriander and an intensely flavoured dressing, then topped with juicy soy-broiled scallops and mushrooms.

1 Line the broiler pan and a baking sheet with foil. To make the baste, mix together the garlic, oil, soy sauce and sugar. Set aside one-third of the baste in a large mixing bowl. Brush some of the remaining baste over both sides of the mushrooms and place on the broiler pan. Brush the scallops with the rest of the baste and place on the baking sheet.

2 Bring a large saucepan of water to a boil and cook the soba for about 6 minutes, or according to the package instructions, until just tender. Drain well.

3 Meanwhile, to make the dressing, add all the dressing ingredients to the baste in the salad bowl and stir until smooth.

4 Add the drained noodles to the dressing and toss to coat. Add the bok choy, bean sprouts, green onions and coriander, and toss well again. Divide among 4 shallow bowls.

5 Preheat the broiler. Cook the mushrooms until tender, turning once. Remove from the heat, then broil the scallops until cooked. Slice the mushrooms and scatter over the salad with any cooking juices. Add the scallops and nori and serve.

350 g large flat mushrooms

250 g large scallops

200 g soba (buckwheat noodles)

120 g bok choy, shredded

2 cups bean sprouts

4 green onions, shredded

¼ cup chopped coriander

1 sheet toasted sushi nori, about
    20 x 15 cm, cut into fine strips

SOY AND GARLIC BASTE

2 garlic cloves, crushed

¼ cup sunflower oil

2 tablespoons reduced-salt
    soy sauce

2 teaspoons caster (superfine) sugar

SOY DRESSING

juice of 1 large lemon

2 teaspoons finely grated fresh ginger

1 tablespoon reduced-salt soy sauce

½ small red chili, seeded and
    finely chopped

scallop and cherry tomato sauté

Scallops are infinitely adaptable. Here, these low-fat, low-cholesterol morsels of succulent seafood are sautéed with cherry tomatoes and enlivened with a vermouth-based sauce. Serve with Asian rice vermicelli or brown rice.

500 g large scallops
4 teaspoons cornstarch
2 teaspoons olive oil
3 garlic cloves, finely chopped
250 g cherry tomatoes
²/₃ cup dry vermouth, white wine
    or reduced-salt chicken stock
¹/₃ cup chopped fresh basil

1 Coat the scallops in 3 teaspoons cornstarch, shaking off the excess. Heat the oil in a large nonstick frying pan over medium heat. Add the scallops and sauté until golden-brown and cooked through, about 3 minutes. With a slotted spoon, transfer the scallops to a bowl.

2 Add the garlic to the pan and cook for 1 minute. Add the tomatoes and cook until they begin to collapse, about 4 minutes. Add the vermouth and basil to the pan. Bring to a boil and cook for 1 minute.

3 Meanwhile, stir together the remaining 1 teaspoon cornstarch with 1 tablespoon cold water in a small bowl. Add the cornstarch mixture to the pan and cook, stirring, until the sauce is slightly thickened, about 1 minute.

4 Return the scallops to the pan, reduce to a simmer, and cook just until heated through, about 1 minute. Serve hot.

30 **C**

preparation time **5 mins**
cooking time **10 mins**
serves **4**

PER SERVING

120 calories

15 g protein

3 g total fat
1 g saturated fat

41 mg cholesterol

5 g total carbohydrate
2 g sugars

1 g fibre

221 mg sodium

HEALTH HINT

The fat used here is heart-friendly olive oil, high in monounsaturated fat that protects beneficial HDL cholesterol levels while lowering harmful LDL levels. The mineral-rich scallops are low in both saturated and total fat.

shrimp and vegetable stir-fry

A simple stir-fry that's ready in thirty minutes! Fresh shrimp, crisp-yet-tender vegetables, a hint of soy and the zing of ginger. Stir-frying is quick, so it limits nutrient loss. Fast food that's healthy, too. Serve on white or brown rice.

1 Blend ⅔ cup water, the soy sauce, wine, cornstarch and ginger in a small bowl until smooth. Set aside.

2 Heat the oil in a large wok or large deep frying pan over medium-high heat until hot. Stir-fry the garlic until soft, about 2 minutes. Add the shrimp and stir-fry until pink, about 3 minutes. Remove the shrimp with a slotted spoon and set aside. Add the broccoli florets to the wok and stir-fry until they are bright green, about 2 minutes. Add the red and yellow pepper strips and snow peas and stir-fry until they are just tender but still crisp, about 1 minute longer.

3 Return the shrimp to the wok. Add the baby corn, water chestnuts and green onions. Pour in the sauce mixture and stir-fry until the sauce thickens and boils, about 1 minute. Serve.

⅓ cup reduced-salt soy sauce

¼ cup white wine

2 tablespoons cornstarch

1½ teaspoons grated peeled fresh ginger

1 tablespoon vegetable oil

2 garlic cloves, finely chopped

500 g large raw shrimp, peeled and deveined

250 g broccoli florets

1 large red pepper, cut into strips

1 large yellow pepper, cut into strips

120 g snow peas

100 g whole baby corn

½ cup sliced water chestnuts

4 green onions, cut diagonally into 5 cm pieces

preparation time **20 mins**

cooking time **10 mins**

serves **4**

PER SERVING

233 calories

24 g protein

7 g total fat
1 g saturated fat

116 mg cholesterol

18 g total carbohydrate
7 g sugars

6 g fibre

1064 mg sodium

COOK'S TIP

Stir-frying is an ideal method for cooking shrimp. If cooked too long or at too high a temperature, shrimp become unpleasantly dry and tough.

poultry

Asian chicken salad

This chicken salad has an Asian twist. Fried chicken is tossed with oranges, green onions, snow peas and lychees and is then crowned with a drizzle of creamy peanut dressing. What a treat for your heart and your taste buds!

500 g romaine lettuce

150 g snow peas

1 can (398 ml) lychees, drained and cut in half

1 large navel orange, peeled and cut into sections

1 red plum, pitted and sliced

4 green onions, thinly sliced

370 g chicken breasts

CREAMY PEANUT DRESSING

⅓ cup reduced-fat mayonnaise

4 tablespoons creamy peanut butter

1 garlic clove, finely chopped

1 Finely shred the lettuce and place in a bowl. Trim the snow peas and remove the strings. Cut the snow peas in half on the diagonal and add them to the bowl. Add the lychees, orange, plum and green onions and toss to combine.

2 Coat a heavy-based frying pan with nonstick cooking spray and set over medium-high heat until hot, about 2 minutes. Fry the chicken until cooked through, about 4 minutes on each side.

3 To make the dressing, whisk the mayonnaise, peanut butter and garlic in a small cup. Cut the chicken diagonally into thin slices and add the strips to the bowl. Just before serving, drizzle the salad with the dressing and toss to coat.

30 **C** **Fb** **GI**

preparation time **20 mins**

cooking time **10 mins**

serves **4**

PER SERVING

404 calories

32 g protein

18 g total fat
4 g saturated fat

75 mg cholesterol

29 g total carbohydrate
26 g sugars

8 g fibre

382 mg sodium

COOK'S TIP

This salad works with many types of cooked lean meat and seafood. In place of the chicken, cook the same amount of boneless lamb, turkey breast, pork fillet, beef fillet or large shrimp.

mango chicken salad

This salad combines new potatoes, tender broiled chicken and asparagus, tossed in a fresh orange dressing and then gently mixed with juicy mango slices and baby salad greens. It makes a delicious and well-balanced meal all on its own.

preparation time **15 mins**

cooking time **35 mins**
plus 15 mins marinating

serves **4**

PER SERVING

428 calories

26 g protein

22 g total fat
3 g saturated fat

61 mg cholesterol

33 g total carbohydrate
9 g sugars

6 g fibre

270 mg sodium

HEALTH HINT

Mango is an excellent source of vitamin C and beta carotene, both antioxidants that help to protect against damage by free radicals. Due to the beta carotene content, mango is also one of the best fruit sources of vitamin A, providing over 50 per cent of the daily needs in half a large fruit.

1 Place the garlic, ginger, soy sauce and sunflower oil in a bowl and whisk together. Add the chicken breasts and turn to coat both sides, then leave to marinate for 15 minutes.

2 Place the potatoes in a saucepan, pour over boiling water to cover and add the mint sprigs. Cook for 15–20 minutes or until tender. Meanwhile, place the asparagus in a steamer basket or metal colander, cover and set over the pan of potatoes to steam. Cook thin spears for 4–5 minutes and thick spears for 8–10 minutes, or until just tender. Drain the potatoes (discard mint) and leave until cool enough to handle, then cut into thick slices. Cut the asparagus diagonally into 6 cm lengths.

3 Preheat the broiler. Remove the chicken from the marinade and place it on the broiler rack. Broil, brushing frequently with the marinade and turning once, until cooked through and the juices run clear when the chicken is pierced with the tip of a knife. Leave to rest for 3–4 minutes, then slice.

4 To make the orange dressing, place the orange rind and juice, mustard, and sunflower and walnut oils in a large serving bowl, and whisk all the ingredients together until slightly thickened. Season with pepper.

5 Transfer the warm sliced chicken, potatoes and asparagus to the serving bowl and gently toss together to coat with the dressing. Add the mango and salad greens and toss gently again. Serve immediately, while still warm.

1 garlic clove, crushed

1 teaspoon grated fresh ginger

1 tablespoon reduced-salt soy sauce

2 teaspoons sunflower oil

300 g chicken breasts

750 g new potatoes, washed

2 large sprigs fresh mint

120 g asparagus spears

1 ripe mango, peeled and sliced

150 g mixed baby salad greens, such as spinach, arugula and romaine lettuce

FRESH ORANGE DRESSING

½ teaspoon finely grated orange rind

1 tablespoon freshly squeezed orange juice

1 teaspoon Dijon mustard

2 tablespoons sunflower oil

1 tablespoon walnut oil

pepper to taste

tarragon chicken with baby spinach

Tahini, a paste made from sesame seeds, is a favourite ingredient in Middle Eastern cooking. Available at most large grocery stores, it adds a nutty taste and thick creaminess to the dressing for this nutritious chicken salad.

300 g chicken breasts
²⁄₃ cup reduced-salt chicken or vegetable stock
1 small bunch fresh tarragon
1 small lemon
3 black peppercorns
2 tablespoons tahini
pepper to taste
1 head endive, about 150 g
150 g baby spinach
2 oranges
½ cup flaked almonds, toasted

1 Place the chicken in a shallow pan and pour over the stock. Remove the tarragon leaves from the stalks and set them aside. Lightly crush the stalks with a rolling pin to release their oils, then add to the pan. Remove a small strip of rind from the lemon and add this to the pan with the peppercorns.

2 Set the pan over medium heat and bring the stock to a boil. Turn down the heat, cover and simmer gently. Cook for 15 minutes or until the chicken is white all the way through.

3 Remove the chicken breasts using a slotted spoon and leave to cool on a plate. Strain the stock into a cup and discard the tarragon stalks, lemon rind and peppercorns. Set the stock aside. When the chicken has cooled, cut it into thick strips.

4 Place the tahini in a bowl and whisk in 5 tablespoons of the reserved stock to make a smooth, creamy dressing. If the dressing is a bit thick, add an extra tablespoon of stock. Squeeze the juice from the lemon and stir it into the dressing. Chop enough of the tarragon leaves to make 1 tablespoon, and add to the dressing with pepper to taste.

5 Cut the endive across on the diagonal into slices 1 cm thick. Arrange the endive and spinach in a large salad bowl.

6 Peel the oranges, then cut between the membrane into segments. Scatter the segments over the salad, followed by the toasted almonds. Place the chicken strips on top, and spoon over the tahini tarragon dressing. Serve immediately.

C Fb GI

preparation time **15 mins**

cooking time **20 mins**

serves **4**

PER SERVING

278 calories	
23 g protein	
17 g total fat	
2 g saturated fat	
50 mg cholesterol	
8 g total carbohydrate	
8 g sugars	
4 g fibre	
297 mg sodium	

HEALTH HINT

Chicken is an excellent source of protein and provides many B vitamins. Removing the skin reduces the fat content considerably, as most of the fat in chicken lies directly beneath the skin.

coronation chicken

Specially created for Queen Elizabeth's coronation, this curry-flavoured salad with a fruity pilaf makes a lovely summer dish. Often made with cream and mayonnaise, this version cuts the fat content down significantly.

 Fb GI

preparation time **30 mins**

cooking time **1 hour 10 mins** plus cooling

serves **6**

PER SERVING

707 calories

35 g protein

31 g total fat
6 g saturated fat

126 mg cholesterol

73 g total carbohydrate
21 g sugars

5 g fibre

528 mg sodium

COOK'S TIP

Using the chicken stock to cook the rice ensures that none of the water-soluble vitamins that seeped into the water while the chicken was being poached are lost.

1 Place the chicken in a large pan and cover with water. Add the onion, carrot and celery and bring almost to a boil, skimming any fat off the surface. When bubbles begin to break through the surface, reduce the heat and simmer. Add the peppercorns and bay leaf and simmer for 45 minutes or until the juices run clear from the chicken when you pierce the thigh.

2 Remove the chicken from the liquid and set aside to cool. Pour the cooking liquid through a fine sieve into a measuring cup. Discard the vegetables.

3 To make the pilaf, place 2⅓ cups of the strained cooking liquid and the rice in a saucepan. Stir in the raisins and mango. Bring to a boil, then reduce the heat, cover and simmer for 8–10 minutes, or according to the package instructions, until all the liquid has been absorbed and the rice is tender.

4 Remove the rice from the heat and set aside, covered, for 5 minutes. Transfer the rice to a bowl to cool completely.

5 To make the curry dressing, place the yogourt, mayonnaise, curry paste and lemon rind and juice in a bowl and mix until well blended. Stir in the chives, mint, parsley and pepper.

6 When the chicken is cool, cut into bite-sized pieces and fold into the curry dressing. Slice the banana and add to the chicken mixture. Stir the pecans into the rice pilaf and spoon onto 6 plates. Arrange the zucchini ribbons on the pilaf and top with the chicken mixture. Garnish with fresh mint sprigs and serve.

1 chicken, about 1.5 kg

1 onion, sliced

1 large carrot, coarsely chopped

1 celery stalk, chopped

6 black peppercorns, lightly crushed

1 bay leaf

1 large banana

2 zucchinis, sliced lengthwise with a vegetable peeler into thin strips

sprigs fresh mint to garnish

MANGO AND RAISIN PILAF

2 cups basmati rice, well rinsed

⅓ cup raisins

50 g dried mango, chopped

⅔ cup pecans

CURRY DRESSING

150 g plain low-fat yogourt

5 tablespoons reduced-fat mayonnaise

2 tablespoons korma curry paste

grated rind of 1 large lemon

1 tablespoon freshly squeezed lemon juice, or to taste

2 tablespoons snipped fresh chives

2 tablespoons chopped fresh mint

2 tablespoons chopped parsley

pepper to taste

warm sesame chicken salad

Strips of chicken in a crisp coating of sesame seeds, breadcrumbs and cornflakes are served on a crunchy vegetable salad dressed with a fresh herb vinaigrette. A little chili powder in the coating gives the salad a bit of a kick.

450 g chicken breasts

1 cup fresh whole-wheat breadcrumbs

50 g cornflakes, lightly crushed

4 teaspoons sesame seeds, plus extra to garnish

1 teaspoon chili powder, or to taste

2 eggs

SALAD

¼ white cabbage

½ chicory

2 heads endive

HERB DRESSING

1 tablespoon chopped parsley

1 tablespoon chopped fresh oregano

1 tablespoon chopped fresh tarragon

1 tablespoon white wine vinegar

5 tablespoons olive oil

1 teaspoon clear honey

pepper to taste

1 Preheat the oven to 400°F (200°C). Slice each chicken breast in half horizontally, then cut lengthwise into strips.

2 Place the breadcrumbs, cornflakes, sesame seeds and chili powder in a plastic bag and shake to mix well. Break the eggs into a shallow dish and beat together lightly.

3 Dip the chicken strips, one at a time, in the egg, then drop into the plastic bag. When a few pieces of chicken are in the bag, shake to coat evenly with the sesame seed mixture. As the chicken strips are coated, transfer to 2 nonstick baking sheets, spreading out the pieces in a single layer.

4 Bake the chicken strips for 15–20 minutes, turning the pieces over halfway through baking time.

5 Meanwhile, to make the salad, finely shred the cabbage and place in a large mixing bowl. Pull the chicory and endive leaves apart and tear any large ones into smaller pieces. Add to the mixing bowl.

6 In a small screwtop jar, shake together the herb dressing ingredients. Season with pepper. Pour the dressing over the salad and toss well.

7 Divide the salad among 4 individual plates and pile the cooked chicken pieces on top. Garnish with a few more sesame seeds, then serve.

Variation For a Chinese-style chicken salad, use 1 egg and beat it with 2 teaspoons five-spice powder, 1 tablespoon poppy seeds, 2 tablespoons tomato sauce, 2 tablespoons sweet sherry and 2 tablespoons reduced-salt soy sauce in a bowl. Stir in the chicken strips. Lift them out, a few at a time, and coat with the breadcrumb mixture (omit the sesame seeds and the chili powder). Bake as above. Meanwhile, finely shred 1 head bok choy, discarding some of the hard white part. Place in a bowl and add 1⅓ cups bean sprouts and 1 bunch green onions, thinly sliced into rings. Toss with the dressing (made with 2 tablespoons each parsley and coriander). Serve the hot chicken strips on top of the salad.

preparation time **15 mins**

cooking time **20 mins**

serves **4**

PER SERVING

507 calories

34 g protein

31 g total fat
6 g saturated fat

188 mg cholesterol

24 g total carbohydrate
5 g sugars

4 g fibre

398 mg sodium

HEALTH HINT

Cabbage belongs to a family of vegetables that contains a number of different phytochemicals that may help to protect against breast cancer. They are also a good source of vitamin C and are among the richest vegetable sources of folate.

sweet and sour chicken pancakes

This is a novel way of serving the popular Chinese dish of stir-fried sweet and sour chicken. Here zucchinis and bean sprouts are added to the chicken, and the whole mixture is folded up in pancakes.

1 cup all-purpose flour
pepper to taste
2 eggs, beaten
¾ cup low-fat milk

CHICKEN FILLING
2 tablespoons tomato sauce
1 tablespoon sunflower oil
grated rind and juice of 1 lemon
1 teaspoon malt vinegar
1 tablespoon brown sugar
2 teaspoons clear honey
450 g chicken breasts, cut into
      long thin strips
1 tablespoon sunflower oil
1 onion, halved and sliced
1 zucchini, cut into 5 cm matchsticks
1 tablespoon sunflower oil
2 cups bean sprouts
1 teaspoon sesame seeds
2 tablespoons reduced-salt soy sauce,
      plus extra to serve
green onions, sliced, to garnish

1 To make the pancakes, sift the flour into a bowl and add pepper. Make a well in the centre. Beat the eggs, milk and ⅓ cup water together and pour into the well; whisk in the flour to form a smooth batter. Cover and leave to stand.

2 To make the filling, mix together the tomato sauce, 1 tablespoon oil, the lemon rind and juice, vinegar, sugar and honey in a bowl. Add the chicken and toss to coat the strips.

3 Heat a wok and add another tablespoon oil. Add the onion and stir-fry for 5 minutes or until softened. Add the zucchini and stir-fry for 3 minutes. Using a slotted spoon, remove the vegetables from the wok and set aside. Reheat the wok, then add the chicken mixture and stir-fry for 3–4 minutes or until cooked. Return the vegetables to the wok. Toss together, then remove from the heat and set aside.

4 Heat a 20 cm (8 in.) nonstick frying pan and grease with a little oil. Pour in some batter and tilt the pan so the batter spreads evenly; tip any excess back into the bowl. Cook the pancake over medium-high heat for 2 minutes, then loosen the edges, flip it over and cook for 30 seconds. Slide the pancake onto a plate and cover with parchment paper. Repeat with the remaining batter to make 8 pancakes. Cover with foil and keep warm over a pan of simmering water. Reheat the filling. Add the bean sprouts, sesame seeds and soy sauce, and stir-fry for approximately 1–2 minutes until everything is hot. Fill the pancakes, fold into quarters and garnish with the green onions. Serve with extra soy sauce to sprinkle.

preparation time **20 mins**
cooking time **35 mins**
serves **4**

PER SERVING

558 calories

42 g protein

26 g total fat
5 g saturated fat

201 mg cholesterol

39 g total carbohydrate
13 g sugars

4 g fibre

557 mg sodium

HEALTH HINT

Bean sprouts, along with other sprouted seeds, are rich in B vitamins and vitamin C. Although some of the vitamin C will be destroyed by cooking, the bean sprouts still contribute good amounts in this recipe.

chicken and cashew pancakes

Chicken, stir-fried with carrots, celery and cabbage, then lightly flavoured with orange and sesame, makes a delicious filling for pancakes. This dish is sure to meet with your whole family's approval.

Fb

preparation time **20 mins**
cooking time **30 mins**
serves **4**

PER SERVING

455 calories

32 g protein

20 g total fat
4 g saturated fat

118 mg cholesterol

36 g total carbohydrate
9 g sugars

5 g fibre

341 mg sodium

HEART SUPERFOOD

Cashews, like all nuts, have been shown to be important for heart health. It could be due to their "healthy" mono-unsaturated fat, their vitamin E or their fibre, minerals or antioxidants.

1 To make the pancakes, sift the flour into a bowl and add pepper. Make a well in the centre. Beat the egg and milk, then pour into the well. Gradually whisk in the flour to form a smooth batter.

2 Heat a 20 cm (8 in.) nonstick frying pan and grease with a little oil. Pour in some batter and tilt the pan so the batter spreads evenly; tip any excess back into the bowl. Cook the pancake over medium-high heat for 2 minutes, then loosen the edges, flip it over and cook for 30 seconds. Slide the pancake onto a plate and cover with parchment paper. Repeat with the remaining batter to make 8 pancakes. Cover with foil and keep warm over a pan of simmering water.

3 To make the filling, heat a wok or large frying pan. Add the cashews and dry-fry over medium heat for a few minutes or until golden. Remove to a plate and set aside. Add the oil to the wok or frying pan and swirl it around, then add the chicken, garlic, ginger and chili. Stir-fry for 3 minutes.

4 Add the carrot and celery sticks, and stir-fry for a further 2 minutes. Add the orange rind and cabbage and stir-fry for 1 minute. Sprinkle over the soy sauce and sesame oil and stir-fry for another minute. Return the cashews to the pan and toss to mix with the other ingredients.

5 Divide the filling among the warm pancakes and fold them over or roll up. Serve immediately, with a little extra soy sauce to sprinkle.

1 cup all-purpose flour
pepper to taste
1 egg, beaten
1¼ cups low-fat milk
1 teaspoon sunflower oil

CHICKEN AND CASHEW NUT FILLING
⅓ cup cashews
1 tablespoon sunflower oil
300 g chicken breasts, cut into strips
1 garlic clove, crushed
1 teaspoon finely chopped fresh ginger
1 small red chili, seeded and finely chopped
2 carrots, cut into 5 cm matchsticks
2 celery stalks, cut into 5 cm matchsticks
grated rind of ½ orange
½ Savoy cabbage, shredded
1 tablespoon reduced-salt soy sauce, plus extra to serve
1 teaspoon sesame oil

spicy chicken and vegetable pastries

There are lots of variations on these savoury Mexican pastries, which are similar to Cornish pasties. The filling here is a blend of lean chicken and vegetables, subtly flavoured with spices, nuts and dried fruit.

¾ cup warm water

250 g whole-wheat bread mix

1 small egg, beaten

¼ teaspoon paprika

SPICY CHICKEN FILLING

1 tablespoon sunflower oil

1 onion, thinly sliced

1 garlic clove, crushed

1 green or red chili, seeded and finely chopped

250 g ground chicken

300 g potatoes, peeled and diced 1 cm thick

½ teaspoon ground cinnamon

½ teaspoon ground coriander

½ teaspoon ground cumin

5 tablespoons dry sherry or white wine

1 large carrot, coarsely grated

⅓ cup raisins

¼ cup blanched almonds, toasted and roughly chopped

2 tablespoons tomato sauce

2 tablespoons chopped fresh coriander

pepper to taste

1 To make the filling, heat the oil in a frying pan and cook the onion, garlic and chili over medium-high heat for 2–3 minutes, stirring, until softened and lightly browned. Add the ground chicken and stir for a further 4–5 minutes.

2 Meanwhile, parboil the diced potatoes in a saucepan of boiling water for 5 minutes. Drain well.

3 Stir the cinnamon, coriander and cumin into the chicken mixture and cook for 30 seconds. Add the sherry or wine and simmer until most of the liquid has evaporated. Stir in the potatoes, carrot, raisins, almonds, tomato sauce, fresh coriander and pepper. Remove from the heat.

4 Stir the water into the bread mix and knead for 2 minutes or until smooth. Cover and leave to rest for 5 minutes, then divide into 5 equal pieces. Roll out each piece on a lightly floured surface to a 20 cm round.

5 Preheat the oven to 425°F (220°C). Divide the filling among the dough rounds, spooning it into the centre. Brush the edge of each round with egg, then fold over into a half-moon shape. Press the edges together and roll over to seal. Place on a nonstick baking sheet, cover with oiled plastic wrap and leave in a warm place for 10–15 minutes or until slightly risen.

6 Uncover the pastries, glaze them with the rest of the beaten egg and sprinkle with the paprika. Bake for 10 minutes, then reduce the temperature to 350°F (180°C) and bake for a further 15 minutes. Serve hot or at room temperature.

preparation time **25 mins**

cooking time **40 mins** plus 15 mins rising

serves **5**

PER SERVING

350 calories

19 g protein

14 g total fat
2 g saturated fat

71 mg cholesterol

36 g total carbohydrate
12 g sugars

6 g fibre

280 mg sodium

HEALTH HINT

Raisins, like other dried fruit, are a very good source of dietary fibre. They are also virtually fat-free and provide useful amounts of iron.

chicken burgers with tropical fruit salsa

There's no need to give up burgers just because you're on a heart-smart diet. These juicy chicken burgers, topped with a Caribbean-inspired salsa, are absolutely delicious. Complete the meal with oven-baked chips.

1 Peel, core, slice and chop the pineapple (you need 2 cups) and place in a bowl. Mix in the mango, onion, coriander, lemon juice and oil. Cover and set aside.

2 Mix the chicken, apple and breadcrumbs in another bowl until blended. Divide the mixture into 4 equal portions and shape into patties about 1 cm thick. Place the patties on a plate, cover, and place in the freezer for 20 minutes.

3 Preheat the broiler or barbecue. Cook the patties until browned and cooked through.

4 For each burger, place a slice of cheese on the bottom of a hamburger bun, cover with lettuce, add a patty, top with about ½ cup salsa, and crown with the top of the bun.

1 small pineapple

1 small mango, peeled and finely chopped

1 small red onion, finely chopped

2 tablespoons finely chopped fresh coriander

1 tablespoon fresh lemon juice

1 teaspoon canola oil

500 g ground chicken

1 large Granny Smith apple, peeled and shredded

¼ cup dry breadcrumbs

4 thin slices reduced-fat Cheddar cheese

4 hamburger buns or soft rolls, preferably whole wheat, split

4 lettuce leaves

preparation time **20 mins**

cooking time **15 mins** plus 20 mins chilling

serves **4**

PER SERVING

581 calories

41 g protein

19 g total fat
6 g saturated fat

105 mg cholesterol

62 g total carbohydrate
24 g sugars

9 g fibre

715 mg sodium

COOK'S TIP

To help patties keep their shape during cooking, mix and shape them from cold meat, then firm them up by chilling in the freezer for 20 minutes or in the refrigerator for 1 hour.

spicy chicken tostadas

"Tostadas" comes from the Spanish word for toasted. These flat, crisply toasted corn tortillas can be topped with all sorts of savoury things. Here a delicious spicy chicken, pepper, bean and tomato mixture is used.

Fb GI

preparation time **30 mins**
cooking time **25 mins**
serves **4**

PER SERVING

506 calories

38 g protein

23 g total fat
6 g saturated fat

96 mg cholesterol

37 g total carbohydrate
12 g sugars

11 g fibre

548 mg sodium

HEALTH HINT

Radishes are low in fat and calories, and provide useful amounts of vitamin C. They contain phytochemicals that may help to protect the body against cancer.

HEART SUPERFOOD

Pulses such as pinto and kidney beans are a good source of protein for vegetarians. They are rich in soluble fibre, which helps sweep "used" cholesterol out of the body. They have little fat, plenty of B vitamins and the minerals potassium and magnesium, all of which help keep your heart in good health.

1 Place the chicken in a saucepan with cold water to cover. Bring to a boil, then reduce the heat and simmer for 10–15 minutes. Remove from the heat and leave to cool in the liquid. When cool enough to handle, drain and shred the meat. Set aside.

2 Meanwhile, heat the olive oil in a frying pan and add the peppers, onion and garlic. Fry over medium heat for 5 minutes or until softened. Add the chili powder, paprika and cumin, stir well, and cook for a few more minutes. Stir in the tomatoes with their juice and the sugar. Simmer for 5–8 minutes or until thick. Season with pepper. Remove from the heat and keep warm.

3 Heat a heavy-based frying pan. Fry the tortillas, one at a time, for about 15 seconds on each side or until slightly crisp and lightly browned. As they are done, keep them warm stacked in a dish towel. Meanwhile, in a small pan, warm the beans in the can liquid. Drain well.

4 Place 2 toasted tortillas on each plate. Spread with the tomato mixture, then spoon on the beans and chicken. Add the diced tomato, pickled jalapeños, if using, lettuce and radishes, piling up these toppings. Finish with a spoonful of reduced-fat sour cream. Serve with Tabasco sauce.

Variation Instead of beans, you can use a mixture of corn and zucchini. Cook 1 corn on the cob and 1 whole zucchini in separate pans of boiling water until tender, about 10 minutes for the corn and 5 minutes for the zucchini. Drain. Dice the zucchini, and cut the kernels of corn from the cob. Scatter the vegetables over each sauce-spread tortilla, then add the chicken.

500 g chicken breasts

2 tablespoons extra virgin olive oil

2 red peppers, seeded and
    coarsely chopped

1 onion, coarsely chopped

2 garlic cloves, thinly sliced

1 tablespoon mild chili powder

2 teaspoons paprika

1 teaspoon ground cumin

1 can (398 ml) diced tomatoes

⅛ teaspoon sugar

pepper to taste

8 corn tortillas

1 can (540 ml) pinto or
    kidney beans

1 tomato, diced

pickled jalapeño chili peppers
    (optional)

½ iceberg lettuce, shredded

8 radishes, sliced

5 tablespoons reduced-fat
    sour cream to serve

Tabasco or other hot chili sauce
    to serve

chicken fajitas with tomato salsa

Although in Mexico "fajitas" refers to a specific cut of beef, the term has come to describe a combination of sizzling chicken with pepper and onion, wrapped in a tortilla. The dish has very little fat, but lots of fresh flavours.

400 g chicken breasts, cut into strips

2 garlic cloves, chopped

1 teaspoon ground cumin

1 teaspoon mild chili powder

1 teaspoon paprika

¼ teaspoon dried oregano

grated rind and juice of ½ orange

juice of ½ lemon

2 tablespoons sunflower oil

1 cup fresh coriander leaves, chopped

2 green peppers, seeded and thinly sliced lengthwise

2 onions, thinly sliced lengthwise

8 flour tortillas

sprigs fresh coriander to garnish

½ cup extra-light sour cream

TOMATO SALSA

4 green onions, thinly sliced

120 g ripe tomatoes, diced

1 medium-hot green chili, seeded and chopped, or to taste

2 tablespoons tomato paste

2 garlic cloves, chopped

½ teaspoon ground cumin

freshly squeezed lemon juice to taste

pepper to taste

1 In a bowl combine the chicken with the garlic, cumin, chili, paprika, oregano, orange rind and juice, lemon juice, 1 tablespoon oil and 4 tablespoons coriander. Mix well so that all the chicken strips are coated, then leave to marinate for at least 15 minutes, or while you prepare the rest of the dish.

2 For the salsa, combine all the ingredients. Add the remaining chopped coriander and mix.

3 Preheat the oven to 350°F (180°C). Heat a heavy-based frying pan until very hot. Brush with the remaining oil. Add the green peppers and onions and cook for 6–8 minutes or until tender and lightly charred (do this in batches, if necessary). Remove from the pan and set aside.

4 Wrap the tortillas, stacked up, in foil to keep warm. Meanwhile, preheat the broiler. Spread out the chicken in a shallow layer in the broiler pan. Broil close to the heat, turning once or twice, until thoroughly cooked.

5 To serve, divide the chicken, onions and pepper among the warm tortillas and roll up. Garnish with sprigs of coriander and serve with the salsa and sour cream. Or serve the ingredients separately, with the tortillas wrapped in a cloth to keep them warm, and let your guests make their own fajitas.

preparation time **30 mins**

cooking time **20 mins**

serves **4**

PER SERVING

553 calories

35 g protein

25 g total fat
6 g saturated fat

93 mg cholesterol

46 g total carbohydrate
11 g sugars

6 g fibre

500 mg sodium

HEART SUPERFOOD

Onions and garlic are not just valuable assets in the kitchen, they have been used throughout history as a cure-all. Recent research suggests that they can help to lower blood cholesterol and so reduce the risk of heart disease. They also prevent blood clotting and are a natural decongestant. Therefore, include onions and garlic in your cooking regularly.

preparation time **20 mins**

cooking time **1 hour**

serves **2**

PER SERVING

467 calories

38 g protein

9 g total fat
2 g saturated fat

87 mg cholesterol

53 g total carbohydrate
7 g sugars

12 g fibre

331 mg sodium

HEALTH HINT

Nutritionists recommend 30 g fibre every day, but most of us consume only half that amount. Much of the fibre in this dish comes from the tomatoes, which also provide healthy amounts of vitamin C and beta carotene.

COOK'S TIP

Roasted garlic can also be stirred into soup, tossed in salad or spread on bread.

chicken breasts with roasted garlic-tomato sauce

Here's a recipe that turns the ordinary into the extraordinary. This chicken dish, simmered in a rich tomato sauce seasoned with roasted garlic, is high in vitamins C, B$_6$, beta carotene and niacin, is low in fat, but fabulous in flavour.

1 Preheat the oven to 350°F (180°C). Cut the top off each bulb of garlic and wrap the bulbs in foil. Bake until soft, about 1 hour.

2 Meanwhile, coat a medium ovenproof pan (with a lid) with nonstick cooking spray and set over medium-high heat. Sprinkle the chicken with pepper and cook until golden-brown, 4–5 minutes on each side. Transfer the chicken to a plate.

3 Add the carrots and shallot to the pan and fry until the shallot is soft, about 2 minutes. Return the chicken, skinned-side down, to the pan. Add the tomatoes, stock, wine and rosemary. Bring to a simmer. Cover and transfer to the oven. Bake the chicken until the juices run clear, 30–45 minutes.

4 Remove the garlic cloves from their skins with the tip of a sharp knife and mash until smooth. Stir the garlic into the sauce and sprinkle with parsley. Serve over the cooked fettuccine.

- 2 bulbs garlic, papery skin removed
- 2 bone-in chicken breast halves, about 150 g each, skin removed
- 1/2 teaspoon pepper
- 2 carrots, thinly sliced
- 1 large shallot, finely chopped
- 4 canned whole tomatoes, seeded and diced
- 1/2 cup reduced-salt chicken stock
- 1/2 cup dry white wine or additional reduced-salt chicken stock
- 1 teaspoon chopped fresh rosemary or 1/4 teaspoon dried rosemary
- 1 tablespoon chopped Italian parsley
- 350 g cooked fettuccine

chicken with lemongrass

A cross between a soup and stew, this dish captures the exciting spicy and sour flavours of Southeast Asia. Lemongrass gives a citrus touch, and light coconut milk—using just the minimum for flavour—adds richness without excessive fat.

1 small red chili, split open lengthwise but left whole

1 garlic clove, cut in half

1 cm piece fresh ginger, peeled and cut into 4 slices

2 stalks lemongrass, bruised and cut in half

650 g bone-in chicken pieces, such as breasts or thighs, skinned

1 shallot, finely chopped

250 g thin green beans, trimmed and cut into bite-sized pieces

1 zucchini, sliced lengthwise with a vegetable peeler into thin strips

⅓ cup reduced-fat coconut milk

finely grated rind and juice of 1 lime

pepper to taste

2 tablespoons chopped fresh coriander to garnish

1 Place 4 cups water in a saucepan over high heat. Spear the chili, garlic and ginger on a wooden cocktail stick or skewer (this makes them easy to remove later) and add to the pan together with the lemongrass. Bring to a boil and boil for 1 minute. Remove from the heat, cover and set aside to infuse for about 30 minutes.

2 Return the liquid to a boil, then reduce the heat to low. Add the chicken pieces, shallot and green beans, and poach for 12–15 minutes or until the chicken is cooked (test with the tip of a knife—the juices should run clear). Add the zucchini slices for the last 2 minutes of cooking.

3 Using a slotted spoon, transfer the chicken, beans and zucchini to a warmed bowl. Add a little of the poaching liquid to keep them moist, then cover tightly and keep warm.

4 Return the liquid to a boil and add the coconut milk, stirring until it dissolves. Continue boiling for about 5–6 minutes or until the liquid has reduced by about one-third.

5 Remove the chicken meat from the bones and shred it roughly. Return the chicken meat, beans and zucchini to the soup and stir, then reheat briefly. Stir in the grated lime rind and juice. Season with pepper.

6 Divide the chicken and vegetables among 4 soup bowls. Spoon over the liquid, discarding the lemongrass and stick of chili, garlic and ginger. Sprinkle with the coriander and serve.

Variation To turn this into a more filling dish, add some noodles. Soak 100 g Chinese egg noodles in boiling water for 3 minutes, or according to the package instructions, then drain. Stir into the reduced cooking liquid with the chicken and vegetables in step 5.

preparation time **25 mins**

cooking time **25 mins** plus 30 mins infusing

serves **4**

PER SERVING

177 calories

22 g protein

8 g total fat
4 g saturated fat

64 mg cholesterol

3 g total carbohydrate
2 g sugars

2 g fibre

60 mg sodium

HEALTH HINT

Green beans are a good source of the B vitamin folate, essential for a healthy pregnancy. It is important to ensure a good intake of folate in the early stages of pregnancy, and three months before, to prevent spina bifida. Folate may also have a role in helping to protect the body against heart disease.

chicken cacciatore

This rich-tasting Italian classic is perfect for a chilly night. Skinless chicken thighs keep the fat figures in check and a combination of mushrooms, tomatoes and herbs provide just the right flavour. Serve with polenta and green beans.

750 g bone-in chicken thighs

½ teaspoon pepper

1 large onion, chopped

2 celery stalks, thinly sliced

250 g button mushrooms, quartered

½ cup dry red wine or reduced-salt chicken stock

1 can (796 ml) crushed tomatoes

1 bay leaf

2 sprigs fresh rosemary

6 sprigs Italian parsley, plus 1 tablespoon chopped to garnish

¼ teaspoon paprika

1 Remove the skin from the chicken thighs, and then sprinkle the thighs with pepper. Lightly coat with nonstick cooking spray (preferably olive oil). Coat a large nonstick frying pan with nonstick cooking spray and set over high heat until hot but not smoking. Pan-fry the chicken until golden-brown, about 5 minutes on each side. Transfer the chicken to a plate.

2 Reduce the heat to medium and add the onion, celery and mushrooms. Fry until the mushrooms are soft, about 5 minutes. Pour in the wine or stock. Reduce the heat to medium-low and simmer for 1 minute. Stir in the tomatoes, bay leaf, rosemary, parsley sprigs and paprika.

3 Return the chicken to the frying pan. Simmer, partially covered, until the juices run clear, about 30 minutes. Remove the bay leaf, rosemary and parsley. Sprinkle the chicken with the extra chopped parsley and serve.

preparation time **20 mins**

cooking time **45 mins**

serves **4**

PER SERVING

268 calories

25 g protein

12 g total fat
3 g saturated fat

108 mg cholesterol

11 g total carbohydrate
9 g sugars

6 g fibre

149 mg sodium

HEALTH HINT

A chicken thigh provides about 50 per cent more iron per 100 g serving than an equal serving of breast meat.

COOK'S TIP

During cooking, the alcohol in the wine evaporates, leaving just its concentrated flavour. The better the wine, the more mellow the flavour!

chicken and spinach roulades

Fresh spinach, roasted red pepper, ricotta and a touch of Parmesan together make a fantastic filling for tender chicken roulades. Braised in stock and vermouth and served with asparagus, this makes an elegant, attractive dish.

Fb

preparation time **30 mins**
cooking time **35 mins**
serves **4**

PER SERVING

426 calories

42 g protein

21 g total fat
10 g saturated fat

191 mg cholesterol

7 g total carbohydrate
5 g sugars

3 g fibre

345 mg sodium

HEALTH HINT

Asparagus is a rich source of many of the B vitamins, especially folate. New research suggests that folate may have a role in helping to protect against heart disease.

1 Roll out the chicken with a rolling pin into rough squares about 5 mm thick. Set aside.

2 Place the spinach in a large pan, with just the water remaining from washing. Cover and cook for 2 minutes or until wilted. Drain well, squeezing out all the excess liquid, then chop the spinach finely and place in a large bowl.

3 Preheat the broiler. Broil the red pepper quarters, skin side up, until the skin is charred. Transfer to a plastic bag and seal. When cool enough to handle, peel and dice.

4 Add the red pepper to the spinach together with the ricotta, egg, Parmesan cheese, breadcrumbs, basil and nutmeg. Season with pepper. Mix well. Divide the filling among the chicken slices, spreading it over them evenly. Roll up each one, folding in the sides to enclose the filling, and secure with wooden cocktail sticks or skewers. Place the roulades in a frying pan and pour over the vermouth and stock. Cover and bring to a boil, then reduce the heat and simmer for 20 minutes.

5 Remove the roulades from the pan and keep hot. Bring the liquid back to a boil and boil until reduced. Stir in the sour cream and boil for a further 1–2 minutes or until thickened.

6 While the liquid is reducing, cook the asparagus spears in boiling water for 2–3 minutes or until just tender. Drain, refresh with cold water and keep warm.

7 Remove and discard the cocktail sticks from the chicken roulades, then cut into neat slices. Serve garnished with the asparagus spears and with the sauce drizzled around.

600 g chicken breasts

150 g spinach leaves

1 small red pepper, seeded and quartered

150 g reduced-fat ricotta cheese

1 egg, beaten

2 tablespoons freshly grated Parmesan cheese

2 tablespoons fresh whole-wheat breadcrumbs

2 tablespoons chopped fresh basil

$\frac{1}{8}$ teaspoon freshly grated nutmeg

pepper to taste

$\frac{2}{3}$ cup dry vermouth

$\frac{2}{3}$ cup reduced-salt chicken stock

5 tablespoons reduced-fat sour cream

250 g thin asparagus spears to serve

chicken with pepper and asparagus

Stir-frying is not just for Chinese dishes. This quick and healthy method of cooking works just as beautifully in this chicken and vegetable sauté, seasoned with garlic and rosemary. A bowl of basmati rice is the perfect complement.

2 teaspoons olive oil

1 yellow pepper, cut into 1 cm wide strips

3 garlic cloves, finely chopped

3 green onions, cut into 2 cm lengths

370 g chicken breasts, cut crosswise into 1 cm wide strips

750 g asparagus, cut into 5 cm lengths

1½ teaspoons grated lemon rind

½ teaspoon fresh chopped rosemary

¾ cup reduced-salt chicken stock

1½ teaspoons cornstarch blended with 1 tablespoon water

2 tablespoons toasted, finely chopped walnuts

1 Heat the oil in a large nonstick frying pan over medium-high heat. Add the pepper, garlic and green onions to the pan and cook until the pepper is crisp-tender, about 2 minutes.

2 Add the chicken, asparagus, lemon rind and rosemary to the frying pan and cook until the chicken is cooked through and the asparagus is tender, about 5 minutes.

3 Add the stock and bring to a boil. Stir in the cornstarch mixture and cook for 1 minute or until the sauce has thickened. Add the walnuts, toss to combine, then serve.

30 **C** **Fb**

preparation time **20 mins**

cooking time **10 mins**

serves **4**

PER SERVING

250 calories

29 g protein

13 g total fat
3 g saturated fat

75 mg cholesterol

5 g total carbohydrate
4 g sugars

3 g fibre

195 mg sodium

COOK'S TIP

The grated lemon rind and rosemary in this dish have such powerful flavours that you will never miss the fat that would ordinarily have been used in a dish like this.

tandoori-style chicken breasts

Tandoori dishes are one of the healthiest options in most Indian restaurants because the food is cooked without fat in a tandoor oven. At home, broiling gives similar results. These lean chicken breasts are served with creamy raita.

30 **C**

preparation time **15 mins**
cooking time **15 mins**
serves **4**

PER SERVING

329 calories

46 g protein

11 g total fat
3 g saturated fat

127 mg cholesterol

10 g total carbohydrate
9 g sugars

1 g fibre

226 mg sodium

HEALTH HINT

Yogourt is an excellent source of protein and calcium, needed for healthy bones and teeth, and it provides useful amounts of phosphorus, riboflavin and vitamin B$_{12}$, as well as beneficial bacteria for digestion.

1 Preheat the broiler. To make the yogourt marinade, place all the marinade ingredients in a large bowl and whisk together well. If you prefer, place the ingredients in a blender or food processor and process until well blended. Transfer to a bowl large enough to hold all the chicken breasts.

2 Score 2 slits on each side of the chicken breasts. Place them in the marinade, turning to coat and rubbing the marinade into the slits. (If you have time, leave the chicken to marinate in the refrigerator overnight.)

3 Brush the broiler rack with oil, then place the chicken breasts on top. Broil, turning and basting with the remaining marinade, until the juices run clear when the chicken is pierced with a knife, and the marinade looks slightly charred.

4 Meanwhile, to make the raita, place the yogourt in a bowl. Coarsely grate the cucumber, then squeeze to remove as much moisture as possible. Add the cucumber to the yogourt together with the tomato, ground coriander, cumin and cayenne pepper. Stir well to mix. Spoon the raita into a serving bowl.

5 Transfer the chicken breasts to a serving plate. Add the lemon or lime wedges and garnish with the coriander sprigs. Serve with the raita on the side.

4 chicken breasts, about
    150 g each
sunflower oil for brushing
lemon or lime wedges to serve
sprigs fresh coriander to garnish

YOGOURT MARINADE

1 garlic clove, crushed

1 tablespoon finely chopped
    fresh ginger

1½ teaspoons tomato paste

1½ teaspoons garam masala

1½ teaspoons ground coriander

1½ teaspoons ground cumin

¼ teaspoon turmeric

⅛ teaspoon cayenne pepper

100 g plain low-fat yogourt

RAITA

350 g plain low-fat yogourt

1 cucumber, cut into quarters
    lengthwise and seeded

1 tomato, very finely chopped

½ teaspoon ground coriander

½ teaspoon ground cumin

⅛ teaspoon cayenne pepper

prosciutto-stuffed chicken breasts

This stylish-looking main course is surprisingly easy to make. The chicken breasts can be prepared in advance and kept covered in the refrigerator. Fettuccine tossed with a little grated lemon rind is a good accompaniment.

1 Preheat the oven to 425°F (220°C). Make a slit along the length of each chicken breast and enlarge to form a pocket.

2 Divide the mozzarella among the chicken breasts, sliding the slices into the pockets. Top the cheese with the tomato slices and crushed garlic. Roughly chop a little of the basil and add a sprinkling to each pocket.

3 Season each chicken breast with pepper. Place a large sprig of basil on each, then wrap in a slice of prosciutto, making sure the ham covers the slit in the chicken. Tie the ham securely in place with three or four pieces of string on each breast.

4 Heat the oil in a heavy-based frying pan (preferably one with an ovenproof handle). Add the chicken breasts and fry over a high heat for 3–4 minutes, turning midway through to brown both sides. Transfer the pan to the oven (or transfer the chicken to an ovenproof dish) and bake for 10–12 minutes or until the chicken is cooked through; the juices should run clear when the thickest part of the chicken is pierced with a knife.

5 Meanwhile, to make the salad, place the oil and lemon juice in a bowl, season with pepper and mix well together. Add the lettuce and watercress. Toss together, then divide among 4 individual serving plates.

6 Remove the string from the chicken breasts. Cut each breast across into slices, holding it together so it keeps its shape. Place on the salad and garnish with the remaining basil. Serve.

Variation As an alternative to the mozzarella filling, use a mixture of ricotta cheese and watercress. Soften ½ finely chopped red onion in 2 teaspoons reduced-salt margarine for 3–5 minutes, then add 80 g watercress sprigs and cook for a further minute or until the watercress has just wilted. Crumble in 100 g ricotta cheese and season with nutmeg and black pepper.

4 chicken breasts, about
 150 g each

100 g mozzarella cheese,
 thinly sliced

1 tomato, thinly sliced

1 garlic clove, crushed

1 bunch fresh basil

pepper to taste

4 slices prosciutto or lean ham,
 about 60 g in total

1 tablespoon extra virgin olive oil

pepper to taste

GREEN SALAD

2 tablespoons extra virgin olive oil

juice of ½ lemon

pepper to taste

120 g mixed salad greens

1 bunch watercress, large stalks
 discarded

Fb

preparation time **25 mins**

cooking time **15 mins**

serves **4**

PER SERVING

458 calories

45 g protein

30 g total fat
8 g saturated fat

130 mg cholesterol

3 g total carbohydrate
3 g sugars

4 g fibre

506 mg sodium

HEALTH HINT

The Greeks and Romans believed that eating watercress could cure madness. We also attribute healing powers to this green leaf, as it contains powerful phytochemicals that help to protect against cancer. It is also a good source of many B vitamins plus vitamins C, E and beta carotene, which the body converts into vitamin A.

Hungarian chicken meatballs

Ground chicken and mushrooms make succulent meatballs—delicious simmered in a smooth tomato sauce with red and green peppers. Paprika warms the flavour and new potatoes turn it into a complete one-dish meal.

2 tablespoons reduced-salt margarine

1 small onion, finely chopped

350 g mushrooms, finely chopped

350 g ground chicken

²/₃ cup fresh whole-wheat breadcrumbs

1 egg, beaten

2 tablespoons chopped parsley

pepper to taste

550 g small new potatoes

5 tablespoons plain low-fat yogourt to serve

Italian parsley to garnish

PAPRIKA AND PEPPER SAUCE

2 tablespoons extra virgin olive oil

1 onion, finely chopped

2 garlic cloves, crushed

1 red pepper, seeded and thinly sliced

1 green pepper, seeded and thinly sliced

1 tablespoon mild paprika

4 cups tomato sauce

⅛ teaspoon caraway seeds

pepper to taste

1 Melt the margarine in a frying pan. Add the onion and mushrooms, and cook over medium heat, stirring frequently, for about 10 minutes, until the mixture is reduced, dark in colour and very thick. Transfer the mixture to a bowl and allow it to cool slightly.

2 Add the chicken to the mushroom mixture and use a fork to combine. Add the breadcrumbs, egg, parsley and pepper. Mix the ingredients until thoroughly combined. Wet your hands, then shape it into 20 walnut-sized balls. Set aside.

3 To make the sauce, heat the oil in a flameproof casserole dish. Add the onion and cook for 4–5 minutes, stirring frequently, until softened. Add the garlic and peppers, then cook, stirring constantly, for 2–3 minutes. Stir in the paprika and cook for 1 minute, then pour in the tomato sauce and bring to a boil over high heat.

4 Stir in the caraway seeds and pepper to taste. Add the meatballs and the potatoes to the simmering sauce, taking care not to break up the meatballs. Bring the sauce back to simmering point, then cover and simmer gently for 35 minutes or until the potatoes are tender.

5 Ladle the meatballs, potatoes and sauce into bowls and swirl on a little yogourt. Garnish with parsley and serve.

preparation time **35 mins**

cooking time **55 mins**

serves **4**

PER SERVING

549 calories

34 g protein

26 g total fat
5 g saturated fat

118 mg cholesterol

46 g total carbohydrate
19 g sugars

13 g fibre

1145 mg sodium

HEALTH HINT

When eaten regularly and in quantity, potatoes are a useful source of vitamin C—new potatoes contain the most, and eating them unpeeled retains the maximum goodness as the nutrients are concentrated under the skin.

preparation time **10 mins**
cooking time **20 mins**
serves **4**

PER SERVING

365 calories

40 g protein

13 g total fat
4 g saturated fat

127 mg cholesterol

20 g total carbohydrate
13 g sugars

1 g fibre

247 mg sodium

HEART SUPERFOOD

An apple a day may not keep the doctor away, but several studies suggest a link between apple consumption and reduced risk of cardiovascular disease. Apples contain flavonoids, a group of antioxidants that protect against heart disease and cancer. They're also a good source of cholesterol-lowering soluble fibre.

brandy chicken with apples

 Looking for a meal that can be on the table in thirty minutes yet is elegant enough to serve at a dinner party? This dish tastes like it came from a French bistro. Serve with wild rice and sautéed green beans.

1 Lightly coat a large frying pan with nonstick cooking spray and set over medium-high heat. Sauté the shallots until soft, about 2 minutes. Add the apples and sauté until lightly browned, about 3 minutes. Add the apple juice, stock and Calvados. Cook, stirring, until the apples are tender, 5 minutes. Transfer to a medium bowl. Wipe the frying pan clean.

2 Meanwhile, combine the flour and pepper on a sheet of parchment paper. Coat the chicken breasts with the seasoned flour, pressing with your hands so the flour adheres and the chicken is flattened evenly.

3 Lightly coat the frying pan again with cooking spray and set over medium-high heat. Cook the chicken until browned and almost cooked through, about 3 minutes on each side. Return the apple mixture and any juices to the frying pan and bring to a boil. Reduce the heat and simmer for 2 minutes. Stir in the cream, remove from heat and serve.

2 medium shallots, finely chopped

2 tart apples, peeled and cut into 5 mm slices

1 cup apple juice

¾ cup reduced-salt chicken stock

1 tablespoon Calvados (apple brandy) or apple juice

¼ cup all-purpose flour

½ teaspoon freshly ground black pepper

4 chicken breasts, about 150 g each

2 tablespoons reduced-fat cream

citrus-grilled chicken with melon salsa

Capture the spirit of the tropics and serve it on your dinner table! This sunny mix of melon, salad greens, chicken and citrus, spiked with jalapeño chili pepper, is healthy carefree eating at its best.

500 g chicken breasts
½ teaspoon pepper
1 jalapeño chili
⅓ cup freshly squeezed lime juice
1 garlic clove, finely chopped
2 teaspoons reduced-salt soy sauce
100 g mixed salad greens

MELON SALSA
1 large cucumber
1 small cantaloupe, diced 2 cm thick
1 cup cherry tomatoes, halved
2 tablespoons very thinly sliced
    fresh basil

1 Sprinkle pepper on both sides of the chicken. Devein and seed the jalapeño chili with a melon baller (wear gloves when handling, as it can burn); chop finely. Stir 2 tablespoons lime juice, garlic, soy sauce and 1 teaspoon jalapeño in a pie dish. Add the chicken and turn to coat. Marinate at room temperature, turning once, while preparing the melon salsa.

2 To make the salsa, halve the cucumber lengthwise. Remove the seeds by dragging the tip of a spoon down the centre. Place the cucumber cut side down on a board, and slice 2 mm thick. Toss the cucumber, cantaloupe, tomatoes, basil and remaining jalapeño and lime juice in a medium bowl. Set aside.

3 Preheat the broiler or barbecue. Discard the marinade from the chicken mixture. Lightly coat both sides of the chicken with nonstick cooking spray (preferably olive oil). Broil or barbecue the chicken until the juices run clear, about 5 minutes on each side, turning only once.

4 Transfer the chicken to a cutting board and cut the meat diagonally into strips, about 1 cm thick. Toss with the melon salsa. Divide the salad leaves among 4 plates and spoon a quarter of the chicken and melon mixture on top of each. Serve.

preparation time **20 mins**
cooking time **10 mins**
serves **4**

PER SERVING

261 calories

34 g protein

9 g total fat
3 g saturated fat

101 mg cholesterol

10 g total carbohydrate
10 g sugars

3 g fibre

227 mg sodium

HEALTH HINT

Cantaloupe is an excellent source of beta carotene, a powerful antioxidant with anticarcinogenic properties that the body converts into vitamin A. Vitamin C in the fruit and lime juice aids in the absorption of iron, which is present in the mix of leafy salad greens.

Chinese-style lemon chicken

A savoury lemon sauce seasoned with a hint of sesame tastes fabulous with tender chicken and crunchy Asian vegetables. Serve with plain egg noodles or rice to add some satisfying starchy carbohydrate.

1 Heat the sunflower oil in a flameproof casserole dish. Add the chicken and cook for about 1 minute or until the meat is just turning white. Add the onion, green pepper, garlic and ginger, and cook over medium heat, stirring often, for 5–6 minutes or until the onion is softened but not browned.

2 Add the carrots and water chestnuts. Pour in the stock and sherry, then heat until simmering, but not boiling rapidly. Cover and simmer for 10 minutes, stirring occasionally.

3 Meanwhile, mix the cornstarch and sugar to a smooth paste with the soy sauce, sesame oil and lemon rind and juice. Stir the cornstarch mixture into the casserole and bring to a boil, still stirring. Add the green beans, cover the casserole and simmer gently for a further 2 minutes. Stir in the bean sprouts and simmer for a final 2 minutes. Serve immediately, before the bean sprouts start to soften.

Variation You can try 200 g baby corn instead of the water chestnuts and 200 g baby bok choy instead of the bean sprouts. A little chili is good with this vegetable mix, so add 1 seeded and chopped small green chili with the vegetables in step 1.

1 tablespoon sunflower oil

450 g chicken breasts, sliced

1 onion, halved and thinly sliced

1 large green pepper, seeded and cut into thin strips

1 garlic clove, chopped

1 tablespoon finely chopped fresh ginger

2 large carrots, thinly sliced on the diagonal

1 can (199 ml) water chestnuts, drained and sliced

1¼ cups reduced-salt chicken stock

4 tablespoons dry sherry

2 tablespoons cornstarch

2 teaspoons caster (superfine) sugar

4 tablespoons reduced-salt soy sauce

1 tablespoon sesame oil

grated rind of 2 large lemons

juice of 1 lemon

150 g thin green beans, cut into 5 cm lengths

1½ cups bean sprouts

preparation time **25 mins**

cooking time **25 mins**

serves **4**

PER SERVING

355 calories

29 g protein

17 g total fat
3 g saturated fat

75 mg cholesterol

18 g total carbohydrate
11 g sugars

6 g fibre

829 mg sodium

COOK'S TIP

Mixed with other vegetables, canned water chestnuts can help to extend a modest amount of chicken or meat to make a satisfying meal.

spicy Jamaican barbecued chicken

Because the flavour of chicken is mild, it benefits from a tasty baste when barbecued or broiled, and this also helps to keep the outside from burning until the chicken is cooked through—especially when cooking over charcoal.

8 chicken drumsticks or thighs, about 670 g, skinned

lime wedges to garnish

JAMAICAN BARBECUE BASTE

4 tablespoons extra virgin olive oil

1 onion, very finely chopped

2 garlic cloves, finely chopped

1 red chili, seeded and finely chopped

$\frac{1}{2}$ teaspoon ground allspice

$\frac{1}{4}$ teaspoon ground cinnamon

grated rind and juice of 1 lime

1 To make the baste, heat the oil in a small frying pan over medium-low heat. Add the onion, garlic and chili and cook, stirring frequently, for about 10 minutes or until the onion is softened and starting to brown. Transfer to a large shallow bowl. Add the spices and the lime rind and juice, and stir well to mix.

2 Make a few shallow slits in each piece of chicken, then add to the bowl. Turn the pieces to coat thoroughly with the baste, rubbing it into the slits in the meat. Cover and leave to marinate at room temperature for 1 hour or in the refrigerator for up to 24 hours.

3 Prepare a charcoal barbecue. When it has burned down to coals covered with grey ash, remove the chicken pieces from the marinating baste and barbecue them for 20–25 minutes, turning and brushing frequently with the baste, until cooked all the way through.

4 Alternatively, preheat the broiler. Arrange the chicken pieces on the broiler rack and cook until done.

5 Serve the chicken hot, garnished with the lime wedges.

Variations For a red wine and thyme baste, fry the onion and garlic in the oil with 2 fresh bay leaves and 1 tablespoon fresh thyme leaves. Add $\frac{3}{4}$ cup red wine and $\frac{1}{2}$ teaspoon coarse black pepper. • For a maple syrup and orange baste, fry the onion and garlic in the oil, then add 4 tablespoons maple syrup, the grated rind and juice of 1 orange, 1 tablespoon snipped fresh chives and 1 tablespoon chopped fresh tarragon.

preparation time **20 mins**

cooking time **25 mins** plus at least 1 hour marinating

serves **4**

PER SERVING

261 calories

20 g protein

19 g total fat
4 g saturated fat

101 mg cholesterol

2 g total carbohydrate
1 g sugars

1 g fibre

87 mg sodium

HEALTH HINT

Chilies are more nutritious than sweet peppers, and the red varieties generally have a higher nutritional content than the green ones. They are very good sources of antioxidants, especially beta carotene and vitamin C.

golden-roasted chicken with old-fashioned stuffing

Always an impressive dish, a whole chicken provides plenty of protein, little saturated fat, and good amounts of B vitamins and zinc. A meal like this is perfect for noteworthy occasions, or just a simple family dinner.

2 tablespoons fresh thyme leaves, plus whole sprigs for stuffing

2 tablespoons chopped fresh sage

freshly ground black pepper to taste

1 whole chicken, about 1.5 kg, without giblets

1 lemon, thinly sliced

3 onions, chopped

3 celery stalks, chopped

1¾ cups reduced-salt chicken stock

4 cups prepared stuffing mix

1 Preheat the oven to 425°F (220°C). Mix the thyme, sage and pepper in a small bowl. Gently separate the chicken skin from the breast and insert a third of the herb mixture and lemon slices under the skin. Sprinkle another third of the herb mixture in the cavities and over the chicken.

2 Lightly coat a large nonstick frying pan with nonstick cooking spray and set over medium-high heat. Sauté the onions and celery until soft, 5 minutes. Stir in the remaining herb mixture. Pour in 1 cup stock and 1 cup water. Bring to a boil. Add the stuffing and toss until the liquid is completely absorbed. Remove from the heat.

3 Loosely stuff the chicken cavities with stuffing, top the stuffing with the thyme sprigs and tie the legs together. Place the chicken, breast side down, on a rack in a roasting pan. Pour in the remaining stock and 1 cup water. Roast for 30 minutes. Turn the chicken breast side up. Reduce the temperature to 350°F (180°C). Roast the chicken, basting every 20 minutes with the drippings, until the juices run clear, about 1½ hours. Transfer the stuffing to a bowl and discard the thyme. Let the chicken stand for 10 minutes before carving. Discard the lemon slices and skin before serving.

preparation time **30 mins**

cooking time **2¼ hours**

serves **6**

PER SERVING

428 calories	
31 g protein	
20 g total fat	
10 g saturated fat	
121 mg cholesterol	
32 g total carbohydrate	
8 g sugars	
4 g fibre	
1035 mg sodium	

COOK'S TIP

To ensure a juicy bird, start roasting it breast side down so that the juices flow over the breast. Finish roasting it breast side up, basting the bird frequently to add extra moisture. Cook with the skin on to seal in the juices, but be sure to discard it before eating, since most of the fat is found in the skin.

roast herb and garlic chicken

Rather than rubbing butter over chicken before roasting, here a paste of fresh herbs and reduced-fat ricotta cheese is pushed under the skin. This keeps the roasting chicken beautifully moist as well as adding a wonderful flavour.

C

preparation time **15 mins**
cooking time **1¾–2 hours**
serves **4**

PER SERVING

276 calories

36 g protein

12 g total fat
4 g saturated fat

135 mg cholesterol

1 g total carbohydrate
1 g sugars

1 g fibre

153 mg sodium

HEALTH HINT

Garlic contains sulphur compounds that may speed the breakdown of carcinogens, which are cancer-causing substances.

1 Preheat the oven to 350°F (180°C). Grate the rind from the lemon, then cut the lemon in half. Hold the chicken on end in a small roasting pan and squeeze the lemon juice inside the cavity. Push the lemon halves inside the cavity and sprinkle in half the rind.

2 Place the chicken in the pan, breast side up. Very carefully ease your fingers under the skin, starting at the neck end. Loosen the skin over the breasts and thighs, without breaking it.

3 Combine the coriander, parlsey and garlic in a blender or food processor and process until finely chopped. Add the ricotta cheese, remaining lemon and pepper, and process again briefly to mix. Push the paste under the skin, easing it along so that it covers the breasts and thighs evenly in a thin layer. Secure the end of the neck skin by folding the wing tips underneath it.

4 Cover the chicken with foil and roast for 45 minutes. Remove the foil and roast, uncovered, for a further 1–1¼ hours or until the juices run clear when a knife is inserted into the thickest part of the thigh. Baste once or twice with the pan juices.

5 Tip the chicken so that the juices can run out of the cavity into the pan. Set the chicken aside on a wooden board to rest. Skim all the fat from the surface of the juices in the pan, then bring to a boil on top of the stove. Add the wine and bring back to a boil, scraping up all the browned bits from the bottom of the pan. Boil the pan sauce for 1 minute. Season with pepper. Carve the chicken and garnish with lemon slices and sprigs of coriander or parsley, and serve with the pan sauce.

1 lemon
1 whole chicken, about 1.5 kg, without giblets
½ cup fresh coriander
½ cup parsley
2 garlic cloves, peeled
2 tablespoons reduced-fat ricotta cheese
pepper to taste
⅔ cup dry white wine
pepper to taste
lemon slices to garnish
sprigs fresh coriander or parsley to garnish

spicy stir-fried duck

Here, strips of duck are stir-fried with onions, water chestnuts, bok choy, bean sprouts and pear. Very little oil is needed for a stir-fry, and adding lots of vegetables keeps the quantity of meat down. Serve with rice noodles.

400 g duck breasts
2 teaspoons five-spice powder
2 tablespoons sunflower oil
4 small onions, thinly sliced
4 small celery stalks, thinly sliced, plus a few leaves to garnish
1 large firm pear, peeled, cored and diced
1 can (199 ml) water chestnuts, drained and sliced
1 tablespoon clear honey
4 tablespoons rice vinegar or sherry vinegar
1 tablespoon reduced-salt soy sauce
200 g bok choy, shredded
1½ cups bean sprouts

1 Remove the skin and all the fat from the duck breasts, then cut them across into thin strips. Sprinkle with the five-spice powder and toss to coat. Set aside.

2 Heat a wok or heavy-based frying pan until very hot, then add the oil and swirl to coat the wok. Add the duck pieces and stir-fry for 2 minutes. Add the onions and celery and stir-fry for 3 minutes or until they are softened. Add the pear and water chestnuts and stir to mix.

3 Add the honey, rice or sherry vinegar and soy sauce. When the liquid is bubbling, reduce the heat to low and simmer for 2 minutes.

4 Turn the heat up to high again. Add the bok choy and bean sprouts, and stir-fry for 1 minute or until the bok choy is just wilted and the bean sprouts are heated through.

5 Transfer to a warmed serving dish and serve immediately, garnished with the celery leaves.

Variation Use chicken or turkey, cut into strips, instead of the duck.

preparation time **15 mins**
cooking time **10 mins**
serves **4**

PER SERVING

366 calories

28 g protein

21 g total fat
4 g saturated fat

141 mg cholesterol

18 g total carbohydrate
14 g sugars

4 g fibre

313 mg sodium

HEALTH HINTS

Removing the skin and fat from duck lowers the fat content substantially. Skinless duck breast contains only a fraction more fat than skinless chicken breast.

Dark green, leafy vegetables such as bok choy provide good amounts of vitamin C, as well as vitamin B$_6$, folate and niacin.

creamy turkey salad with grapes and pecans

With its wonderfully contrasting tastes and textures, this salad makes a satisfying main course that is luxurious without containing a lot of saturated fat. It is the perfect recipe for roast turkey leftovers.

1 Cook the pasta in boiling water for 10–12 minutes, or according to the package instructions, until al dente. Drain and rinse with cold water, then drain again and leave to cool.

2 Meanwhile, mix the yogourt with the mayonnaise, white wine vinegar, mustard and tarragon in a large bowl. Stir until all the ingredients are combined and the dressing is smooth.

3 Add the pasta, turkey, celery, grapes, toasted pecan nuts and pepper to taste. Toss until the ingredients are all evenly coated with the creamy dressing.

4 Transfer to a serving dish or plates and garnish with sprigs of tarragon. Serve with a mixed green salad, if desired.

Variations Use 50 g natural roasted cashews instead of the pecans, and 2 cored and chopped dessert apples instead of the grapes. Add ⅓ cup sultanas. • For a spicy Indian flavour, stir in 2 tablespoons tikka masala curry paste (or to taste) with the yogourt. Garnish with chopped fresh coriander instead of the tarragon. • To make a tempting vegetarian salad, try 220 g firm smoked tofu instead of the turkey.

200 g fusilli (pasta spirals)
150 g plain low-fat yogourt
4 tablespoons low-fat mayonnaise
1 teaspoon white wine vinegar
2 teaspoons Dijon mustard
4 tablespoons chopped fresh tarragon
250 g skinless boneless roast turkey, cubed
2 celery stalks, cut into fine strips
120 g black grapes, or a mixture of black and green grapes, halved
⅓ cup pecans, toasted and roughly chopped
pepper to taste
sprigs fresh tarragon to garnish
mixed green salad to serve (optional)

preparation time **20 mins** plus cooling

cooking time **10 mins**

serves **4**

PER SERVING

394 calories

27 g protein

14 g total fat

2 g saturated fat

46 mg cholesterol

39 g total carbohydrate

10 g sugars

4 g fibre

318 mg sodium

HEALTH HINTS

Turkey, without skin, is an excellent source of low-fat protein, and it contains more vitamin B_{12}, niacin and zinc than chicken.

Black grapes provide useful amounts of bioflavonoids, the antioxidants that help to protect against the damaging effect of free radicals linked with cancer.

pan-fried turkey escalopes with citrus honey sauce

The tanginess of citrus fruit marries well with poultry, especially turkey, which can sometimes be a little light on flavour. Here orange and lemon with honey create a tasty sauce. For a simple accompaniment, steam some new potatoes.

1 Place the turkey between sheets of plastic wrap and pound them to flatten to about 5 mm thickness. Set aside.

2 Melt the margarine in a large frying pan, add the shallots and garlic, and cook, stirring, for 2–3 minutes or until softened but not brown. Remove the shallots and garlic from the pan with a slotted spoon and set aside.

3 Place the turkey escalopes in the pan, in a single layer, and fry them for 2–3 minutes on each side.

4 Meanwhile, cook the beans in a saucepan of boiling water for 3–4 minutes or until just tender. Drain and rinse briefly in cold water to stop them cooking. Keep the beans warm.

5 Mix the honey with the rind and juice of the orange and lemon. Remove the turkey escalopes from the pan and keep hot. Pour the honey mixture into the pan, return the shallots and garlic, and add pepper. Bring to a boil and cook for about 2 minutes, stirring constantly.

6 Make a pile of beans on 4 plates and place a turkey escalope on top of each pile. Spoon over the citrus honey sauce, and serve.

Variation Replace the turkey breasts with 4 small boneless duck breasts, about 550 g in total. Remove the skin and all fat from the breasts. Pan-fry for 3 minutes on each side if you like duck a little pink, or a little longer for well-done. For the sauce, use the rind and juice from a pink grapefruit instead of the orange and lemon.

4 small turkey breasts, about 120 g each
2 tablespoons reduced-salt margarine
4 large shallots, thinly sliced
1 garlic clove, crushed
400 g thin French beans, trimmed
2 tablespoon clear honey
grated rind and juice of 1 orange
grated rind and juice of 1 lemon
pepper to taste

preparation time **15 mins**
cooking time **15 mins**
serves **4**

PER SERVING

263 calories

29 g protein

9 g total fat
2 g saturated fat

60 mg cholesterol

16 g total carbohydrate
15 g sugars

3 g fibre

237 mg sodium

HEART SUPERFOOD

Turkey contains even less fat than chicken, making it one of the lowest fat meats available.

HEALTH HINT

Studies have shown a correlation between a regular intake of vitamin C and better lung function in children with asthma.

roast turkey with lemon couscous

A small whole turkey is amazingly economical. It will give enough meat for at least 8 portions, or you can serve 4 people and have plenty of leftovers for sandwiches, salads and other dishes and make stock with the carcass.

4 large lemons

2 cups couscous

1 teaspoon turmeric

1 teaspoon ground cumin

1 teaspoon ground cinnamon

4 cups hot reduced-salt chicken stock

110 g dried apricots, chopped

5 tablespoons chopped fresh mint

1 whole turkey, about 2.5 kg, without giblets

⅔ cup dry sherry

pepper to taste

sprigs fresh mint to garnish

1 Halve the lemons lengthwise and squeeze all the juice into a cup. Pull the pulp from each lemon half to leave a shell. Discard the pulp. Cut a thin slice off the base of each lemon so it will stand firmly when upturned. Set aside.

2 Place the couscous in a bowl. Add ⅓ cup lemon juice, the spices, 3 cups stock, the apricots and mint, and mix well. Soak for 10 minutes or until the couscous has absorbed all the stock.

3 Preheat the oven to 400°F (200°C). Place the turkey on a rack in a roasting pan and pour over ⅔ cup hot water.

4 Using a spoon stuff some couscous into the neck end of the turkey, mounding it a little. Secure the skin flap underneath the bird with the wing tips. Spoon 2 tablespoons lemon juice over. Cover the turkey loosely with oiled foil and roast for 1¾ hours. Baste with the juices occasionally, and remove the foil for the last 30 minutes of cooking to brown the skin. The turkey is cooked when the juices run clear.

5 Meanwhile, fill the lemon halves with couscous. Spread the rest of the couscous in a small ovenproof dish and sit the filled lemon halves on top. Cover with foil and place in the oven for the last 20 minutes of the turkey's roasting time. When the turkey is cooked, remove it from the pan and let it rest on a board for 10 minutes. Skim the fat from the surface of the juices in the pan, then add the sherry and the remaining stock. Bring to a boil on the stove, scraping up the browned bits. Boil for 5 minutes. Season with pepper.

6 Carve the turkey and serve with the couscous-filled lemons, the extra couscous and the pan sauce. Garnish with mint.

preparation time **20 mins**

cooking time **1¾ hours**

serves **8**

PER SERVING

529 calories

65 g protein

20 g total fat
5 g saturated fat

157 mg cholesterol

17 g total carbohydrate
8 g sugars

2 g fibre

758 mg sodium

HEALTH HINT

Couscous is low in fat and high in starchy carbohydrate. It closely resembles pasta in nutritional value. It is high in thiamine and nicacin, as well as protein.

orange-glazed chickens

 In this recipe small chickens are glazed with a delicious orange-tea marmalade. In addition, a wealth of heart-healthy vitamins and minerals come in each chicken. Serve on a bed of wild rice.

preparation time **20 mins**

cooking time **1 hour** plus 10 mins standing

serves **4**

PER SERVING

340 calories

47 g protein

14 g total fat
4 g saturated fat

174 mg cholesterol

6 g total carbohydrate
5 g sugars

2 g fibre

176 mg sodium

HEALTH HINT

Chickens with skins removed are relatively low in total fat, especially saturated fat.

1 Preheat the oven to 375°F (190°C). Fit a roasting pan with a wire rack. Steep the tea bag in ¼ cup boiling water for 5 minutes in a small saucepan. Discard the tea bag. Squeeze the juice from 1 orange into the tea, and then stir in the marmalade until melted. Cut the remaining orange into quarters.

2 Remove and discard the giblets from the chickens. Wash the chickens and dry thoroughly, and then sprinkle the cavities with pepper. Loosen the breast skin slightly. Stuff the cavity of each chicken with 1 orange quarter, a quarter of the onion slices, 1 rosemary sprig and 1 thyme sprig. Tie the legs together with kitchen string. Place the chickens, breast side up, on the rack in the roasting pan. Brush the chickens over and under the skin with about a quarter of the glaze. Pour enough water into the pan to cover the bottom (the water should not reach the rack).

3 Roast the chickens on the middle oven rack, basting over and under the skin every 20 minutes with the remaining glaze, until browned and the juices run clear, about 1 hour. Let the chickens stand for 10 minutes. Discard the rosemary, thyme, onions and orange from the cavities of the chickens. Garnish with the remaining rosemary and thyme sprigs. Discard the skin before serving the chickens.

1 tea bag, such as Earl Grey

2 medium oranges, unpeeled

½ cup no-sugar-added orange marmalade

4 small chickens, about 500 g each

½ teaspoon pepper

2 onions, sliced

8 sprigs fresh rosemary

8 sprigs fresh thyme

beef, lamb, pork & veal

filet mignon salad

How can steak be part of a smart diet? Very easily! Broil or barbecue the finest and one of the leanest of steaks, filet mignon, and arrange it on top of fresh salad greens and plenty of vegetables to make a "composed" salad.

4 red peppers
300 g filet mignon
½ teaspoon pepper
2 garlic cloves
500 g green beans, trimmed
4 tablespoons balsamic vinegar
2 teaspoons extra virgin olive oil
2 tablespoons finely chopped shallot
120 g mixed salad greens
6 tomatoes, cut into 5 mm wedges

1 Preheat the broiler or barbecue. Place the red peppers in the broiler pan or on the barbecue. Cook until the skins are blistered and blackened, turning frequently. Place in a plastic bag, seal tightly, and let steam for 10 minutes. Peel away the blackened skins from the peppers, seed them and cut them into chunks.

2 Meanwhile, lay the filet flat on a cutting board and slit it lengthwise three-quarters of the way through. Open it up like a book and press it flat. Sprinkle with ¼ teaspoon pepper. Cut 1 garlic clove in half and rub the cut sides all over the beef. Barbecue or broil the beef until it is done to your taste, about 3 minutes on each side for medium. Thinly slice the beef.

3 Cook the beans in boiling water until crisp-tender, about 5 minutes. Drain and rinse immediately with cold water.

4 Crush the remaining garlic clove. Whisk the vinegar, oil, garlic, shallot and remaining pepper in a small bowl. Divide the mixed salad greens among 4 plates and arrange the steak, pepper, beans and tomatoes on top. Drizzle with dressing and serve.

preparation time **20 mins**
cooking time **20 mins**
serves **4**

PER SERVING

199 calories	
21 g protein	
7 g total fat	
2 g saturated fat	
39 mg cholesterol	
13 g total carbohydrate	
12 g sugars	
8 g fibre	
58 mg sodium	

COOK'S TIP

Extra virgin olive oil is the result of the first pressing of olives, and is the finest kind of olive oil. It ranges in colour from light golden to greenish.

preparation time **15 mins**

cooking time **30 mins**
plus 30 mins marinating

serves **4**

PER SERVING

311 calories

30 g protein

7 g total fat

3 g saturated fat

66 mg cholesterol

31 g total carbohydrate

7 g sugars

6 g fibre

191 mg sodium

HEALTH HINT

There are two good reasons to serve meat and potatoes on a bed of salad greens: the fresh greens provide a delicious contrast to the meat; and at the same time, they round out the meal with important nutrients, such as carotenoids, vitamin C, folate and fibre.

broiled steak with mustard-glazed potatoes

 Here lean beef is flavoured with a honey-mustard marinade and served with potatoes that are first boiled, then tossed in the marinade and broiled with the meat for a barbecued effect. Both are served on a bed of peppery watercress.

1 Combine the mustard, honey, vinegar, garlic and pepper in a large bowl and stir well to combine. Place the beef in a shallow bowl. Measure out 2 tablespoons of mustard mixture and rub all over the beef. Marinate the beef for 30 minutes at room temperature or up to overnight in the refrigerator.

2 With a vegetable peeler, remove a strip of skin from around each potato. Drop the potatoes in a large pan of boiling water and cook until they are just tender, about 20 minutes. Drain the potatoes well. Add to the bowl of mustard mixture, tossing to coat. With a slotted spoon, transfer the potatoes to the broiler. (Leave room in the broiler pan for the onion wedges and beef.)

3 Add the onion to the mustard mixture in the bowl, turning the wedges to coat. Add to the broiler pan with the potatoes.

4 Preheat the broiler. Add the beef to the potatoes and onion in the pan. Broil 8 cm from the heat for 8 minutes, turning the beef, potatoes and onion midway through cooking. Let the beef stand for 5 minutes before slicing. Serve with watercress.

¼ cup Dijon mustard

1 tablespoon clear honey

1 tablespoon cider vinegar

2 cloves garlic, finely chopped

¼ teaspoon pepper

500 g lean beef, such as beef tenderloin

750 g new potatoes

1 large onion, cut into 8 wedges

1 bunch watercress, tough ends trimmed

pepper steak with leek mashed potatoes

Potatoes—as fries, baked or mashed—are a popular partner for steak. Here mashed potatoes with leeks and mustard accompany pepper-coated tenderloin steaks. Serve with a fresh seasonal green vegetable such as green beans.

2 tablespoons mixed or black peppercorns, coarsely crushed

4 beef tenderloin steaks, 2 cm thick, about 150 g each, trimmed of fat

1 teaspoon extra virgin olive oil

chopped parsley or snipped fresh chives to garnish

LEEK AND MUSTARD MASHED POTATOES

900 g potatoes, peeled and cut into chunks

2 teaspoons extra virgin olive oil

200 g leeks, finely chopped

½ cup low-fat milk

1 tablespoon whole-grain mustard

1½ tablespoons reduced-salt margarine

pepper to taste

1 To make the leek and mustard mashed potatoes, place the potatoes in a saucepan and pour over boiling water to cover by 5 cm. Bring back to a boil, then reduce the heat and cook for 15–20 minutes or until the potatoes are very tender.

2 Meanwhile, spread out the crushed peppercorns on a plate and press the steaks into them until they are coated with peppercorns on all sides. Set aside.

3 Heat the oil for the mashed potatoes in a nonstick frying pan. Add the leeks and cook, stirring constantly, for 3–5 minutes or until tender. Transfer to a plate lined with a double thickness of paper towel to drain. Heat the milk in a saucepan until hot.

4 When the potatoes are tender, drain them, shaking the colander or sieve to remove any excess water, and return them to the pan. Pour the hot milk over the potatoes, then mash them until they are completely smooth. Add the leeks, mustard and margarine, and season with pepper. Beat well to mix, then cover and keep warm.

5 Heat a ridged cast-iron broil pan over a high heat until hot. Brush the pan with the olive oil, then reduce the heat to medium-high. Place the steaks in the pan and cook for 3 minutes on each side for rare, 3½ minutes on each side for medium-rare, 4 minutes on each side for medium, or 5 minutes on each side for well done.

6 Spoon a mound of potatoes on each warmed plate and place a steak next to it. Drizzle any pan juices over the steaks and sprinkle with parsley or chives. Serve immediately.

Variation Veal loin chops can be cooked in the same way. Use 4 chops, 2 cm thick and about 250 g each. (This weight includes the bone; it should give about 150 g meat.) Brush the chops with oil and season with pepper to taste, omitting the peppercorns. Cook as for the steaks, allowing 3 minutes on each side for medium-rare; 3½ minutes on each side for medium; or 4½ minutes on each side for well done.

preparation time **20 mins**

cooking time **40 mins**

serves **4**

PER SERVING

403 calories

36 g protein

16 g total fat
5 g saturated fat

80 mg cholesterol

29 g total carbohydrate
5 g sugars

5 g fibre

146 mg sodium

HEALTH HINT

Adding leeks to mashed potatoes not only boosts their flavour but also adds thiamine, vitamin B$_6$ and folate. If you include the green part of the leeks this will also provide beta carotene. Eaten regularly, leeks are believed to help reduce the risk of heart disease and stroke.

succulent grilled steak
with crispy potatoes

In this recipe, slices of beef are marinated in a tangy green herb-based sauce, called chimichurri sauce, which hails from Argentina, making them tender and juicy. They are complemented nicely by crispy grilled potatoes.

1 round steak, 2 cm thick,
    about 500 g

¹⁄₂ teaspoon pepper

4 medium baking potatoes, washed
    and sliced lengthwise into
    1 cm slices

CHIMICHURRI SAUCE

¹⁄₃ cup reduced-salt chicken stock

1 tablespoon extra virgin olive oil

2 teaspoons freshly squeezed
    lemon juice

2 large garlic cloves, finely chopped

1 tablespoon chopped fresh oregano
    or 1 teaspoon dried oregano

¹⁄₂ teaspoon crushed dried chilies,
    or to taste

1 small onion, finely chopped

¹⁄₂ cup finely chopped
    Italian parsley

1 Put all the sauce ingredients in a sealable plastic bag and shake to mix well. Rub the steak on both sides with half the pepper, and then put the steak in the bag and close. Refrigerate for 30 minutes, or up to 2 hours, turning once.

2 Meanwhile, place a wire cooling rack over paper towel. Bring the potatoes, remaining pepper and enough water to cover to a boil in a saucepan over high heat. Reduce the heat to medium and simmer until the potatoes are almost tender, about 10 minutes. Transfer the potatoes to the rack. Lightly coat the potatoes on both sides with nonstick cooking spray (preferably olive oil).

3 Remove the steak from the sauce. Boil the sauce vigorously in a small saucepan for 3 minutes, stirring constantly. Remove from the heat and cover to keep warm. Meanwhile, coat a grill pan with nonstick cooking spray and set over medium-high heat. Cook the steak and potatoes until the steak is done to taste (3 to 4 minutes on each side for medium-rare, 4 to 5 minutes for medium) and the potatoes are crispy, about 4 minutes per side. Thinly slice the steak across the grain. Divide the potato and steak slices among 4 plates. Spoon about 2 tablespoons warm sauce over each serving.

preparation time **15 mins**

cooking time **25 mins**
plus 30 mins marinating

serves **4**

PER SERVING

300 calories

29 g protein

13 g total fat
4 g saturated fat

62 mg cholesterol

17 g total carbohydrate
1 g sugars

3 g fibre

118 mg sodium

COOK'S TIP

The ideal potato to use for this recipe is Yukon Gold.

seared beef with garden vegetables

A scrumptious sirloin is flash-cooked to seal in all its fabulous flavours and surrounded by plenty of fresh veggies. Sirloin is among the leanest cuts of steak, and trimming away any visible fat before eating makes it even better.

1 Preheat the oven to 375°F (190°C). Mash the garlic and ¼ teaspoon pepper with the side of a knife to form a chunky paste. Rub the mixture on both sides of the steak. Set aside.

2 Bring the potatoes and enough water to cover to a boil in a saucepan. Reduce the heat and simmer for 5 minutes. Add the beans and cook until the potatoes are tender and the beans are just tender, 3–4 minutes. Drain, rinse with cool water and transfer to a large bowl.

3 Place the onion in a colander and rinse with hot tap water. Mix the vinegar, oil, the remaining pepper and the sugar in a small bowl. Set the vinaigrette aside.

4 Heat a large heavy-based ovenproof pan over medium-high heat until very hot but not smoking. Add the steak and sear until browned, about 3 minutes on each side. Transfer to the oven. For medium-rare (480°F–525°F/250°C–275°C), cook 15–18 minutes; medium (525°F–550°F/275°C–290°C), 20 to 23 minutes. Let stand for 5 minutes. Trim any remaining fat and thinly slice the steak. Arrange the potatoes, beans and onions around the steak and drizzle with the vinaigrette before serving.

2 garlic cloves, finely chopped
½ teaspoon pepper
1 bone-in beef sirloin steak 2 cm thick, about 1.2 kg
500 g potatoes, quartered
500 g green beans
1 large red onion, very thinly sliced
2 tablespoons white wine vinegar
2 teaspoons extra virgin olive oil
¼ teaspoon sugar

preparation time **15 mins**
cooking time **35 mins**
serves **8**

PER SERVING

261 calories

31 g protein

10 g total fat
4 g saturated fat

69 mg cholesterol

11 g total carbohydrate
2 g sugars

3 g fibre

66 mg sodium

HEALTH HINT

Lean trimmed beef is a highly nutritious food. It is an excellent source of iron, niacin, riboflavin, vitamin B$_{12}$ and zinc.

Sunday special roast beef

Succulent roast beef, crispy roast potatoes and root vegetables, and feather-light, old-fashioned Yorkshire puddings make one of the best loved of Sunday lunches. This healthy version will please everyone, even the traditionalists.

1.5 kg boned, rolled and tied lean sirloin tip, trimmed of fat

pepper to taste

4 teaspoons prepared English mustard (optional)

1.5 kg potatoes, peeled and cut into even-sized pieces

650 g baby parsnips, halved lengthwise

650 g baby carrots, halved lengthwise

3 tablespoons sunflower oil

650 g broccoli florets

1¾ cups reduced-salt beef stock

pepper to taste

YORKSHIRE PUDDINGS

½ cup all-purpose flour

1 egg

⅓ cup low-fat milk

2 teaspoons sunflower oil

1 Preheat the oven to 350°F (180°C). Put the meat, fat side up, on a rack in a roasting pan. Season with pepper, then spread with 3 teaspoons of the English mustard, if using. Roast the meat in the oven according to the weight (see the cook's tip). Baste occasionally with the juices in the pan.

2 Meanwhile, prepare the Yorkshire pudding batter. Place the flour in a bowl. Make a well in the centre and add the egg. Add a little of the milk and beat together, gradually beginning to work in the flour. Slowly beat in the remaining milk and 5 tablespoons water until all the flour is incorporated and the batter is smooth. Set aside.

3 Place the potatoes in a large saucepan of boiling water and boil for 5 minutes. Drain well and return to the pan, then cover and shake vigorously to roughen the surface of the potatoes (this helps to make them crisp).

4 Place the parsnips and carrots in another large saucepan of boiling water and boil for 3 minutes, then drain.

5 One hour before the end of the roasting time for the beef, put 2 tablespoons of the oil in a nonstick roasting pan and the remaining 1 tablespoon oil in another nonstick roasting pan. Heat on top of the stove, then add the potatoes to the 2 tablespoons oil and the parsnips and carrots to the 1 tablespoon oil. Baste each piece of vegetable with oil, then quickly place the pans in the oven with the beef. (With a gas oven, put the potatoes above the meat, and the carrots and parsnips below.) After 30 minutes, turn all the vegetables so they crisp and brown evenly.

6 When the beef is cooked, remove it from the oven and increase the heat to 425°F (220°C). Place the beef on a warmed plate, cover with foil and keep warm. Divide the oil for the Yorkshire puddings among 12 cups in a nonstick muffin pan and place the pan in the top of the oven to heat for 2–3 minutes. (Move the potatoes down a shelf.) Stir the batter, pour it into the pan and bake for 15 minutes or until the puddings are risen and golden-brown.

7 Meanwhile, steam the broccoli for 10 minutes or until tender. To make the gravy, pour the fat very slowly out of the roasting pan, leaving the sediment behind. Place the pan on top of the stove and pour in the stock. Bring to a boil,

preparation time **20 mins**

cooking time **2–2½ hours**

serves **8**

PER SERVING

563 calories

51 g protein

21 g total fat
6 g saturated fat

118 mg cholesterol

42 g total carbohydrate
11 g sugars

11 g fibre

377 mg sodium

COOK'S TIP

For rare roast beef, cook for 20 minutes per 500 g plus 20 minutes. For medium, cook for 25 minutes per 500 g plus 25 minutes. For well done, cook for 30 minutes per 500 g plus 30 minutes.

stirring and scraping up the browned cooking residue on the bottom of the pan, then simmer until slightly reduced. Season with pepper and stir in the remaining mustard, if using.

8 To serve, transfer the meat to a warmed serving platter and surround with the roast potatoes, carrots and parsnips and the Yorkshire puddings. Place the broccoli in a warmed serving dish. Add any meat juices that have collected on the plate to the gravy and stir to combine, then skim off any fat. Pour the gravy into a gravy boat and serve immediately.

roast beef tenderloin in red wine

Cancel those dinner reservations—you can make the kind of dinner you find in fine restaurants, and you don't have to be a chef to do it. The tenderloin almost cooks itself, and the vegetables complement the meat perfectly.

1 beef tenderloin roast, about 2 kg, trimmed

1½ teaspoons coarsely ground black pepper

2 cups dry red wine

1 kg onions, chopped

3 garlic cloves, crushed

6 sprigs fresh thyme

300 g button mushrooms, trimmed

1 tablespoon sugar

370 g baby carrots

2 cups red or yellow cherry tomatoes

500 g wide egg noodles

1 Preheat the oven to 450°F (230°C). Rub the roast with pepper. Tuck the ends under and tie with string. Mix the red wine with 1½ cups water. Coat a frying pan with cooking spray and set over medium-high heat. Add the beef, a third of the onions and the garlic and sear the meat until browned on all sides, 10 minutes. Discard the garlic and onion and transfer the tenderloin to a roasting pan. Pour in half the wine mixture. Add 3 thyme sprigs and place the pan in the oven.

2 Meanwhile, set aside 5 mushrooms and slice the remaining ones. Sauté the sliced mushrooms, remaining onions and sugar in the frying pan until brown, about 7 minutes. Cook the carrots in boiling water in a saucepan until they are just tender, 5–7 minutes. Drain.

3 After the meat has been roasting for 20 minutes, add the carrots and sautéed vegetables to the pan. Pour in the remaining wine mixture. Roast until done to your taste, about 25 minutes longer for medium. Transfer the meat to a board and let stand 10 minutes. Add the tomatoes to the pan, cover and let stand.

4 Meanwhile, cook the noodles according to the package directions. Trim the reserved mushrooms and flute with a paring knife. Coat a frying pan with cooking spray and set over medium heat. Sauté the mushrooms for 5 minutes. Arrange the noodles and vegetables on a platter. Slice the beef and add to the platter. Garnish with mushrooms and thyme. Serve with the pan juices.

 Fb GI

preparation time **15 mins**

cooking time **50 mins**

serves **10**

PER SERVING

536 calories

49 g protein

13 g total fat

5 g saturated fat

105 mg cholesterol

52 g total carbohydrate

9 g sugars

7 g fibre

131 mg sodium

HEALTH HINT

Cooking mushrooms breaks down their fibrous cell walls, making their nutrients more available to the body.

sirloin steaks with port sauce

Thin steaks can be quickly fried, and the pan juices turned into a tasty sauce with the help of a little port. A colourful stir-fry of new potatoes, mushrooms, red pepper and sugar snap peas makes the perfect accompaniment.

Fb

preparation time **10 mins**
cooking time **25 mins**
serves **4**

PER SERVING

468 calories

40 g protein

21 g total fat
6 g saturated fat

75 mg cholesterol

27 g total carbohydrate
9 g sugars

7 g fibre

357 mg sodium

HEALTH HINT

New potatoes provide vitamin C and the B vitamin folate. The preparation method makes a big difference to the amount of dietary fibre provided: new potatoes cooked in their skins offer one-third more fibre than peeled potatoes.

1 Place the potatoes in a pan and cover with boiling water. Bring back to a boil, reduce heat and simmer 10–12 minutes.

2 Meanwhile, heat the oil in a frying pan, add the mushrooms, peas and pepper and stir-fry for 1 minute. Mix ½ cup stock with the Worcestershire sauce, mustard and sugar, and stir into the vegetables. Reduce heat and simmer gently for 3 minutes or until the vegetables are just tender, stirring frequently.

3 Season the steaks on both sides with pepper and set aside. Heat a ridged cast-iron grill pan. Meanwhile, drain the cooked potatoes and add to the vegetables. Stir gently, then cover and leave over very low heat until ready to serve.

4 Place the margarine in the hot pan and turn up the heat to high. When the margarine starts to foam, add the steaks. For steaks 1 cm thick, allow 1 minute on each side for rare, 1½–2 minutes on each side for medium, and 2½–3 minutes on each side for well done. Lift the steaks onto warmed dinner plates. Keep the steaks warm while making the sauce.

5 Add the shallot and garlic to the juices in the pan and cook, stirring, over low heat for 1 minute. Add the port and increase the heat so the sauce is bubbling. Cook for about 1 minute, stirring. Pour in the remaining stock and let it bubble for 1 minute. Spoon the sauce over the steaks and serve immediately, with the vegetables.

500 g small new potatoes, washed and any larger ones halved

1 tablespoon extra virgin olive oil

250 g large mushrooms, quartered

250 g sugar snap peas

1 large red pepper, seeded and cut into thin strips

¾ cup reduced-salt beef or vegetable stock

1 tablespoon Worcestershire sauce

1 teaspoon Dijon mustard

½ teaspoon dark brown sugar

4 thin sirloin steaks, about 150 g each, trimmed of visible fat

pepper to taste

1½ tablespoons reduced-salt margarine

1 shallot, finely chopped

2 garlic cloves, crushed

5 tablespoons port

beef in red wine and brandy

Long, slow cooking gives this traditional casserole its inimitable flavour. The cooking liquid is reduced simply by removing the casserole lid, resulting in a wonderfully aromatic sauce that glazes the meat and vegetables.

1 Preheat the oven to 300°F (150°C). Dice the beef 1 cm thick.

2 Heat the sunflower oil in a large flameproof casserole dish. Add the sliced onion and cook over medium-high heat for about 5 minutes or until softened and beginning to brown.

3 Add the stewing beef to the casserole dish and fry for a further 5 minutes, stirring frequently, until the pieces of beef are browned on all sides. Stir in the baby carrots and parsnips, the button mushrooms and the garlic.

4 Pour in the red wine, then stir in the orange rind and juice, thyme, rosemary and bay leaf and season with pepper. Bring the mixture to a boil, then cover the casserole and transfer it to the oven. Cook the casserole for 1¼ hours.

5 Remove the lid of the pan and cook the casserole for a further 30 minutes, stirring once or twice. Stir in the broad beans and cook, uncovered, for another 30 minutes, again stirring once or twice.

6 Taste and add pepper if necessary, and stir in the chopped parsley. Warm the brandy in a small saucepan and pour it over the casserole. Immediately set the brandy alight and carry the casserole to the table still flaming.

Variations You can vary the vegetables in this recipe. Small broccoli florets or shelled fresh or frozen peas can be added instead of the broad beans. Also, large carrots and parsnips, cut into equal-sized chunks, are more economical for an everyday stew than baby vegetables. • Also, flaming the casserole with brandy is completely optional. • For an everyday version, you might prefer to use 3 cups reduced-salt beef stock or light ale instead of the wine.

500 g lean stewing beef
2 tablespoons sunflower oil
1 large onion, sliced
250 g baby carrots
250 g baby parsnips
250 g button mushrooms
1 garlic clove, finely chopped
1 bottle full-bodied red wine
grated rind and juice of 1 orange
1 sprig fresh thyme
1 sprig fresh rosemary
1 bay leaf
pepper to taste
200 g shelled fresh broad beans or frozen broad beans, thawed
2 tablespoons chopped parsley
4 tablespoons brandy

preparation time **20 mins**
cooking time **2½ hours**
serves **4**

PER SERVING

538 calories

52 g protein

21 g total fat
6 g saturated fat

94 mg cholesterol

19 g total carbohydrate
11 g sugars

9 g fibre

140 mg sodium

HEALTH HINTS

Robust broad beans go well with beef and they bring valuable dietary fibre to the dish.

Research shows that, in moderation, red wine consumption may help protect the body against certain cancers and heart disease, and can reduce bad cholesterol levels.

spicy steak with garlic toast

This is a delicious combination of juicy sliced steak, confetti-bright corn relish, and a hefty hunk of garlic toast, all totally heart-healthy. You can cook the steak and toast under the broiler, or barbecue them outdoors.

2 teaspoons ground cumin

1½ teaspoons chili powder

¾ teaspoon oregano

½ teaspoon black pepper

⅔ cup spicy tomato-vegetable juice

4 tablespoons freshly squeezed lime juice

2 cups frozen corn, thawed

2 green onions, thinly sliced

1 small red pepper, seeded and diced

370 g well-trimmed flank steak

1 loaf Italian bread, about 250 g, halved horizontally, then halved crosswise

1 clove garlic, peeled and halved

1 Stir together the cumin, chili powder, oregano and black pepper in a small bowl. Place the tomato-vegetable juice and lime juice in a measuring cup. Measure out 2½ teaspoons of spice mixture and stir into the tomato-lime juice mixture.

2 Combine the corn, green onions, red pepper and ½ cup of the tomato-lime juice mixture in a medium bowl. Stir to combine. Refrigerate until serving time.

3 Preheat the broiler. Rub the remaining spice mixture onto both sides of the steak. Broil the steak 8 cm from the heat until medium-rare, about 4 minutes per side. Remove the steak but leave the broiler on. Let the steak stand for 10 minutes before thinly slicing across the grain, on the diagonal.

4 Place the bread under the broiler, cut side up, until lightly toasted, about 30 seconds. Rub the toasted side of the bread with the cut garlic and with the remaining tomato-lime juice mixture and cook until lightly browned, about 1 minute. Serve the steak with the corn relish and the toast.

preparation time **10 mins**

cooking time **10 mins** plus 10 min standing

serves **4**

PER SERVING

376 calories

27 g protein

9 g total fat
3 g saturated fat

46 mg cholesterol

46 g total carbohydrate
6 g sugars

5 g fibre

441 mg sodium

HEALTH HINT

Garlic bread is usually soaked with butter, but this grilled toast is fine without the fat because it's rubbed with garlic, then brushed with a pleasantly spicy tomato-lime mixture.

beef in beer

Topped with thick slices of garlic and herb bread, this casserole is hearty and satisfying. It's an ideal dish for entertaining because it can be prepared ahead. Serve with mashed potatoes and steamed seasonal greens for a complete meal.

Fb

preparation time **15 mins**
cooking time **2¾ hours**
serves **4**

PER SERVING

714 calories

43 g protein

33 g total fat
7 g saturated fat

71 mg cholesterol

53 g total carbohydrate
10 g sugars

6 g fibre

840 mg sodium

HEALTH HINT

A casserole such as this makes a particularly healthy meal. Water-soluble vitamins—C and B complex—and minerals that seep from the food during the cooking process are usually thrown away with the cooking water. In casseroles, more of the nutrients are retained in the gravy.

1 Preheat the oven to 350°F (180°C). Heat 1 tablespoon of the oil in a flameproof casserole dish, add the beef and cook over medium-high heat for 4–5 minutes or until browned all over. Transfer the meat and its juices to a plate.

2 Add the remaining 1 tablespoon oil to the pan and reduce the heat to low, then add the onion, carrots, parsnip and garlic. Cook, stirring frequently, for 5 minutes. Return the beef and its juices to the pan together with the stout, stock, mixed herbs, vinegar, mustard and sugar. Stir well and bring to a boil. Cover the casserole and transfer to the oven. Cook for 2 hours or until the beef is tender.

3 Meanwhile, to make the garlic bread, cut baguette into 8 thick slices. Mix together the garlic, parsley, thyme and oil and spoon evenly over one side of each slice of bread.

4 Uncover the casserole and add pepper to season. Lay the slices of bread, oiled side up, in a circle around the edge of the casserole dish, overlapping them slightly. Return the casserole to the oven to cook for 20–30 minutes or until the bread is golden and crisp. Serve hot.

Variation For beef in red wine, use 12 whole shallots or baby onions in place of the onion, carrots and parsnips, and a full-bodied red wine instead of the stout. Omit the vinegar, mustard and sugar and add 1 tablespoon redcurrant jelly instead.

2 tablespoons extra virgin olive oil

450 g lean braising steak, trimmed of visible fat and cut into 5 cm cubes

1 large onion, cut into wedges

2 large carrots, thickly sliced on the diagonal

1 large parsnip, cut into cubes

1 large garlic clove, crushed

1 bottle (341 ml) stout beer

1¼ cups reduced-salt beef stock

1 teaspoon dried mixed herbs

1 tablespoon red wine vinegar

1 tablespoon whole-grain mustard

1 teaspoon dark brown sugar

pepper to taste

GARLIC AND HERB BREAD

1 piece of long baguette, about 250 g

1 large garlic clove, crushed

1 tablespoon chopped parsley

1 tablespoon chopped fresh thyme

4 tablespoons extra virgin olive oil

keema curry with cucumber raita

 This mellow curry of ground beef has just a hint of chili, so it's ideal for children who like to be a little adventurous with their food. Serve with steamed basmati rice and warm nan bread.

500 g lean ground beef
1 onion, finely chopped
450 g potatoes, peeled and diced
3 garlic cloves, chopped
2 cm piece fresh ginger, finely chopped
1 cinnamon stick, halved
1 teaspoon turmeric
1 teaspoon cumin seeds,
    roughly crushed
1 teaspoon coriander seeds, crushed
$1/2$ teaspoon crushed dried chilies
1 can (540 ml) diced tomatoes
$1^1/4$ cups reduced-salt beef stock
pepper to taste
150 g baby spinach
fresh mint leaves to garnish

CUCUMBER RAITA
150 g plain low-fat yogourt
$1/4$ cucumber, finely diced
4 teaspoons chopped fresh mint
pepper to taste

1 Fry the beef and onion in a large saucepan for 5 minutes or until evenly browned, stirring to break up the meat. Add the potatoes, garlic, ginger, spices and chili and fry for 2 minutes, stirring. Add the tomatoes with their juice and the stock and season with pepper. Bring to a boil, then cover and simmer for 20 minutes, stirring occasionally.

2 Meanwhile, to make the cucumber raita, mix the yogourt, cucumber and mint together with a little pepper. Spoon into a small bowl and chill.

3 Stir the baby spinach into the curry and heat through for about 1 minute, then add a little more pepper. Spoon the curry onto warmed plates and sprinkle with fresh mint leaves. Serve immediately, with the chilled cucumber raita.

Variations If you prefer, you can cook the curry in the oven. Brown the beef and onion in a flameproof casserole dish, then add the other ingredients and bring to a boil. Cover and cook in a preheated 350°F (180°C) oven for 1 hour. Add the spinach, toss with the meat, then cover and return to the oven to cook for 10 minutes. • For a fruity curry, you can add $1/2$ cup sultanas and 1 sliced dessert apple with the potatoes. Omit the spinach. Garnish the curry with 1 diced banana tossed with the juice of $1/2$ lemon and 2 tablespoons chopped fresh coriander.

preparation time **15 mins**
cooking time **30 mins**
serves **4**

PER SERVING

296 calories

33 g protein

8 g total fat
3 g saturated fat

67 mg cholesterol

22 g total carbohydrate
8 g sugars

5 g fibre

406 mg sodium

HEALTH HINT

A raita or sauce of yogourt, cucumber and mint is often served with curries to act as a cooling agent against the heat of the chilies and spices. Yogourt is also extremely nutritious—it is a valuable source of calcium and it provides useful amounts of phosphorus, the B vitamin riboflavin and vitamin B_{12}. Live yogourt also provides beneficial bacteria that can help to maintain a healthy digestive tract.

lamb kebabs with Greek salad

Cubes of lamb flavoured with a mixture of garlic, lemon and fresh oregano are cooked on skewers and served with a Greek-style tomato and cabbage salad and pita bread for a deliciously aromatic main dish.

1 Preheat the broiler or heat a ridged cast-iron grill pan. Put the olive oil, garlic, lemon juice and oregano in a bowl and stir to combine. Add the lamb and turn until well coated. Thread the cubes onto 4 skewers.

2 Cook the lamb under the broiler or in the pan for about 7–8 minutes or until tender, turning frequently. Toward the end of cooking, warm the pita bread under the broiler.

3 Place all the salad ingredients in a bowl. Toss gently. Serve the kebabs with the salad, pita bread and yogourt, if using.

Variation For chili beef kebabs, use 4 beef tenderloin steaks cut into cubes. Mix together 1 teaspoon chili powder, ¼ teaspoon ground cumin, 1 tablespoon extra virgin olive oil, 2 crushed garlic cloves, juice of ½ lime and pepper. Coat steak with the spice mixture, then thread onto 4 skewers. Cook with 1 sliced onion under the broiler for 4–6 minutes. Remove skewers from the broiler and continue cooking the onion until tender. Mix 1 can (540 ml) kidney beans, rinsed, with 1 diced avocado, juice of 1 lime, 2 tablespoons extra virgin olive oil, ½ red onion, finely chopped, 1 green chili, seeded and finely chopped, 300 g cherry tomatoes, halved, and ⅔ cup chopped fresh coriander. Remove the steak from the skewers and divide with the onion among 8 warmed flour tortillas. Add some of the salad to each tortilla, and roll up into wraps. Serve with the rest of the salad.

1 tablespoon extra virgin olive oil

2 large garlic cloves, crushed

juice of ½ lemon

1 tablespoon chopped
fresh oregano

450 g boneless leg of lamb,
trimmed of visible fat
and diced 2 cm thick

4 whole-wheat pita breads, cut
into triangles, to serve

Greek-style yogourt to
serve (optional)

GREEK-STYLE SALAD

6 tomatoes, thickly sliced

1 red onion, finely chopped

1 baby or small white cabbage,
about 220 g, core removed
and thinly shredded

5 tablespoons chopped
fresh mint

¼ cucumber, halved
and thinly sliced

juice of ½ lemon

1 tablespoon extra virgin olive oil

30 Fb

preparation time **20 mins**

cooking time **10 mins**

serves **4**

PER SERVING

420 calories

30 g protein

19 g total fat
6 g saturated fat

80 mg cholesterol

31 g total carbohydrate
9 g sugars

9 g fibre

296 mg sodium

HEALTH HINT

Cabbage is not only an excellent source of vitamin C but it is high in fibre. Chemicals found in cabbage have long been known to lower the risk of colon cancer.

Indian lamb with spiced lentils

Freshly ground spices make this lamb curry fabulously fragrant, while green lentils give texture and substance, as well as extra good health. Serve with plain yogourt and saffron rice.

6 black peppercorns

1 tablespoon cumin seeds

seeds from 8 cardamom pods

2 tablespoons sunflower oil

1 large onion, sliced

2 garlic cloves, crushed

5 cm piece fresh ginger, finely chopped

1 red chili, seeded and finely chopped

1 cinnamon stick

1 teaspoon turmeric

500 g lean boneless leg of lamb or shoulder, trimmed of visible fat and cut into cubes

2¹⁄₃ cups hot reduced-salt beef stock

220 g green lentils

4 Italian tomatoes, quartered

juice of ¹⁄₂ lemon

2 tablespoons chopped fresh coriander

pepper to taste

1 Crush the peppercorns with the cumin and cardamom seeds in a mortar and pestle or a spice mill. Set aside.

2 Heat the oil in a large flameproof casserole dish, add the onion and fry gently for 5 minutes or until softened. Add the garlic, ginger and chili and fry for a further 3 minutes, then add the crushed spices and the cinnamon stick and turmeric. Fry gently for 30 seconds, stirring constantly.

3 Add the lamb and stir to coat with the spices. Fry gently for about 4 minutes or until the meat is browned all over. Gradually pour in the stock, stirring well, and bring to a boil. Reduce the heat, cover and cook gently for 1 hour or until the lamb is almost cooked and tender.

4 Meanwhile, rinse and drain the lentils, then place them in a saucepan and cover with cold water. Bring to a boil. Boil, uncovered, for 15 minutes. Drain.

5 Add the lentils and tomatoes to the curry and cook for about 15–20 minutes or until the lamb and lentils are both tender. Stir in the lemon juice and fresh coriander and season with pepper. Serve hot.

Variation If it's more convenient, you can cook the curry in the oven. In step 3, after bringing to a boil, cover the casserole dish and place it in a preheated 350°F (180°C) oven. Cook for 1¹⁄₄ hours. Add the lentils and tomatoes and cook for a further 20 minutes or until tender. Health food stores sell a wide range of lentils. Any of them can be used, but check first whether they are best soaked before cooking, because you may need to plan ahead. Red split lentils and split peas are a good choice because they do not need soaking.

C Fb GI

preparation time **30 mins**

cooking time **1¹⁄₂ hours**

serves **4**

PER SERVING

379 calories

35 g protein

20 g total fat
6 g saturated fat

89 mg cholesterol

15 g total carbohydrate
6 g sugars

5 g fibre

640 mg sodium

HEART SUPERFOOD

Lentils are an excellent source of dietary fibre, particularly the soluble kind responsible for keeping levels of bad cholesterol down. They are also a useful source of thiamine and vitamin B₆.

teriyaki lamb chops

 Yes, you can have lamb chops on a heart-healthy diet, provided you trim away the fat. These are juicy, bursting with flavour, and brightened with Asian accents. Pair them with warm noodles and a fresh salad.

6 green onions

2 tablespoons sesame seeds

¼ cup reduced-salt soy sauce

2 tablespoons cider vinegar

2 tablespoons clear honey

1 small garlic clove, finely chopped

¾ teaspoon ground ginger

8 bone-in lamb loin chops, about 120 g each, trimmed of visible fat

250 g cellophane noodles

4 carrots

1 red pepper

½ of 1 can (398 ml) whole baby corn, drained

1½ teaspoons cornstarch

1 Cut 2 green onions into thin slices and the rest into 4 cm pieces. Toast the sesame seeds in a nonstick frying pan for about 3 minutes. Remove from the heat. Stir in the soy sauce, vinegar, honey, garlic, ginger and the sliced green onions.

2 Roll the narrow end of the chops into medallions and secure with toothpicks. Place them in a baking dish and pour in the soy sauce mixture. Cover and refrigerate for 1–2 hours.

3 Cook the noodles according to the package directions. Drain. Cut the carrots and pepper into matchsticks and blanch in water to cover, 3 minutes. Add the remaining green onions and corn. Blanch until the vegetables are crisp-tender, about 2 minutes longer. Drain and toss with the noodles.

4 Preheat the broiler. Remove the chops from the marinade; pour the marinade into a small saucepan. Broil the chops 12 cm from the heat until done to taste, 4 minutes on each side for medium. Transfer to a platter, remove the toothpicks and keep warm. Bring the marinade to a boil. Cook, stirring, for 2 minutes. Dissolve the cornstarch in ⅓ cup water and whisk into the marinade. Boil over medium-high heat, whisking, until the sauce thickens, about 2 minutes. Toss half of the sauce with the noodles, drizzle the remaining half over the chops and serve.

 Fb GI

preparation time **15 mins**

cooking time **25 mins**
plus 1–2 hrs marinating

serves **4**

PER SERVING

515 calories

42 g protein

19 g total fat
8 g saturated fat

150 mg cholesterol

43 g total carbohydrate
19 g sugars

6 g fibre

860 mg sodium

COOK'S TIP

Loin chops are a good choice of lamb for this recipe. It is a tender cut, which is suitable for fast-cooking methods, such as broiling.

Mediterranean stuffed vegetables

 An array of colourful stuffed vegetables makes an appetizing main dish, ideal for an informal help-yourself meal when entertaining guests. Serve with lots of crusty whole-wheat bread and a mixed leaf salad.

preparation time **25 mins**

cooking time
1 hour 5 mins

serves **4**

PER SERVING

326 calories

21 g protein

13 g total fat
4 g saturated fat

90 mg cholesterol

32 g total carbohydrate
11 g sugars

7 g fibre

78 mg sodium

HEALTH HINT

The Mediterranean-style vegetables used in this dish are high in phytochemicals and antioxidant vitamins. Among these is beta carotene from the peppers, spinach, tomatoes and zucchinis. The antioxidant properties of beta carotene help to protect cells from damage by free radicals that are produced in the body in response to stress.

1 Cook the rice in boiling water for 10–12 minutes, or according to the package instructions, until tender. Drain.

2 Meanwhile, place the lamb and onion in a nonstick frying pan and fry until the lamb is lightly browned and cooked through and the onion softened. Place a sieve over a bowl and tip the meat and onions into it. The fat will drip through and can be discarded.

3 Cut each pepper in half lengthwise and remove the core and seeds. Cut the tops off the tomatoes and hollow them out. Chop the tops and hollowed-out flesh and place in a bowl. Cut the zucchinis in half lengthwise and hollow out the centres to leave shells 5 mm thick. Chop the removed zucchini flesh and add it to the chopped tomatoes.

4 Preheat the oven to 350°F (180°C). Heat the oil in a nonstick frying pan, add the garlic and chopped vegetables, and cook, stirring, until they soften. Add the spinach and cook over medium heat until wilted. Remove from the heat and add the basil, rice and lamb. Add the egg and pepper and mix well.

5 Spoon the stuffing into the vegetable shells. Arrange the peppers and zucchinis in a single layer in 1 or 2 roasting pans. Cover with foil or a lid and place in the oven for 15 minutes. Add the tomatoes and roast for 15 minutes or until the vegetables are almost tender. Uncover the vegetables and roast for a further 15–20 minutes or until they are tender and the tops are lightly browned. Serve either warm or cool, sprinkled with the additional shredded fresh basil.

1 cup long-grain rice

250 g lean ground lamb

1 onion, chopped

4 mixed-colour peppers

4 large tomatoes, ripe but firm

2 very large zucchinis

1 tablespoon extra virgin olive oil

3 garlic cloves, coarsely chopped

170 g baby spinach leaves

2 tablespoons shredded fresh basil, plus additional 2–4 tablespoons to serve

1 egg, lightly beaten

pepper to taste

leg of lamb with double mint sauce

Treat yourself to roast lamb! A small leg serves six, plus it's extra lean and surprisingly low in fat. Lamb deserves the crowning jewel of a fresh mint sauce that can be prepared in minutes, yet tastes as if it took a lot of effort.

1 boneless leg of lamb, about 1 kg, trimmed of visible fat

2 garlic cloves, chopped

1 tablespoon chopped fresh rosemary

1/2 teaspoon pepper

1 large lemon, halved

2/3 cup dry white wine or reduced-salt chicken stock

MINT SAUCE

2/3 cup mint jelly

2 tablespoons freshly squeezed lemon juice

1/4 cup chopped fresh mint

1 Preheat the oven to 400°F (200°C). Lightly coat a roasting pan with nonstick cooking spray. To make the mint sauce, combine the mint jelly, lemon juice and fresh mint in a small saucepan. Stir constantly over medium heat until the jelly melts, about 5 minutes. Remove from the heat and set aside.

2 Meanwhile, cut the lamb horizontally three-quarters through with a sharp knife. Open and spread flat like a book. Place the meat between two pieces of plastic wrap and pound with a meat mallet or rolling pin to about 2 cm thick.

3 Brush about 2 tablespoons mint sauce on the lamb, and then sprinkle with the garlic, rosemary and pepper. Squeeze the juice from one lemon half over the lamb. Roll up the lamb from one wide side. Tie with kitchen string, in both directions. Transfer to a pan, seam side down. Squeeze the remaining lemon half over the lamb and pour on the wine or stock.

4 Roast for about 50 minutes, or until done to your taste. Let the meat stand for 10 minutes before slicing. Reheat the remaining sauce. Remove the strings from the lamb and cut the lamb into 1 cm slices. Serve with the mint sauce.

preparation time **15 mins**

cooking time **55 mins** plus standing

serves **6**

PER SERVING

289 calories

34 g protein

13 g total fat
7 g saturated fat

118 mg cholesterol

8 g total carbohydrate
8 g sugars

0.4 g fibre

95 mg sodium

HEALTH HINT

The lamb in this dish serves up excellent amounts of vitamin B_{12}, which is needed to make red blood cells and build nerve fibres. It's also an excellent source of the B vitamin niacin, which is needed for the release of energy from food.

preparation time **20 mins**

cooking time
1 hour 20 mins

serves **4**

PER SERVING

420 calories

28 g protein

30 g total fat
12 g saturated fat

107 mg cholesterol

12 g total carbohydrate
10 g sugars

4 g fibre

127 mg sodium

HEALTH HINT

Research has shown that adenosine, a substance found in onions, helps prevent clot formation, which may help prevent heart attacks.

fragrant lamb with spinach

This enticing curry is warmly spiced rather than fiery hot with chilies. Serve it with basmati rice, chapatis or whole-wheat pita breads and a fresh tomato and cucumber salsa for a healthy Indian-style meal.

1 Heat the oil in a large saucepan or flameproof casserole dish. Add the onions, garlic and ginger, and fry for about 5 minutes, stirring frequently, until the onions are golden.

2 Stir in the chili, paprika, cumin, coriander, white pepper, cinnamon, cardamom seeds and bay leaves. Stir briefly over medium heat, then stir in the yogourt and $2/3$ cup water. Add the lamb, mix well and cover the pan. Simmer gently for $1\frac{1}{4}$ hours or until the lamb is tender.

3 Add the tomatoes, spinach and chopped coriander. Cook for 2–3 minutes, stirring, until the tomatoes have softened slightly and the spinach has wilted. Taste for pepper and remove the bay leaves. Serve garnished with fresh coriander.

2 tablespoons sunflower oil
2 onions, finely chopped
4 garlic cloves, crushed
5 cm piece fresh ginger, peeled and chopped
1 large mild red chili, seeded and sliced
2 teaspoons paprika
2 teaspoons ground cumin
2 teaspoons ground coriander
1 teaspoon ground white pepper
$\frac{1}{2}$ teaspoon ground cinnamon
seeds from 8 green cardamom pods, crushed
2 bay leaves
200 g Greek-style yogourt
500 g lean boneless lamb, cubed
2 large tomatoes, chopped
250 g baby spinach
4 tablespoons chopped fresh coriander
sprigs fresh coriander to garnish

old-fashioned shepherd's pie

In this version of a long-time family favourite, the ground lamb filling contains plenty of vegetables and red lentils, giving a rich flavour and texture. A generous serving of peas will make the meal even more nutritious.

1 Heat the oil in a large heavy saucepan. Add the lamb and cook over a high heat, stirring well with a wooden spoon to break up the meat, for about 5 minutes or until lightly browned. Push the meat to one side of the pan and add the onion. Reduce the heat to low and cook for 5 minutes, stirring occasionally, until the onion is softened and lightly browned.

2 Add the carrots, celery and leeks and stir well, then add the tomato sauce, Worcestershire sauce, stock and lentils. Increase the heat and bring to a boil, stirring frequently. Partially cover with a lid, then reduce the heat to low and simmer for about 20 minutes, stirring occasionally.

3 While the meat mixture is cooking, preheat the oven to 400°F (200°C) and prepare the topping. Place the potato and parsnip chunks in a saucepan and pour over boiling water to cover by 5 cm. Bring back to a boil, then reduce the heat and cook for 15–20 minutes or until the potatoes and parsnips are very tender. Heat the milk in a small saucepan until hot.

4 Drain the potatoes and parsnips well, and return them to the pan. Pour the hot milk over them, then mash them until they are completely smooth. Beat in the margarine and add pepper.

5 Remove the meat mixture from the heat, add the chopped parsley and stir well. Spoon into a large ovenproof dish, about 2.5 litre capacity. Top with the mashed vegetables, spreading in an even layer. Bake for 20 minutes or until bubbling and lightly browned. Serve hot, garnished with parsley sprigs.

Variation For a special occasion, you can replace the lamb with lean ground venison. Omit the leeks and stir 250 g fresh or frozen peas into the meat mixture after it has simmered for 15 minutes. In the topping, you can replace the parsnips with celeriac.

1 tablespoon extra virgin olive oil
500 g lean ground lamb
1 large onion, finely chopped
3 carrots, finely chopped
3 celery stalks, thinly sliced
2 leeks, thinly sliced
1 tablespoon tomato sauce
1 tablespoon Worcestershire sauce
1$\frac{1}{3}$ cups reduced-salt beef stock
$\frac{1}{2}$ cup split red lentils
3 tablespoons chopped parsley
parsley sprigs to garnish

POTATO AND PARSNIP TOPPING

500 g potatoes, peeled and
    cut into chunks
500 g parsnips, cut into chunks
$\frac{1}{3}$ cup low-fat milk
2 tablespoons reduced-salt
    margarine
pepper to taste

Fb

preparation time **15 mins**
cooking time **55 mins**
serves **4**

PER SERVING

501 calories

34 g protein

23 g total fat
8 g saturated fat

74 mg cholesterol

40 g total carbohydrate
16 g sugars

11 g fibre

593 mg sodium

HEALTH HINTS

This well-balanced dish of lean meat, vegetables and pulses provides plenty of soluble fibre, mainly from the lentils but also from the parsnips, carrots and leeks. Soluble fibre controls levels of cholesterol and sugar in the blood.

Carrots provide vitamin A in the form of beta carotene. Cooking carrots makes it easier for the body to absorb and use the beta carotene.

lamb burgers with fruity relish

 The advantage of making your own burgers is that you know exactly what's in them, they look and taste better than the fast-food variety, while being a really healthy meal. An orange and raspberry relish adds a lovely fresh flavour.

400 g lean ground lamb

1 carrot, grated

1 small onion, finely chopped

⅔ cup fresh whole-wheat breadcrumbs

⅛ teaspoon freshly grated nutmeg

2 teaspoons fresh thyme leaves or
    1 teaspoon dried thyme

pepper to taste

1 large egg, beaten

2 teaspoons extra virgin olive oil

4 whole-wheat buns

shredded lettuce to garnish

ORANGE AND RASPBERRY RELISH

1 orange

100 g fresh or thawed frozen
    raspberries

2 teaspoons dark brown sugar

1 Preheat the broiler. Place the lamb in a large bowl. Add the carrot, onion, breadcrumbs, nutmeg and thyme, and season with pepper. Mix roughly with a spoon. Add the egg and use your hands to mix the ingredients together thoroughly.

2 Divide the mixture into 4 and shape each portion into a patty about 10–12 cm in diameter, or about 2 cm bigger than the diameter of the buns. Brush both sides of the patties with oil, then place them in the broiler pan. Cook for 4–5 minutes on each side, depending on their thickness.

3 Meanwhile, to make the relish, cut the peel and pith from the orange with a sharp knife and, holding it over a bowl to catch the juice, cut between the membranes to release the segments. Roughly chop the segments and add them to the juice. Add the raspberries and sugar, lightly crushing the fruit with a fork to mix it together.

4 Toast the buns briefly under the broiler. Put a lamb patty in each bun and add some lettuce to garnish and a good spoonful of relish. Serve with the remaining relish.

 30 Fb

preparation time **20 mins**

cooking time **10 mins**

serves **4**

PER SERVING

427 calories

28 g protein

16 g total fat
6 g saturated fat

121 mg cholesterol

43 g total carbohydrate
9 g sugars

7 g fibre

487 mg sodium

HEALTH HINTS

Using whole-wheat buns instead of white ones doubles the amount of fibre. The bread also provides B vitamins and small amounts of iron and calcium.

A fruity relish provides a huge bonus of protective antioxidants. It also provides useful amounts of potassium and fibre, especially from the raspberries.

Irish stew

Traditional recipes for Irish stew use a tough, fatty cut of lamb and only potatoes, onions and herbs. This up-to-date version with lamb leg steaks is leaner, and more colourful with the addition of carrots.

1 Preheat the oven to 325°F (160°C). In a large casserole dish, make layers of the lamb, potatoes, onion and carrots, sprinkling each layer with parsley, thyme, chives and pepper. Finish with a layer of potatoes, then pour over the stock.

2 Cover the casserole with a tight-fitting lid and place in the oven to cook for about 2 hours or until both the meat and vegetables feel tender when tested with a skewer.

3 Increase the oven temperature to 400°F (200°C). Remove the casserole lid and cook for a further 20 minutes or until the potatoes on top are golden-brown and crisp. Serve hot, sprinkled with more thyme and parsley.

Variations Add 120 g whole small button mushrooms, layering them in the casserole with the onion and carrots. • If you want the cooking liquid to be slightly thickened, sprinkle 1 tablespoon pearl barley between the first few layers along with the herbs. • For a real taste of Ireland, you can replace half of the stock with Guinness.

500 g boneless lean lamb leg steaks, trimmed of visible fat and each steak cut into 4 pieces

1 kg potatoes, peeled and thickly sliced

1 large onion, sliced

500 g carrots, thickly sliced

2 tablespoons chopped parsley

1 teaspoon fresh thyme leaves

1 tablespoon snipped fresh chives

pepper to taste

1¾ cups hot reduced-salt vegetable stock

chopped fresh thyme and parsley to garnish

C Fb

preparation time **20 mins**

cooking time **2 hours 20 mins**

serves **4**

PER SERVING

383 calories

33 g protein

10 g total fat
5 g saturated fat

89 mg cholesterol

39 g total carbohydrate
12 g sugars

9 g fibre

583 mg sodium

HEALTH HINT

Carrots are not traditional in Irish stew, but they are well worth including, both for their colour and flavour and also their nutritional properties. They provide vitamins A and C as well as potassium.

sticky pork spare ribs

In this dish, pork spare ribs are simmered first to tenderize the meat and to remove some of the fat, before being roasted in a deliciously sticky orange and mustard glaze. Choose the meatiest ribs you can find.

12 meaty pork spare ribs, about 1 kg in total

4 tablespoons red wine vinegar

2 teaspoons sunflower oil

large strip of orange rind

²⁄₃ cup freshly squeezed orange juice

1 tablespoon tomato sauce

2 tablespoons dark brown sugar

2 tablespoons Worcestershire sauce

1 tablespoon Dijon mustard

¹⁄₂–1 teaspoon chili powder, or to taste

1 Preheat the oven to 400°F (200°C). Trim as much fat as possible off the spare ribs, then place them in a saucepan. Cover with cold water and add 2 tablespoons of the vinegar. Bring to a boil, then simmer for 20 minutes, skimming the fat from the surface from time to time.

2 Meanwhile, combine the remaining 1 tablespoon vinegar, the oil, orange rind and juice, tomato sauce, brown sugar, Worcestershire sauce, mustard and chili powder in a small pan and bring to a boil. Simmer for 4–5 minutes or until the mixture is slightly reduced.

3 Drain the spare ribs and arrange them in a single layer in a large roasting pan. Pour over the orange juice mixture and turn the ribs to coat them evenly. Loosely cover the ribs with foil and roast for 20 minutes.

4 Remove the foil and roast for a further 20–25 minutes, turning and basting occasionally, until the ribs are dark brown and sticky. Transfer to a large serving dish and serve warm.

preparation time **15 mins**

cooking time
1 hour 10 mins

serves **4**

PER SERVING

247 calories

28 g protein

9 g total fat
3 g saturated fat

84 mg cholesterol

12 g total carbohydrate
12 g sugars

0.5 g fibre

268 mg sodium

COOK'S TIP

Spare ribs are one of the fattier cuts of pork. Trimming off any visible fat, simmering in water and then roasting until crisp are clever ways to reduce their fat content.

t207

pork medallions with peppers

This quick sauté makes an excellent dinner party dish, with its well-balanced sweet and sour elements coming from balsamic vinegar, oranges and olives. It is especially good—and extra nutritious—served with broccoli.

preparation time **25 mins**

cooking time **25 mins**

serves **4**

PER SERVING

534 calories

38 g protein

9 g total fat
2 g saturated fat

112 mg cholesterol

74 g total carbohydrate
16 g sugars

7 g fibre

149 mg sodium

HEALTH HINT

Wild rice is not a true rice, but the seeds of a wild aquatic grass. It is gluten-free, like the basmati rice it is mixed with here, and contains useful amounts of B vitamins, particularly niacin, as well as dietary fibre.

1 Place the rice in a saucepan and pour over the boiling water. Bring back to a boil, then reduce the heat to low. Cover and simmer for about 15 minutes, or according to the package instructions, until the rice is tender and all the water has been absorbed.

2 Meanwhile, peel the oranges and cut them crosswise into slices about 1 cm thick. Stack the slices 3 or 4 at a time and cut into quarters. (If possible, use a chopping board with a well to catch the juices.) Set the orange slices and juice aside.

3 Heat the oil in a large nonstick frying pan over medium-high heat. Cook the pork medallions, in batches, for 2–3 minutes on each side. Remove the meat with a slotted spoon and set aside.

4 Reduce the heat to medium and add the onion, pepper strips, carrot and garlic to the pan. Cover and cook, stirring frequently, for 5–6 minutes or until the vegetables start to soften. Add 2 tablespoons water, then the orange juice and balsamic vinegar. Stir well to mix. Cover and cook for 3–4 minutes or until the vegetables are tender.

5 Return the pork to the pan. Add the olives, orange slices and their juice and the basil leaves. Cook for 1 minute to reheat the pork, stirring well. Add pepper to taste.

6 To serve, divide the rice among 4 warmed plates and place the pork medallions and vegetables on top. Drizzle over any juices remaining in the pan and serve immediately.

2 cups mixed basmati and wild rice

2⅓ cups boiling water

2 oranges

1 tablespoon extra virgin olive oil

350 g pork fillet, sliced across into medallions 1 cm thick

1 large red onion, halved lengthwise and thinly sliced into half rings

1 red pepper, seeded and sliced into strips

1 yellow pepper, seeded and sliced into strips

1 large carrot, grated

1 garlic clove, finely chopped

⅓ cup freshly squeezed orange juice

4 tablespoons balsamic vinegar

¼ cup pitted black olives, chopped or sliced

½ cup fresh basil leaves

pepper to taste

sesame pork and noodle salad

*With its typical Chinese flavours—ginger, sesame, soy sauce and rice vinegar—
this salad makes a delectable dish for either lunch or dinner. It is particularly
nutritious as most of the vegetables are raw.*

preparation time **20 mins**
cooking time **15 mins**
serves **4**

PER SERVING

574 calories
48 g protein
15 g total fat
3 g saturated fat
128 mg cholesterol
58 g total carbohydrate
5 g sugars
8 g fibre
655 mg sodium

400 g pork fillet
2 teaspoons grated fresh ginger
1 large garlic clove, finely chopped
1$\frac{1}{2}$ teaspoons sesame oil
4 tablespoons reduced-salt soy sauce
2 tablespoons dry sherry
2 teaspoons rice vinegar
250 g fine Chinese egg noodles
1 red pepper, seeded and cut
    into matchstick strips
1 large carrot, cut into
    matchstick strips
6 green onions, cut into
    matchstick strips
1$\frac{3}{4}$ cups bean sprouts
150 g snow peas
2 tablespoons sesame seeds
1 tablespoon sunflower oil

1 Trim all visible fat from the pork fillet. Cut the pork across into slices about 5 cm thick, then cut each slice into thin strips.

2 Combine the ginger, garlic, sesame oil, soy sauce, sherry and vinegar in a bowl. Add the pork strips and toss to coat, then leave to marinate while you prepare the other ingredients.

3 Place the noodles in a large mixing bowl and pour over enough boiling water to cover generously. Leave to soak for about 4 minutes, or cook according to the package instructions, until tender. Drain well and transfer back into the bowl. Add the pepper, carrot, green onions and bean sprouts.

4 Drop the snow peas into a pan of boiling water and cook for about 1 minute or until just tender but still crisp. Drain and refresh under cold running water. Add the snow peas to the noodle and vegetable mixture and toss to mix. Set aside.

5 Toast the sesame seeds in a large frying pan over medium heat for 1–2 minutes or until golden, stirring constantly. Tip the seeds onto a piece of paper towel. Heat the sunflower oil in the frying pan, increase the heat slightly and add the pork with its marinade. Stir-fry for about 4–5 minutes or until the pork is no longer pink.

6 Add the pork and any cooking juices to the noodle and vegetable mixture, and stir gently to combine. Divide the pork and noodle mixture among 4 shallow bowls, sprinkle with the toasted sesame seeds and serve.

HEALTH HINT

In the past, pork has had a reputation for being rather fatty, but this is no longer the case. Pork now contains considerably less fat, and it also contains higher levels of the "good" unsaturated fats.

spinach, prosciutto and asparagus salad with rye croutons

 Here, pan-fried pieces of asparagus and prosciutto are combined with wilted baby spinach and crisp-baked croutons in a delicious warm salad for two. Serve with a side dish of new potatoes tossed with a little extra virgin olive oil.

1 Preheat the oven to 400°F (200°C). Toss the bread cubes with 1 tablespoon of the olive oil, then spread out on a baking sheet. Bake for about 5 minutes or until crisp.

2 Meanwhile, heat the remaining oil in a wok or frying pan. Add the asparagus in a single layer, and cook over medium heat for 5 minutes, without stirring. Turn the asparagus over, add the garlic and shallots, and cook for a further 3 minutes. Add the prosciutto and cook for 2 more minutes, stirring constantly.

3 Using a slotted spoon, remove the asparagus, prosciutto and shallot mixture from the wok and put it in a bowl. Keep warm. Add the balsamic vinegar, lemon juice and honey to the wok, and stir to mix with the cooking juices. Add the spinach and cook, stirring and turning, until just wilted.

4 Season the spinach with pepper then divide between 2 plates. Arrange the asparagus, prosciutto and shallot mixture on top. Spoon on any cooking juices and scatter over the croutons and shavings of Parmesan cheese. Serve immediately.

60 g crustless dark rye bread, cut into cubes

2 tablespoons extra virgin olive oil

250 g asparagus spears, cut into short pieces

2 garlic cloves, thinly sliced

4 shallots, cut into wedges

6 slices prosciutto, about 90 g, trimmed of visible fat and torn into pieces

1 tablespoon balsamic vinegar

2 tablespoons lemon juice

1 teaspoon clear honey

250 g baby spinach

pepper to taste

few shavings of Parmesan cheese, about 15 g in total

pesto pork chops

Lean pork is now on the heart-healthy menu. To keep these chops healthy but succulent, top them with homemade pesto. It uses just a tiny bit of oil but seals in all the pork's juices at the same time.

180 g wide egg noodles or rice noodles

2 cups fresh basil leaves

3 garlic cloves, peeled

½ teaspoon freshly ground black pepper

2 tablespoons whole-wheat breadcrumbs

2 tablespoons extra virgin olive oil

4 lean pork loin chops, 1 cm thick, about 120 g each

1 Prepare the noodles according to the package instructions. Drain and keep hot. Meanwhile, preheat the broiler.

2 Place the basil, garlic and pepper in a food processor. Pulse until roughly chopped. Add the breadcrumbs and process for 30 seconds. With the motor running, slowly add the oil through the feed tube until puréed. Set aside.

3 Coat a large heavy frying pan and the broiler pan with nonstick cooking spray. Set the frying pan over high heat until it is very hot but not smoking. Sprinkle both sides of the chops with the remaining pepper. Sauté the chops until browned, about 1 minute on each side. Remove from the heat. Spread the chops on both sides with the pesto and transfer to the broiler pan.

4 Broil the chops until the pesto is slightly darker and the juices run clear, about 2 minutes on each side. Divide the noodles evenly among 4 plates, top with a pork chop and serve.

30

preparation time **10 mins**

cooking time **10 mins**

serves **4**

PER SERVING

451 calories

34 g protein

17 g total fat
4 g saturated fat

76 mg cholesterol

41 g total carbohydrate
1 g sugars

4 g fibre

112 mg sodium

COOK'S TIP

How can you tell when a pork chop is done? Near the end of the suggested cooking time, make a slit with a small knife in the centre of the chop. It's ready to eat when the juices run clear, the meat shows just a hint of pink, and the chop is still juicy and tender. Pork is perfectly safe to eat at this stage.

sweet and sour pork

Sweet and sour sauce doesn't have to be a thick bright orange. This modern, light version allows the succulence of the meat and the fresh flavours and different textures of a variety of vegetables and noodles to shine through.

Fb GI

preparation time **30 mins**
cooking time **15 mins**
serves **4**

PER SERVING

531 calories

38 g protein

15 g total fat
3 g saturated fat

112 mg cholesterol

58 g total carbohydrate
22 g sugars

8 g fibre

925 mg sodium

HEALTH HINT

Bean sprouts are rich in vitamin C and several of the B vitamins; they also provide some potassium. Adding them at the last minute preserves as much of their vitamin C content as possible.

1 Place the pork strips in a bowl, sprinkle over the soy sauce and pepper and stir to coat the meat. Sprinkle over the cornstarch and stir again. Cover and set aside.

2 To make the sauce, mix together the cornstarch, sugar, vinegar, rice wine or sherry, ketchup, soy sauce and reserved pineapple juice in a small bowl. Set aside.

3 Cook the egg noodles in a saucepan of boiling water for 3 minutes, or cook or soak them according to the package instructions. Drain well and set aside.

4 Heat a wok or heavy-based frying pan until really hot, then add 1 tablespoon of the sunflower oil and swirl to coat the wok. Add the pork and leave for 1 minute to brown, then stir-fry over high heat for 3–4 minutes. Remove the pork with a slotted spoon and set aside.

5 Heat the remaining oil in the wok, then add the corn and stir-fry for 1 minute. Add the carrot, garlic and ginger and stir-fry for another minute. Sprinkle over 6 tablespoons water and let the vegetables steam for 2–3 minutes.

6 Pour in the sauce mixture, stir well and bring to a boil. Put the meat back in the wok and add the noodles, pineapple and bean sprouts. Heat through, stirring and tossing. Add the green onions and sesame oil and serve.

350 g pork fillet, trimmed of visible fat and cut into 5 x 1 cm strips

1 tablespoon reduced-salt soy sauce

pepper to taste

2 teaspoons cornstarch

140 g medium egg noodles

2 tablespoons sunflower oil

8 baby corn, about 80 g in total, quartered lengthwise

1 large carrot, cut into matchstick strips

1 large garlic clove, finely chopped

1 tablespoon finely diced fresh ginger

300 g bean sprouts

4 green onions, sliced diagonally

1 teaspoon sesame oil

SWEET AND SOUR SAUCE

1 tablespoon cornstarch

1 tablespoon light brown sugar

1 tablespoon rice wine vinegar

2 tablespoons rice wine or dry sherry

2 tablespoons tomato ketchup

4 tablespoons reduced-salt soy sauce

1 can (398 ml) pineapple slices in natural juice, drained and chopped, with juice reserved

Normandy pork with apples, celery and walnuts

Fresh and fruity, this casserole comes from northwestern France, where cider apples grow in profusion. A dish of rice is cooked in the oven at the same time, making this a very simple meal to prepare. Serve with green vegetables.

2 tablespoons sunflower oil

500 g pork fillet, trimmed of visible fat and cut into cubes

8 celery stalks, cut across into 5 cm lengths, leaves reserved and chopped

1 onion, roughly chopped

1¾ cups dry cider or apple juice

1 bay leaf

pepper to taste

1½ cups long-grain rice

4 cups boiling reduced-salt chicken stock

3 crisp dessert apples, preferably red-skinned

¾ cup broken walnuts

1 Preheat the oven to 325°F (160°C). Heat the oil in a flameproof casserole dish, add the pork and fry, stirring frequently, for 5 minutes or until browned on all sides. Add the celery and onion and fry gently for about 10 minutes or until softened.

2 Pour in the cider or apple juice and add the bay leaf. Season with pepper. Bring to a boil, then cover the casserole and transfer to the oven. Cook the casserole for 1¼ hours or until the pork is tender.

3 About 40 minutes before the pork is ready, place the rice in an ovenproof dish and pour over the boiling stock. Stir well, then cover and place in the oven to cook with the pork.

4 About 25 minutes before the end of the cooking time, quarter and core the apples but do not peel them. Slice the quarters thickly, then add to the pork and continue cooking.

5 Meanwhile, heat a small frying pan over medium heat, add the walnuts and cook, stirring, until lightly toasted. When the pork is tender, stir in the walnuts and taste for pepper. Garnish with the chopped celery leaves and serve hot, with the rice.

Variation Add 1 chopped garlic clove and 1 teaspoon chopped fresh ginger to the onion and use freshly squeezed orange juice instead of the fresh apple cider or apple juice. Replace the apple slices with the segments of 2 oranges, adding them 10 minutes before the end of the cooking time. Garnish the casserole with shreds of orange rind. Cook the rice in a mixture of orange juice and vegetable stock.

 Fb

preparation time **15 mins**

cooking time **1½ hours**

serves **4**

PER SERVING

855 calories

52 g protein

31 g total fat
4 g saturated fat

160 mg cholesterol

85 g total carbohydrate
22 g sugars

6 g fibre

808 mg sodium

HEART SUPERFOOD

Some studies indicate that a small quantity of walnuts eaten regularly can help to reduce high blood cholesterol levels. Walnuts may also guard against cardiovascular disease and cancer because of the antioxidants they contain: selenium, zinc, copper and vitamin E.

stir-fried pork with Chinese greens

 Stir-fries do not have to be complicated, with numerous ingredients, as this simple recipe shows. Here strips of pork fillet are marinated then stir-fried with green vegetables. Egg noodles make the perfect accompaniment.

preparation time **10 mins**
cooking time **10 mins**
serves **4**

PER SERVING

546 calories

37 g protein

15 g total fat
3 g saturated fat

97 mg cholesterol

56 g total carbohydrate
4 g sugars

7 g fibre

287 mg sodium

HEALTH HINT

Bok choy, a variety of Chinese cabbage or greens, has broad white stalks topped with large, dark green leaves. Like other dark green, leafy vegetables, it is a particularly good source of folate, a B vitamin that may help to protect against heart disease.

300 g pork fillet, trimmed of visible fat
4 tablespoons dry sherry
4 teaspoons sesame oil
1 tablespoon reduced-salt soy sauce
1 bunch green onions, about 170 g
200 g snow peas
350 g bok choy
250 g medium Chinese egg noodles
1 tablespoon peanut oil

1 Cut the pork across into 5 mm slices, then cut each slice into 5 mm strips. Place in a bowl with sherry, 1 teaspoon sesame oil and soy sauce. Toss to mix well, then set aside to marinate while preparing the vegetables.

2 Cut the green onions in half across, then into shreds lengthwise. Halve the snow peas lengthwise. Trim the bok choy and tear it into large bite-sized pieces.

3 Bring a large pan of water to a boil. Add the egg noodles and cook, according to the package instructions.

4 Meanwhile, heat a wok or large frying pan until hot, then add the peanut oil. Add the pork, reserving the marinade, and stir-fry over high heat for 3 minutes or until the meat is lightly browned and tender. Remove from the wok and set aside.

5 Add the snow peas to the wok and stir-fry for 30 seconds, then add the green onions and bok choy and stir-fry for another minute. Return the pork to the wok, together with the reserved marinade, and stir-fry all together for another 1–2 minutes or until everything is piping hot. The bok choy should have wilted, but still be a bit crisp.

6 Drain the noodles well and toss with the remaining sesame oil. Spoon onto warmed serving plates. Divide the stir-fried pork and greens among the plates and serve.

cidered pork stew with herb dumplings

 A spoonful of mustard peps up this simple, vegetable-rich pork stew. Fluffy dumplings served on top help to mop up every bit of the full-flavoured sauce, and turn the stew into a well-balanced meal in a bowl.

Fb

preparation time **30 mins**
cooking time **1½ hours**
serves **4**

PER SERVING

543 calories

37 g protein

16 g total fat
3 g saturated fat

119 mg cholesterol

58 g total carbohydrate
11 g sugars

9 g fibre

714 mg sodium

HEALTH HINT

Turnip is a member of the cruciferous family of vegetables. It is rich in cancer-fighting phytochemicals and a useful source of vitamin C and beta carotene.

1 Heat the oil in a flameproof casserole dish and add the pork. Cook over high heat for 10 minutes or until browned, stirring frequently. Use a slotted spoon to transfer the meat to a plate.

2 Reduce the heat to medium and add the carrots, celery, leeks, bay leaves and sage. Cook for 5 minutes, stirring often, until the leeks are softened. Pour in the cider and stock. Return the pork to the casserole with any juices. Add the mustard and mix well.

3 Bring to a boil, then reduce the heat to low and cover. Simmer gently for 45 minutes. Stir in the potatoes and turnip. Bring back to simmering point, cover again and cook over low heat for 30 minutes or until the pork and vegetables are cooked.

4 Meanwhile, for the dumplings, mix the breadcrumbs, flour, baking powder, chives and parsley in a bowl. Make a well in the centre and add the egg, milk and oil. Mix the liquids together, then gradually stir in the dry ingredients to make a dough.

5 Bring a pan of water to a boil. Dust your hands with flour, then divide the dumpling mixture into 12 portions and roll each one into a round dumpling. Add the dumplings to the water, adjust the heat so that they simmer gently and cook for about 10 minutes or until risen and firm.

6 Use a slotted spoon to lift the dumplings out of the water, shaking gently to drain them well, and arrange them on top of the casserole. Serve at once.

1 tablespoon extra virgin olive oil

450 g lean boneless pork, cut into 2 cm chunks

2 carrots, cut into 1 cm cubes

2 celery stalks, sliced

2 leeks, sliced

2 bay leaves

2 tablespoons finely shredded fresh sage or 1 teaspoon dried sage

1¼ cups dry cider

1¼ cups reduced-salt chicken stock

1 tablespoon Dijon mustard

670 g potatoes, peeled and cut into 1 cm cubes

220 g turnip, cut into 1 cm cubes

FRESH HERB DUMPLINGS

100 g fresh whole-wheat breadcrumbs

½ cup self-raising flour

½ teaspoon baking powder

4 tablespoons snipped fresh chives

4 tablespoons chopped parsley

1 egg, lightly beaten

4 tablespoons low-fat milk

1 tablespoon sunflower oil

quick Hungarian goulash

This short-cut version of classic Hungarian goulash is rich and delicious. Strips of lean pork, shredded red cabbage and green pepper cook quickly and taste excellent with the traditional flavourings of paprika and caraway seeds.

2 tablespoons extra virgin olive oil

1 large onion, finely chopped

2 garlic cloves, crushed

300 g thick lean pork loin steaks, cut into thin strips

1 tablespoon all-purpose flour

¾ cup reduced-salt chicken stock

½ cup dry white vermouth

2 tablespoons paprika

1 teaspoon caraway seeds

1 teaspoon caster (superfine) sugar

1 large can (796 ml) tomatoes, drained

1 large green pepper, seeded and chopped

200 g red cabbage, finely shredded

pepper to taste

4 tablespoons Greek-style yogourt to serve

paprika to serve

fresh chives to serve

1 Heat the oil in a large frying pan or saucepan. Add the onion, garlic and pork, and cook over high heat for about 3 minutes or until the meat has changed colour and become firm and the onion is slightly softened. Meanwhile, blend the flour with 5 tablespoons of the chicken stock to make a smooth paste; set aside.

2 Add the vermouth, paprika, caraway seeds and sugar to the pan and stir, then add the tomatoes, breaking them up as you mix them in. Stir in the remaining stock, and the flour and stock mixture. Bring to a boil, stirring, and cook until the juices thicken.

3 Stir in the pepper and red cabbage until both are thoroughly coated in the cooking juices. Reduce the heat, cover the pan and simmer for about 15 minutes or until the meat is cooked and the vegetables are just tender, but still slightly crisp.

4 Taste the goulash and season with pepper. Ladle into bowls and top each portion with a spoonful of Greek-style yogourt and a sprinkling of paprika. Garnish with chives and serve.

preparation time **10 mins**

cooking time **25 mins**

serves **4**

PER SERVING

319 calories

21 g protein

15 g total fat
4 g saturated fat

50 mg cholesterol

18 g total carbohydrate
14 g sugars

6 g fibre

195 mg sodium

HEART SUPERFOOD

Studies have shown that eating garlic can reduce the risk of heart attack and stroke by making the blood less sticky and likely to clot. Garlic can also help to reduce high blood pressure.

preparation time **5 mins**

cooking time **50 mins**

serves **4**

PER SERVING

218 calories

38 g protein

5 g total fat
1 g saturated fat

135 mg cholesterol

3 g total carbohydrate
1 g sugars

1 g fibre

252 mg sodium

HEALTH HINT

Compared with many beef and lamb cuts, veal is lower in both fat and saturated fat. It's also a good source of two B vitamins, niacin and riboflavin, which both aid in metabolizing fat. Studies show that niacin plays a part in lowering cholesterol levels, and that riboflavin, as its coenzyme, supports niacin in this role.

veal steaks with lemon-garlic sauce

There's a whole bulb of garlic in this recipe, but after slow-roasting it comes out of the oven tasting mild and sweet. Serve the veal with lightly steamed asparagus and boiled new potatoes sprinkled with chopped parsley.

1 Preheat the oven to 375°F (190°C). Wrap the garlic in foil and bake until tender (the package will feel soft when pressed), about 45 minutes. When cool enough to handle, cut the top off the bulb of garlic, squeeze out the garlic pulp into a small bowl, and mash until smooth.

2 Preheat the broiler. Brush the veal with mustard. Top each steak with 3 lemon slices. Broil the veal about 8 cm away from the heat until cooked through, about 2 minutes. Transfer the veal to a platter and cover loosely with foil to keep warm.

3 In a small saucepan, whisk the stock and lemon juice into the cornstarch. Add the roasted garlic. Bring to a boil over medium heat and boil until the sauce is slightly thickened, about 1 minute. Spoon the sauce over the veal and serve.

1 bulb garlic

4 veal steaks, about 120 g each

1 tablespoon Dijon mustard

1 lemon, very thinly sliced

²/₃ cup reduced-salt chicken stock

¼ cup freshly squeezed lemon juice

2 teaspoons cornstarch

veal escalopes with herbs

 In this light summery dish, ultra-thin, tender veal escalopes are quickly fried, and the pan is then deglazed with wine to make a sauce. New potatoes and spinach make the perfect accompaniments.

1 kg small new potatoes, washed

4 veal steaks, about 125 g each, pounded until 5 mm thick

2 tablespoons all-purpose flour

pepper to taste

2 tablespoons extra virgin olive oil

3 tablespoons reduced-salt margarine

400 g baby spinach

grated rind and juice of 1 lemon

pepper to taste

1/3 cup dry white wine

5 tablespoons chopped mixed fresh herbs, such as parsley, chervil, chives and tarragon

lemon wedges to serve

1 First cook the potatoes. Place them in a large saucepan of boiling water and boil for 15 minutes or until tender.

2 Meanwhile, pat the veal dry with paper towel. Season the flour with a little pepper, then toss the veal in the flour to coat it lightly and evenly all over. Shake off any excess flour.

3 Heat half the oil in a large nonstick frying pan over medium heat. Add half the margarine and heat until it starts to foam, then add the veal. Fry for 2–3 minutes on each side or until the juices run clear. Remove the veal from the pan, place on a warmed serving dish and keep hot.

4 Drain the potatoes in a colander. Add the remaining oil to the hot saucepan in which you cooked the potatoes and set over low heat. Add the potatoes and toss gently until they are coated with oil. Add the spinach to the pan in 4 batches, gently tossing and stirring so that it wilts in the heat from the potatoes. Add the lemon juice and season with pepper. Stir gently to mix. Cover and keep warm while you make the sauce.

5 Return the frying pan to the heat and add the white wine. Increase the heat so the liquid bubbles, then stir vigorously to dislodge any bits of sediment in the bottom of the pan. Boil for 1 minute or until reduced and syrupy. Remove the pan from the heat and add the rest of the margarine. Stir until it has melted. Scatter the mixed herbs over the veal, then drizzle with the wine sauce. Sprinkle the lemon rind over the potatoes and spinach. Serve the vegetables alongside the veal, with lemon wedges for squeezing.

 Fb

preparation time **15 mins**

cooking time **25 mins**

serves **4**

PER SERVING

563 calories

46 g protein

25 g total fat
4 g saturated fat

135 mg cholesterol

38 g total carbohydrate
2 g sugars

7 g fibre

212 mg sodium

HEALTH HINT

This dish is especially rich in B vitamins. There is B_6 in the veal and the new potatoes, and B vitamins niacin and B_{12} in the veal. The veal, spinach and new potatoes together provide an excellent source of folate.

veal Marsala

This dish is elegant enough to serve at a dinner party, yet easy enough for everyday cooking. Lean veal is cooked with Marsala, and mushrooms are added for flavour but no additional fat. Serve on a bed of orzo or other small pasta.

1 Preheat the oven to 265°F (130°C). Place a baking sheet on the middle rack of the oven. Trim the ends off the mushrooms and thinly slice the mushrooms. Set aside.

2 Place the veal between pieces of parchment paper and pound with a meat mallet until 2 mm thick. Sprinkle with pepper. Place the flour in a sealable plastic bag. Add the veal, a few slices at a time, and shake to coat.

3 Coat a large nonstick frying pan with nonstick cooking spray and set over high heat. Melt 1 piece margarine in the pan. Sauté a few pieces of the veal at a time until browned, about 1 minute on each side, turning only once (do not crowd the pan). Transfer the veal to the baking sheet in the oven. Repeat with the remaining veal, adding margarine as needed.

4 Sauté the mushrooms in the frying pan until golden, about 3 minutes. Pour in the Marsala, scraping up any browned bits left in the pan. Cook until the pan juices are reduced to ½ cup, about 2 minutes. Return the veal to the pan, stacking if necessary. Turn to coat with the pan juices. Sprinkle with parsley and serve immediately while still hot.

12 large white mushrooms

500 g veal steaks

½ teaspoon pepper

¼ cup all-purpose flour

2 tablespoons reduced-salt margarine, cut into 4 pieces

¾ cup dry Marsala wine

4 tablespoons chopped Italian parsley

preparation time **10 mins**
cooking time **10 mins**
serves **4**

PER SERVING

369 calories

40 g protein

14 g total fat
3 g saturated fat

136 mg cholesterol

9 g total carbohydrate
2 g sugars

2 g fibre

161 mg sodium

COOK'S TIP

To save on your grocery bill, you can substitute equal amounts of chicken breasts for the more expensive veal.

vegetable dishes & salads

crunchy nut coleslaw

This fresh-tasting coleslaw is made with white cabbage, carrot and radishes, flecked with green onions, sultanas and peanuts.

200 g white cabbage, finely shredded

1 large carrot, coarsely grated

⅓ cup sultanas

4 green onions, finely chopped, with the white and green parts kept separate

2 tablespoons low-fat mayonnaise

150 g plain low-fat yogourt

pepper to taste

30 g radishes, sliced

⅓ cup unsalted roasted peanuts

4 tablespoons chopped parsley or snipped fresh chives, or a mixture of the two (optional)

1 Mix together the cabbage, carrot, sultanas and white parts of the green onions in a large bowl.

2 Stir the mayonnaise and yogourt together and season with pepper. Stir this dressing into the cabbage mixture and toss well to coat all the ingredients.

3 Just before serving, stir in the radishes and peanuts and sprinkle with the chopped green parts of the green onions and the parsley or chives, if using.

Variation For a celeriac coleslaw, use 250 g peeled celeriac cut into matchstick strips, instead of white cabbage. Flavour the yogourt and mayonnaise dressing with 2 teaspoons whole-grain mustard, or 1 teaspoon Dijon mustard and 1 tablespoon mango chutney.

preparation time **10 mins**

serves **4**

PER SERVING

166 calories

7 g protein

7 g total fat
1 g saturated fat

2 mg cholesterol

20 g total carbohydrate
18 g sugars

5 g fibre

165 mg sodium

apple and sprout salad

The dressing for this vibrant salad, with tones of ginger, complements the flavours of the sprouts, apple and vegetables.

1 carrot

1 celery stalk

1 red-skinned dessert apple

1 cup mung bean sprouts

¾ cup alfalfa sprouts

½ cup sunflower kernels

ORIENTAL DRESSING

1 tablespoon lime juice

1 tablespoon finely chopped coriander

2 tablespoons sunflower oil

½ teaspoon sesame oil

½ teaspoon reduced-salt soy sauce

1 teaspoon grated fresh ginger

pepper to taste

1 Cut the carrot into 4 cm lengths. Slice thinly lengthwise, then cut into very fine matchsticks. Cut the celery into matchsticks the same size. Core the apple and cut into 8 wedges, then thinly slice the wedges crosswise to make fan-shaped pieces.

2 Combine the carrot, celery, apple, mung bean sprouts, alfalfa sprouts and sunflower kernels in a mixing bowl.

3 To make the dressing, whisk together all the ingredients, seasoning with pepper. Pour the dressing over the salad, toss well to coat evenly and serve.

Variation For a more substantial salad to serve as a light main dish, you can replace the mung bean sprouts with sprouted green or brown lentils, and stir in 100 g diced tofu.

preparation time **15 mins**

serves **4**

PER SERVING

222 calories

6 g protein

20 g total fat
2 g saturated fat

0 mg cholesterol

6 g total carbohydrate
6 g sugars

4 g fibre

43 mg sodium

HEALTH HINT

Sprouted beans and seeds are a good source of vitamin C and folate, as well as phytochemicals including lutein, coumarins and xanthophylls.

garlicky tomato salad

When tomatoes are at their peak of sweetness, this salad is particularly delicious. It's eye-catching, too, if you make it with a mixture of different-coloured tomatoes—new varieties are coming on the market all the time.

1 To make the garlic vinaigrette, whisk together the garlic, vinegar, oil and pepper in a small mixing bowl.

2 Place a layer of lettuce leaves on a serving platter or on 4 plates and arrange the sliced tomatoes and then the cherry tomatoes on top. Drizzle over the vinaigrette.

3 Scatter the basil leaves and the pumpkin and sunflower seeds over the tomatoes, and serve at once.

Variation Try a salad of cherry tomatoes and sugar snap peas. Trim 250 g sugar snap peas and steam for about 3 minutes or until tender but still crisp. Refresh under cold running water, then cool. Mix with 370 g cherry tomatoes, halved if large, and 6 thinly sliced green onions. Make the garlic vinaigrette as in the main recipe and drizzle it over the tomatoes and peas. Add 4 tablespoons chopped fresh mint, or 1 tablespoon each chopped fresh tarragon and parsley, and toss to mix.

1 large leaf lettuce, large leaves torn into smaller pieces

4 large or 6 small ripe Italian tomatoes, about 500 g in total, sliced

2 cups cherry tomatoes, halved

16 fresh basil leaves

2 tablespoons toasted pumpkin seeds

2 tablespoons toasted sunflower seeds

GARLIC VINAIGRETTE

1 small garlic clove, finely chopped

1½ teaspoons red wine vinegar

2 tablespoons extra virgin olive oil

pepper to taste

preparation time **10 mins**

serves **4**

PER SERVING

164 calories

4 g protein

14 g total fat
2 g saturated fat

0 mg cholesterol

5 g total carbohydrate
4 g sugars

5 g fibre

22 mg sodium

HEALTH HINT

Tomatoes are a rich source of vitamin C, an important nutrient for maintaining immunity and healthy skin. The vitamin C is concentrated in the jelly-like substance surrounding the seeds.

new potato salad

A potato salad with a creamy dressing is always a winner, and the version here, with cucumber, green onions and fresh herbs, is sure to become a firm favourite. Potatoes are full of goodness, particularly if the skins are left on.

900 g tiny new potatoes, washed

2 tablespoons dry white vermouth
    or dry white wine

1 teaspoon white wine vinegar,
    or to taste

pepper to taste

1 garlic clove, finely chopped

4 tablespoons low-fat mayonnaise

6 tablespoons plain low-fat yogourt

½ large firm cucumber, diced

80 g green onions, thinly sliced

4 tablespoons chopped fresh dill

2 tablespoons chopped fresh tarragon

fresh dill and tarragon leaves
    to garnish

1 Cook the potatoes in a saucepan of boiling water for about 10 minutes or until they are just tender. Drain and return them to the pan. Set over a low heat and shake them around for a few minutes to evaporate any moisture. Transfer the potatoes to a mixing bowl and leave to cool for about 5 minutes.

2 Sprinkle the vermouth or wine and wine vinegar over the potatoes. Season with pepper. Turn the potatoes to mix, then leave to cool completely.

3 Meanwhile, mix together the garlic, mayonnaise and yogourt in a small bowl until smooth.

4 When the potatoes are cool, add the cucumber, green onions, dill and tarragon. Spoon on the mayonnaise and yogourt mixture, and stir gently to mix everything together. Serve at room temperature or chilled, garnished with dill and tarragon leaves.

preparation time **15 mins**

cooking time **25 mins**
plus cooling

serves **4**

PER SERVING

200 calories

8 g protein

1 g total fat
0.1 g saturated fat

1 mg cholesterol

37 g total carbohydrate
8 g sugars

5 g fibre

204 mg sodium

HEALTH HINT

Using herbs in a salad helps to reduce the need for salt. Our taste for salt is something we develop the more we eat it. If you gradually reduce the amount of salt you use, your palate adapts as the salt receptors on the tongue become more sensitive to salt. The process takes about 4 weeks.

rustic broiled vegetable and rigatoni salad

Broiled vegetables are delicious with chunky pasta in a tangy dressing. Serve this salad as a light lunch or as an accompaniment to broiled poultry or meat, when it will serve 6 or 8 people.

preparation time **15 mins**

cooking time **20 mins**
plus 30 mins marinating

serves **4**

PER SERVING

356 calories

13 g protein

18 g total fat
4 g saturated fat

7 mg cholesterol

36 g total carbohydrate
7 g sugars

8 g fibre

160 mg sodium

HEALTH HINTS

Broiling or baking is a healthy cooking method for vegetables like eggplants, which can absorb large amounts of fat when they are fried.

Adding a little Parmesan cheese to pasta dishes contributes useful calcium as well as a wonderful cheesy flavour.

1 Cook the rigatoni in boiling water for 10–12 minutes, or according to the package instructions, until al dente. Drain the pasta and rinse under cold running water, then drain again thoroughly and set aside to cool.

2 Meanwhile, broil the pepper halves, skin side up, until blistered and blackened. Place in a plastic bag, then leave until cool enough to handle.

3 Broil the onion and eggplant for about 2 minutes or until slightly charred. Turn them over so that they cook evenly. Add the zucchini, mushrooms and tomatoes to the broiler, and broil all the vegetables for a further 2–3 minutes. Remove the pieces as they are ready. Place them in a large salad bowl.

4 Cut the eggplant slices into 2 cm strips. Peel the pepper and cut into 2 cm strips. Add the eggplant and pepper strips to the salad bowl, with the arugula. Mix in the pasta.

5 To make the dressing, mix the balsamic vinegar or lemon juice with the olive oil, basil, capers, garlic, if using, and pepper in a small bowl. Lightly toss this dressing into the salad. Sprinkle with shavings of Parmesan cheese and serve.

200 g rigatoni or penne

1 large red pepper, seeded and halved

½ red onion, thickly sliced

1 eggplant, trimmed and sliced lengthwise

1 zucchini, thickly sliced

150 g button mushrooms, halved

200 g cherry tomatoes

80 g arugula

2½ tablespoons shaved Parmesan cheese

DRESSING

2 tablespoons balsamic vinegar or lemon juice

4 tablespoons extra virgin olive oil

2 tablespoons shredded fresh basil

1 tablespoon chopped capers

1 large garlic clove, crushed (optional)

pepper to taste

fruity pasta salad

Pineapple and pear give this salad a sweet accent, while balsamic vinegar adds a delightful piquancy. With lean ham, cheese, fruit and vegetables all adding their own nutrients to balance the pasta, the result is a marvellous dish.

1 Top and tail the green beans. Dice the ham or cut it into fine strips, if you prefer. Peel, core and dice the pear.

2 Cook the mixed pasta shapes in boiling water for approximately 10–12 minutes, or according to the package instructions, until al dente. Drain and rinse the pasta in cold water, then drain again.

3 Cook the beans in boiling water for about 3 minutes or until bright green and just tender, but still crisp. Drain and rinse under cold water, then drain again. Set aside.

4 Combine the cooked pasta with the Cheddar cheese, ham, pear, pineapple, onion, mayonnaise, yogourt, gherkin, if using, and sugar. Add a little extra gherkin or sugar, if desired. Mix together well, then adjust the flavour of the dressing with lemon juice, pepper and cayenne pepper, if using.

5 Dress the mixed salad greens with the sunflower oil, if using, the balsamic vinegar and a squeeze of lemon juice. Divide the dressed leaves among 4 plates and top with the pasta mixture.

6 Arrange the green beans, walnuts and dried cranberries, if using, around the salad and serve immediately.

Variations Omit the gherkin and instead season the pasta with a sprinkling of curry powder, stirring it in well. • Sprinkle with cashews instead of walnuts. • Low-fat mayonnaise can be used instead of the traditional type, for extra heart health. • Use 1 can (540 ml) chickpeas, well drained, instead of the ham. • Use 3 slices canned pineapple in natural juice, drained and diced, instead of fresh pineapple.

50 g fine green beans
125 g lean cooked ham
1 pear
350 g mixed coloured pasta shapes
75 g 25% reduced-fat mature Cheddar cheese, grated
100 g peeled fresh pineapple, diced
½ small onion, finely chopped
4 tablespoons mayonnaise
4 tablespoons plain low-fat yogourt
½ teaspoon chopped pickled gherkin, or to taste (optional)
1 teaspoon caster (superfine) sugar, or to taste
juice of ¼ lemon, or to taste
pepper to taste
cayenne pepper (optional)
120 g mixed salad greens, such as arugula, watercress or baby spinach
1 tablespoon sunflower oil (optional)
½ teaspoon balsamic vinegar, or to taste
2 tablespoons coarsely chopped walnuts
2 tablespoons dried cranberries (optional)

preparation time **20 mins**
cooking time **15 mins**
serves **4**

PER SERVING

479 calories

22 g protein

15 g total fat
4 g saturated fat

35 mg cholesterol

64 g total carbohydrate
12 g sugars

6 g fibre

766 mg sodium

HEALTH HINT

Cheese is a good source of protein and a valuable source of calcium, phosphorus, niacin and vitamin B$_{12}$. Using a strongly flavoured cheese, such as mature Cheddar, means that less is required for flavour in the dish, thus keeping the total fat content down.

crispy potatoes

You might think that only deep-frying could make potatoes truly crispy, but we are happy to prove you wrong. These crunchy potato cakes, lightly glazed with fragrant Parmesan cheese, require just 2 teaspoons of oil!

750 g all-purpose potatoes, unpeeled
2 teaspoons olive oil
¾ teaspoon rosemary, finely chopped
¼ teaspoon pepper
¼ cup grated Parmesan cheese

1 Preheat the oven to 475°F (240°C). Spray 2 large baking sheets lightly with nonstick cooking spray. Grate the potatoes in a food processor or with a grater. Transfer the potato mixture to a large bowl. Add the olive oil, chopped rosemary and pepper. Toss the mixture well to coat.

2 Divide the potato mixture into 8 equal portions and spread out 4 large rounds, each about 5 mm thick, on each baking sheet. Bake the potatoes for 20 minutes in the oven.

3 Preheat the broiler. Remove the potatoes from the oven. With a spatula, carefully turn the potatoes over on the baking sheets. Sprinkle them with Parmesan cheese. Broil the potatoes about 8 cm from the heat until the tops are golden-brown and the potatoes are cooked through, about 3 minutes. Serve hot.

preparation time **10 mins**
cooking time **25 mins**
serves **4**

PER SERVING

162 calories

7 g protein

4 g total fat
1 g saturated fat

5 mg cholesterol

24 g total carbohydrate
1 g sugars

4 g fibre

82 mg sodium

HEALTH HINT

Rosemary is rich in flavonoids, which are phytochemicals that may help prevent blood clots.

COOK'S TIP

You can cook the potatoes ahead up to step 2 and refrigerate for up to 8 hours. At serving time, preheat the broiler, sprinkle Parmesan cheese over the potatoes, and broil until golden-brown.

cauliflower with crispy crumbs

The crispy golden topping in this simple side dish is usually made by frying the breadcrumbs in a generous quantity of butter. This version uses a modest portion of olive oil and fresh herbs to flavour the topping.

1 Prepare a saucepan of boiling water with a steamer over the top. Steam the cauliflower for aproximately 15 minutes or until tender but not soft.

2 Meanwhile, to make the topping, heat the olive oil in a nonstick frying pan or saucepan. Add the breadcrumbs and stir well to coat the crumbs as evenly as possible with the oil. Cook over medium heat, stirring often, for about 10 minutes or until the crumbs are well browned and crisp. As the crumbs cook, the oil will seep out of those that absorbed it initially, allowing the rest to become evenly crisp.

3 Transfer the cauliflower to a warm serving dish. Season the crumbs with pepper and mix in the thyme, tarragon and parsley. Sprinkle the crumb mixture over the cauliflower. Garnish with sprigs of herbs, if using, and serve.

1 cauliflower, trimmed and broken into florets

CRISPY CRUMB TOPPING
2 tablespoons extra virgin olive oil
1¼ cups fresh breadcrumbs
pepper to taste
1 tablespoon chopped fresh thyme
1 tablespoon chopped fresh tarragon
2 tablespoons chopped parsley
sprigs fresh herbs to garnish (optional)

preparation time **5 mins**
cooking time **15 mins**
serves **4**

PER SERVING

166 calories	
4 g protein	
10 g total fat	
1 g saturated fat	
0 mg cholesterol	
15 g total carbohydrate	
2 g sugars	
2 g fibre	
144 mg sodium	

HEALTH HINT

Cauliflower is a member of the brassica family of cruciferous vegetables. It contains sulphurous compounds thought to help protect against cancer. It also provides vitamin C and fibre.

butternut squash gratin

Hiding inside a butternut squash's skin is dense, mildly sweet orange flesh that's an excellent source of disease-battling beta carotene. A big butternut can be a bit tricky to cut up; you'll do best with a large, sturdy chef's knife.

1 butternut squash, about 1 kg, halved crosswise, then lengthwise, seeded and peeled

1 medium red onion, halved and thinly sliced

1½ cups frozen corn kernels, thawed

2¼ teaspoons extra virgin olive oil

⅓ cup grated Parmesan cheese

1 Preheat the oven to 400°F (200°C). Quarter the butternut squash pieces lengthwise and then cut each piece crosswise into 1 cm thick chunks. Combine the squash, onion, corn and oil in a large bowl, tossing to coat.

2 Arrange the vegetables in a 30 x 20 cm (13 x 9 in.) baking dish. Bake until the butternut squash is tender, about 40 minutes, stirring halfway through cooking time.

3 Sprinkle the Parmesan cheese over the vegetables and bake until melted and golden, about 5 minutes.

Variation For an unusual pasta dish, prepare and bake the vegetables as in steps 1 and 2 above. Chop the vegetables and stir into them a good-quality bottled tomato pasta sauce. Toss the sauce with hot cooked pasta.

preparation time **15 mins**

cooking time **45 mins**

serves **4**

PER SERVING

219 calories

10 g protein

6 g total fat
3 g saturated fat

7 mg cholesterol

30 g total carbohydrate
13 g sugars

5 g fibre

112 mg sodium

HEALTH HINT

Both butternut squash and corn contain soluble fibre, which may help reduce LDL ("bad") cholesterol by blocking its absorption into the body.

snow peas with apples and ginger

Slices of firm apple, briefly stir-fried, have the same crunch as water chestnuts, so they partner well with crisp, fresh snow peas.

1 Heat the oil in a large nonstick frying pan over low heat. Add the ginger and garlic and cook until tender, about 2 minutes.

2 Add the snow peas and apples to the frying pan and cook, stirring frequently, until the peas are crisp-tender, about 7 minutes. Serve.

Variation For an unusual main-dish salad, fold the cooled snow pea and apple combination into a big bowl of slightly chilled cooked rice along with cubes of cooked chicken breast or pork fillet.

2 teaspoons extra virgin olive oil

2 tablespoons finely peeled, slivered fresh ginger

3 cloves garlic, finely chopped

500 g snow peas, strings removed

2 crisp red-skinned apples, unpeeled, cut into thin wedges

lemony sugar snap peas

The very essence of summer, emerald-green sugar snaps are so tender you can eat them pods and all. These sweetest of peas shine in a simple stir-fry accented with shallots, garlic and lemon rind.

1 Remove the strings from both sides of the sugar snap peas.

2 Heat the oil in a large nonstick frying pan over medium heat. Add the shallots and garlic and cook, stirring, until the shallots are softened, about 3 minutes.

3 Add the peas and lemon rind to the pan and cook, stirring, until the peas are just tender, about 4 minutes, and serve.

750 g sugar snap peas

2 teaspoons extra virgin olive oil

3 shallots, thinly sliced

1 clove garlic, finely chopped

1 tablespoon grated lemon rind

spiced couscous tomatoes

Choose ripe, well-flavoured tomatoes for this dish. Hollowed out, tomatoes make the perfect container for a spicy eggplant, dried apricot and nut couscous. Serve the stuffed tomatoes with sesame breadsticks.

8 large tomatoes, about 170 g each
2 tablespoons extra virgin olive oil
50 g flaked almonds
1 small eggplant, diced 1 cm thick
1 teaspoon ground coriander
$\frac{1}{2}$ teaspoon ground cumin
$\frac{1}{8}$ teaspoon ground cinnamon
1 cup boiling reduced-salt
    vegetable stock
125 g couscous
2 tablespoons chopped fresh mint
50 g dried apricots, chopped
1 teaspoon harissa (chili paste)
pepper to taste

1 Cut the tops off the tomatoes and scoop out the insides. Place the tomatoes and cut-off tops on one side. Place the seeds and scooped-out flesh in a sieve set over a small bowl and press with the back of a spoon to extract the juices; you will need about 5 tablespoons juice. Leave the bowl of juice on one side and discard the seeds and flesh.

2 Place the hollowed-out tomatoes upside-down on a plate covered with paper towel and leave to drain.

3 Heat $\frac{1}{2}$ tablespoon olive oil in a nonstick saucepan. Add the flaked almonds and cook over low heat for 2–3 minutes or until golden-brown. Remove from the pan with a slotted spoon and set aside.

4 Add the remaining oil to the saucepan. Stir in the eggplant and cook for 5 minutes, turning frequently, until browned and tender. Stir in the coriander, cumin and cinnamon, and cook for a few more seconds, stirring constantly.

5 Pour in the stock and bring to a rapid boil, then add the couscous in a steady stream, stirring constantly. Remove from the heat, cover, and leave to stand for 5 minutes.

6 Uncover the pan, return to low heat and cook for 2–3 minutes, stirring with a fork to separate the couscous grains. Stir in the toasted almonds, mint and dried apricots. Add the harissa to the reserved tomato juices and stir to mix, then pour over the couscous. Add pepper and mix well. Spoon the couscous mixture into the tomatoes, replace the tops and serve.

preparation time **20 mins**
cooking time **15 mins**
plus 5 mins standing
serves **4**

PER SERVING

263 calories

9 g protein

15 g total fat
1 g saturated fat

0 mg cholesterol

23 g total carbohydrate
17 g sugars

9 g fibre

290 mg sodium

HEALTH HINT

Couscous is low in fat and high in starchy carbohydrates and fibre. It has a moderate score on the Glycemic Index, which means that it is digested and absorbed relatively slowly, releasing glucose gradually into the blood stream. This helps to keep blood sugar levels steady.

three-vegetable mash

Here's a chef-worthy accompaniment you can do yourself. These vivid vegetables are all based on mashed potatoes tinted and flavoured three different ways—with health-giving sweet potatoes, spinach and beets.

1 Preheat the oven to 375°F (190°C). Wrap the sweet potato chunks in a large pocket of heavy-duty foil. Combine the all-purpose potatoes, garlic and ¼ cup water in a roasting pan, tossing to coat. Cover the pan with foil. Place the roasting pan and the sweet potato pocket in the oven and bake until both types of potato are tender, about 45 minutes.

2 Transfer the all-purpose potatoes and the garlic to a large bowl. Add the sour cream and coarsely mash with a potato masher. Divide the potato mixture among 3 medium bowls.

3 Add the spinach, lemon rind and marjoram to one bowl of potatoes and coarsely mash together.

4 Drain the beets, reserving 1 tablespoon liquid. Add the beets, reserved liquid, orange rind and coriander to another bowl of potatoes and coarsely mash together.

5 Add the sweet potato, ginger and cayenne pepper to a third bowl and coarsely mash together. Serve.

370 g sweet potatoes, peeled and cut into large chunks

1.25 kg all-purpose potatoes, peeled and cut into large chunks

8 cloves garlic, peeled

½ cup reduced-fat sour cream

300 g frozen chopped spinach, thawed and drained

1 teaspoon grated lemon rind

½ teaspoon marjoram

1 can (398 ml) sliced beets

1 teaspoon grated orange rind

¼ teaspoon ground coriander

½ teaspoon ground ginger

¼ teaspoon cayenne pepper

preparation time **25 mins**

cooking time **45 mins**

serves **8**

PER SERVING

211 calories

7 g protein

6 g total fat
3 g saturated fat

15 mg cholesterol

33 g total carbohydrate
9 g sugars

6 g fibre

190 mg sodium

HEALTH HINT

Beets are a good source of cholesterol-lowering fibre as well as phyto-chemicals, such as saponins, which show potential for reducing the risk of heart disease. Also high in folate, just 1 cup of beets provides about one-third of the daily requirement for this cardioprotective B vitamin.

roast root vegetables with herbs

Use this recipe as a basic guide for roasting single vegetables, such as potatoes or parsnips, as well as for a superb dish of mixed root vegetables. Serve them in generous quantities with roast poultry or meat.

1 kg mixed root vegetables, such as potatoes, sweet potatoes, carrots, parsnips, turnip and kohlrabi

220 g shallots or pickling onions

2 tablespoons extra virgin olive oil

1 teaspoon cracked black peppercorns

few sprigs fresh thyme

few sprigs fresh rosemary

sprigs fresh thyme or rosemary to garnish (optional)

1 Preheat the oven to 425°F (220°C). Wash or peel the root vegetables, according to their type and your taste. Halve or quarter large potatoes. Cut large carrots or parsnips in half lengthwise, then cut the pieces across in half again. Cut sweet potato, turnip or kohlrabi into large chunks (about the same size as the potatoes). Leave shallots or pickling onions whole.

2 Place all the vegetables in a large saucepan and pour in enough boiling water to cover them. Bring the water back to a boil, then reduce the heat and simmer for 5–7 minutes or until the vegetables are lightly cooked, but not yet tender.

3 Drain the vegetables and place them in a roasting pan. Brush the vegetables with olive oil and sprinkle with cracked black peppercorns. Add the herb sprigs to the pan and place the pan in the oven.

4 Roast for 30–35 minutes or until the vegetables are golden-brown, crisp and tender. Turn the vegetables over halfway through cooking time. Serve hot, garnished with extra sprigs of thyme or rosemary, if desired.

Variations If part of a complete roast meal, the vegetables can be roasted at the same time as a joint of meat or poultry. Allow 45 minutes at 400°F (200°C), or longer at a lower temperature, if necessary. • Baby new vegetables can also be roasted in this dish with delicious results. For example, try new potatoes, carrots and beets. • As well as root vegetables, baby squash and asparagus are also delicious roasted. Sprinkle them with herbs and a little balsamic vinegar or lemon juice.

preparation time **10 mins**

cooking time **40 mins**

serves **4**

PER SERVING

241 calories

6 g protein

10 g total fat
1 g saturated fat

0 mg cholesterol

32 g total carbohydrate
14 g sugars

6 g fibre

103 mg sodium

HEALTH HINT

Combining different root vegetables instead of serving roast potatoes alone provides a good mix of flavours and nutrients, including vitamin C from the potatoes and beta carotene from the carrots. Turnips are part of the brassica family, which offer cancer-fighting phytochemicals.

Boston baked beans

 These oven-baked beans are cooked slowly to create a richly flavoured vegetable dish—a revelation if you've only ever eaten the canned variety. Serve alongside grilled meat, together with potatoes or bread.

220 g dried white navy beans, soaked
    for at least 8 hours
1 tablespoon sunflower oil
5 shallots, finely chopped
2 garlic cloves, crushed
2 celery stalks, finely chopped
1 can (796 ml) diced tomatoes
2 teaspoons dried mixed herbs
2 cups dry cider
pepper to taste
2 tablespoons dark brown sugar
1 tablespoon black treacle
1 teaspoon Dijon mustard
sprigs fresh Italian parsley
    to garnish

1 Drain the soaked beans and rinse under cold running water. Place them in a saucepan, cover with plenty of fresh cold water and bring to a boil. Boil rapidly for 10 minutes, then reduce the heat and simmer for 50–60 minutes or until tender. Drain well and place in a flameproof casserole dish.

2 Preheat the oven to 325°F (160°C). Heat the oil in a saucepan, add the shallots, garlic and celery, and sauté for about 5 minutes or until softened, stirring occasionally.

3 Stir in the canned tomatoes with their juice, the dried herbs, cider and pepper. Cover and bring to a boil, then reduce the heat and simmer for 10 minutes, stirring occasionally.

4 Add the sugar, treacle and mustard to the tomato sauce, and mix. Pour the sauce over the beans and stir to mix. Cover the casserole and bake for 3½ hours, stirring occasionally. Serve the beans hot, garnished with Italian parsley.

Variation Instead of white navy beans, you can substitute other dried beans, such as black-eyed beans or cannellini beans.

C **Fb** **GI**

preparation time **15 min**
cooking time **5 hours**
plus 8 hours soaking
serves **6**

PER SERVING

146 calories

4 g protein

4 g total fat
0.4 g saturated fat

0 mg cholesterol

19 g total carbohydrate
16 g sugars

5 g fibre

61 mg sodium

HEALTH HINT

Treacle is a sticky fluid refined from molasses. Though it is primarily carbohydrate in the form of sugar, black treacle can provide useful amounts of potassium, calcium and iron.

orange-maple sweet potatoes

Try this method of cooking sweet potatoes and you'll discover how subtly delicious they are. Here, they are glossed with an orange-maple glaze. Beta carotene and fibre are the sweet potato's secret weapons against heart disease.

1 Preheat the oven to 450°F (230°C). Place the sweet potatoes and garlic in a medium saucepan. Add enough water to just cover the potatoes. Bring to a boil over medium heat and cook until the potatoes are tender, about 20 minutes.

2 Drain and transfer the sweet potatoes and garlic to a medium bowl. Add pepper and 2 teaspoons oil. With a potato masher, mash the sweet potatoes and garlic until not quite smooth, with some texture remaining.

3 Transfer to a 28 x 18 cm (11 x 7 in.) baking dish. Combine the remaining 2 teaspoons oil, maple syrup and orange rind in a small saucepan and bring to a boil over low heat. Drizzle the mixture over the potatoes. Bake for 25 minutes or until the top is lightly browned. Serve. This recipe can be cooked ahead and refrigerated. Reheat, covered, in a 265°F (130°C) oven.

1 kg sweet potatoes, peeled and thickly sliced
6 cloves garlic, peeled and thinly sliced
½ teaspoon pepper
4 teaspoons extra virgin olive oil
4 tablespoons maple syrup
2 teaspoons grated orange rind

preparation time **10 mins**
cooking time **45 mins**
serves **6**

PER SERVING

162 calories

3 g protein

3 g total fat
0.4 g saturated fat

0 mg cholesterol

30 g total carbohydrate
17 g sugars

4 g fibre

16 mg sodium

HEALTH HINT

Sweet potatoes are a nutritional "super food" because they're bursting with vitamins, minerals and fibre. So don't just think of them for Sunday lunch—find ways to get them into your diet on a regular basis. Sweet potatoes can be sliced and steamed, baked or mashed and they will still maintain their goodness.

sesame stir-fried asparagus and peas

When asparagus is in season, run to the nearest grocery store and buy a big bunch. Cook it quickly and lightly. Stir-frying asparagus, rather than boiling it, preserves the water-soluble vitamins, including folate.

2 teaspoons hulled sesame seeds
750 g asparagus
1 teaspoon extra virgin olive oil
½ cup thinly sliced red onion
1 clove garlic, slivered
1 cup frozen peas

1 Toast the sesame seeds in a small heavy frying pan over low heat, stirring frequently until golden-brown, about 3 minutes. Transfer to a plate to prevent further cooking.

2 Cut the asparagus on the diagonal into 4 cm lengths. Spray a large nonstick frying pan with nonstick cooking spray. Add the oil and heat over medium heat. Add the onion and garlic, and cook, stirring, until the onion is tender, about 5 minutes.

3 Add the asparagus and peas to the pan and cook, stirring frequently, until the asparagus is crisp-tender and the peas are heated through, about 5 minutes.

4 Sprinkle the sesame seeds over the asparagus and peas and toss well to combine, then serve.

preparation time **5 mins**
cooking time **15 mins**
serves **4**

PER SERVING

75 calories

7 g protein

2 g total fat
0.3 g saturated fat

0 mg cholesterol

7 g total carbohydrate
4 g sugars

5 g fibre

7 mg sodium

HEALTH HINT

Six asparagus spears provide remarkable amounts of folate— one-quarter of the day's requirement. This heart-healthy B vitamin is also plentiful in peas. Folate helps to reduce blood levels of homocysteine, a substance linked to increased risk of cardiovascular disease.

baked eggplant with yogourt

In this delicious dish, grilled slices of eggplant and zucchini are layered with a rich tomato sauce and cumin-flavoured yogourt, then baked. Thick slices of multi-grain bread and a crisp green salad are perfect accompaniments.

Fb **GI**

preparation time **15 mins**
cooking time **1½ hours**
serves **4**

PER SERVING

336 calories

17 g protein

21 g total fat
4 g saturated fat

120 mg cholesterol

18 g total carbohydrate
18 g sugars

8 g fibre

256 mg sodium

HEALTH HINT

The normal digestive tract flora can be upset by antibiotics, stress and poor diet. Including yogourt in the diet helps to maintain the "good" bacteria in the gut and prevent the growth of less desirable bacteria.

1 Heat 1½ tablespoons oil in a saucepan, add the onion and cook for about 8 minutes or until softened. Add the garlic and cook for a further minute, stirring. Stir in the diced tomatoes with their juice, the tomato paste, wine and bay leaf. Cover and simmer gently for 10 minutes.

2 Uncover the pan and let the sauce bubble for a further 10 minutes or until thickened, stirring occasionally. Remove the bay leaf. Stir in the parsley and pepper.

3 While the sauce is simmering, preheat the broiler. Lightly brush the eggplant and zucchini slices with the remaining 2½ tablespoons oil. Cook under the broiler, in batches, for 3–4 minutes on each side or until browned and very tender.

4 Preheat the oven to 350°F (180°C). Stir the cumin into half of the yogourt. Arrange one-third of the eggplant slices, in one layer, in a large ovenproof dish with a capacity of about 2.5 litres (2½ quarts). Spoon over half of the tomato sauce. Arrange half of the zucchini slices on top, in one layer, then drizzle with half of the cumin-flavoured yogourt. Repeat the layers, then finish with a layer of the remaining eggplant slices.

5 Mix the remaining 200 g yogourt with the beaten eggs and half of the Parmesan cheese. Spoon the yogourt mixture over the top layer of eggplant, spreading with the back of the spoon to cover evenly. Sprinkle with the remaining Parmesan cheese.

6 Bake for 40–45 minutes or until the top is lightly browned and set, and the sauce is bubbling. Serve hot, in the baking dish.

4 tablespoons extra virgin olive oil
1 red onion, finely chopped
2 garlic cloves, finely chopped
1 can (398 ml) diced tomatoes
2 teaspoons sundried tomato paste
½ cup dry red wine
1 bay leaf
2 tablespoons chopped parsley
pepper to taste
3 small eggplants, about 700 g in total, cut into 1 cm slices
3 zucchinis, about 450 g in total, thinly sliced
½ teaspoon ground cumin
400 g plain low-fat yogourt
2 eggs, beaten
2½ tablespoons freshly grated Parmesan cheese

vegetable tart Provençale

Brimming with the sunny flavours typical of southern France, this delectable tart is perfect for a lunch or light dinner. An easy-to-assemble, herb-scented crust is the perfect partner for heart-healthy fresh vegetables.

2 large onions, sliced
all-purpose flour for dusting
half of one puff pastry package
2 zucchinis
4 tomatoes, cut into 5 mm slices
2 tablespoons freshly grated
    Parmesan cheese

1 Coat a large nonstick frying pan with nonstick cooking spray and set over medium-high heat until hot. Reduce the heat to medium-low and sauté the onions until very soft and golden, 20 minutes. Transfer to a plate.

2 Preheat the oven to 400°F (200°C). Lightly sprinkle a work surface with flour and form the pastry into a 32 x 22 cm (12 x 8 in.) rectangle or 27 cm (10 in.) round. Fold in half and transfer to a 28 x 18 cm (11 x 7 in.) tart pan or a 23 cm (9 in.) round tart pan with a removable bottom. Trim pastry edges.

3 Cut the zucchini on the diagonal into long slices 5 mm thick. Lightly coat the frying pan again with cooking spray and set over medium heat. Sauté the zucchini until golden, about 5–7 minutes.

4 Arrange the zucchini, tomatoes and onions in rows on the pastry, standing them up and overlapping them slightly. Sprinkle with Parmesan cheese. Bake until the crust is golden, about 20 minutes. Serve hot, warm or at room temperature.

preparation time **10 mins**
cooking time **45 mins**
serves **4**

PER SERVING

393 calories
9 g protein
23 g total fat
3 g saturated fat
26 mg cholesterol
38 g total carbohydrate
8 g sugars
5 g fibre
80 mg sodium

HEART SUPERFOOD

Centuries ago, folk healers recommended onions as a heart tonic. Modern science supports this ancient practice. Studies indicate that flavonoids, compounds present in onions, may raise the levels of HDL ("good") cholesterol, thus protecting against the artery-clogging damage of LDL ("bad") cholesterol. These and onion's sulphur compounds can hinder the formation of blood clots, which may further help protect against heart attacks.

millet with spinach and pine nuts

Bright green spinach and orange apricots add rich colour and flavour to this easy-to-make grain and vegetable side dish. Serve it instead of potatoes or rice, with stews and casseroles that have plenty of sauce.

1 Place the millet and dried apricots in a large saucepan and stir in the stock and 1 cup of water. Bring to a boil, then lower the heat. Simmer for 15–20 minutes or until all the liquid has been absorbed and the millet is tender.

2 Meanwhile, toast the pine nuts in a small nonstick frying pan until they are golden-brown and fragrant. Set aside.

3 Add the spinach and lemon juice to the millet and season with pepper. Cover the pan and leave to cook over a very low heat for 4–5 minutes to wilt the spinach. Stir the millet and spinach mixture gently, then spoon into a serving bowl. Scatter the toasted pine nuts on top and serve immediately.

Variation For eggplant with millet and sesame seeds, dice 2 eggplants. Brown eggplant in a frying pan with 2 tablespoons extra virgin olive over high heat. Remove from the heat and stir in 200 g millet, 2½ cups reduced salt vegetable stock and 1 cup water. Return to the heat and bring to a boil. Stir, reduce the heat and simmer for 15–20 minutes or until the liquid has been absorbed and the millet is tender. Season with pepper. Transfer to a serving bowl and scatter over chopped fresh coriander, thinly sliced green onions and toasted sesame seeds.

200 g millet
50 g dried apricots, roughly chopped
2½ cups reduced-salt vegetable stock
60 g pine nuts
250 g baby spinach
juice of ½ lemon
pepper to taste

preparation time **5 mins**
cooking time **25 mins**
serves **4**

PER SERVING

335 calories

9 g protein

13 g total fat
1 g saturated fat

0 mg cholesterol

46 g total carbohydrate
10 g sugars

4 g fibre

673 mg sodium

HEALTH HINT

Millet provides useful amounts of iron and B vitamins and, as it is not highly milled, it retains all its nutritional value. Being gluten-free, it can be an additional source of starchy carbohydrate for celiacs.

pasta with roasted vegetables

Oven-roasted vegetables, tender and scented with garlic, make a chunky dressing that is great with wide pasta noodles. A sprinkling of crunchy sunflower seeds adds texture as well as additional nutritional benefits.

preparation time **20 mins**
cooking time **45 mins**
serves **4**

PER SERVING

521 calories

17 g protein

22 g total fat
3 g saturated fat

0 mg cholesterol

64 g total carbohydrate
13 g sugars

13 g fibre

128 mg sodium

HEALTH HINT

As well as all the benefits from the excellent mixture of vegetables in this dish, the sunflower seeds provide a useful source of zinc, thiamine and niacin, plus plenty of vitamin E.

COOK'S TIP

Pappardelle are wide pasta noodles with straight or rippled sides. Lasagnette are also wide ribbons of pasta with ruffled edges. You could also use bow ties.

1 Preheat the oven to 375°F (190°C). Arrange the eggplant, zucchinis, red and green peppers, tomatoes, red onions and whole garlic cloves in a single layer in a large ovenproof dish or roasting pan. Sprinkle with about 2 tablespoons olive oil, cayenne pepper, half the chopped garlic and pepper.

2 Roast for about 45 minutes or until the vegetables are tender but not soft and mushy, and are charred in places. Turn the vegetables once or twice during cooking, and increase the heat slightly if they are not cooking quickly enough.

3 Meanwhile, toast the sunflower seeds. Lightly brush a frying pan with just a few drops of olive oil, then heat the pan. Add the sunflower seeds and toss and turn them for a few minutes until they begin to toast. Add the soy sauce and turn the seeds quickly, letting the soy sauce evaporate as the seeds toast and brown lightly. This should take about 4–5 minutes in total. Remove from the heat just before the seeds are crisp and leave them to cool in the pan. They will become crisper as they cool.

4 Cook the pasta in boiling water for 10–12 minutes, or according to the package instructions, until al dente. Drain well and keep hot.

5 Cut the roasted vegetables into bite-sized chunks. Toss the vegetables and garlic with the remaining raw chopped garlic, the tomato sauce and basil or parsley.

6 Toss the pasta with the vegetables and serve immediately, sprinkled with the toasted sunflower seeds.

Variations Crush a few saffron threads in a mortar and pestle and add them to the roasted vegetables along with the tomato sauce for an added touch. • You could also serve each portion of roasted vegetable pasta topped with a spoonful of low-fat fresh goat cheese instead of toasted sunflower seeds. • Pumpkin seeds can be used instead of sunflower seeds.

1 eggplant, cut into large chunks

2 zucchinis, cut into large chunks

2 red peppers, quartered and seeded

1 green pepper, quartered and seeded

4 ripe tomatoes, halved

2 red onions, quartered

1 head garlic, cloves separated but unpeeled, plus 2 garlic cloves, chopped

4 tablespoons extra virgin olive oil

cayenne pepper to taste

pepper to taste

1/3 cup sunflower seeds

1 teaspoon reduced-salt soy sauce

350 g wide pasta noodles, such as pappardelle or lasagnette

4 tablespoons tomato sauce, or to taste

1 handful of fresh basil leaves, coarsely chopped if large, or 2 tablespoons chopped parsley

falafel pitas

Falafels, the traditional Middle Eastern bean patties, are usually deep-fried. This updated version, delicately spiced and crunchy with grated carrot, is baked for a lower-fat result, but is just as delicious and is served in pita bread with salad.

1 can (540 ml) chickpeas, drained and rinsed
1 teaspoon extra virgin olive oil
½ teaspoon ground cumin
⅛ teaspoon cayenne pepper
⅛ teaspoon turmeric
1 garlic clove, crushed
1 tablespoon freshly squeezed lemon juice
1 carrot, finely grated
1 tablespoon chopped fresh coriander
pepper to taste
4 whole-wheat pita bread pockets, about 70 g each
½ romaine lettuce, shredded
2 Italian tomatoes, thinly sliced
⅔ cup plain low-fat yogourt
2 tablespoons chopped fresh mint
pepper to taste

1 Preheat the oven to 400°F (200°C). Cover a baking sheet with parchment paper. Place the chickpeas in a bowl with oil and use a potato masher to mash them until smooth. Mix in the cumin, cayenne pepper, turmeric, garlic, lemon juice, carrot, coriander and pepper. Alternatively, mix all the ingredients, except the carrot and coriander, in a food processor. Transfer the mixture to a bowl and stir in the carrot and coriander.

2 Shape the mixture into 16 flat, round patties, each about 3 cm across, and place them on the baking sheet. Bake for 15–20 minutes or until crisp and lightly browned, turning them over halfway through cooking time.

3 About 3 minutes before the falafels have finished cooking, place the pita breads in the oven to warm. Then split the bread in half widthwise and gently open out each half to make a pocket.

4 Half-fill the pita bread pockets with shredded lettuce and sliced tomatoes, then divide the falafels among them. Mix together the yogourt and mint, season with pepper to taste, and drizzle over the falafels. Serve hot.

preparation time **15 mins**
cooking time **20 mins**
serves **4**

PER SERVING

279 calories

13 g protein

4 g total fat
1 g saturated fat

2 mg cholesterol

48 g total carbohydrate
7 g sugars

6 g fibre

469 mg sodium

HEALTH HINT

Chickpeas are an important source of protein in many parts of the world. They also contain useful amounts of fibre, which helps to maintain bowel health.

stir-fried vegetable curry

A selection of ground and whole spices and a hint of coconut flavour the mixed vegetables in this contemporary curry, which is cooked in stages so that all the individual tastes remain distinct and delicious. Serve with boiled rice.

Fb

preparation time **25 mins**

cooking time **1 hour** plus overnight soaking

serves **4**

PER SERVING

323 calories

11 g protein

17 g total fat
3 g saturated fat

0 mg cholesterol

33 g total carbohydrate
13 g sugars

12 g fibre

517 mg sodium

HEALTH HINT

To preserve the vitamins under the skin of potatoes, just wash them rather than peeling them before cooking.

1 Blanch the onions in boiling water for 3 minutes. Drain well and set aside until cool enough to handle, then peel. Set aside.

2 Meanwhile, add the beans to the pan of boiling water and boil rapidly for 10 minutes, then reduce the heat and simmer for 20–25 minutes or until tender. Drain well and set aside.

3 Bring the stock to a boil, add the coconut cream and stir well to mix. Set aside.

4 Using a mortar and pestle, pound the ginger and garlic to a paste. Stir in the ground coriander, garam masala, turmeric and chilies until well blended.

5 Heat a large wok over high heat. Add 2 tablespoons oil. When hot, add the coriander, cumin and mustard seeds. Fry for 30 seconds or until the seeds give off their aroma. Use a slotted spoon to transfer the seeds to paper towel on a plate. Add the remaining oil and the spice paste to the wok. Reduce the heat to medium and stir-fry for 1 minute. Stir in the carrots, parsnips, potatoes and 2 tablespoons water, and stir-fry for 2 minutes.

6 Pour in the coconut stock and bring to a boil, stirring. Reduce the heat to low, cover and simmer for 5 minutes. Add the cauliflower, peas and onions. Cover and simmer for a further 5 minutes, stirring occasionally. Uncover and bring back to a boil, then boil for about 5 minutes or until most of the liquid has evaporated and all of the vegetables are just tender.

7 Add the cabbage, beans and fried spice seeds and stir-fry to wilt the cabbage. Add pepper and serve immediately, sprinkled with chopped fresh coriander, if using.

120 g small pickling onions (unpeeled)

120 g dried mung beans, soaked overnight, drained and rinsed

1¾ cups reduced-salt vegetable stock

¼ cup reduced-fat coconut cream

1 tablespoon finely chopped fresh ginger

1 large garlic clove, crushed

2 tablespoons ground coriander

1 tablespoon garam masala

½ teaspoon turmeric

⅛ teaspoon crushed dried chilies

4 tablespoons sunflower oil

1 teaspoon coriander seeds, crushed

1 teaspoon cumin seeds

1 teaspoon brown mustard seeds

250 g carrots, diced

250 g parsnips, diced

250 g small new potatoes, halved

250 g cauliflower, cut into small florets

150 g frozen peas

120 g white cabbage, shredded

pepper to taste

chopped fresh coriander to garnish (optional)

roasted vegetable and pasta bake

A hearty vegetarian dish packed with flavour, this selection of vegetables—butternut squash, asparagus and leeks—is roasted in garlicky olive oil, then tossed with chunky pasta shapes and a cheese sauce.

1 small butternut squash, peeled, seeded and cut into 5 cm cubes, about 500 g peeled weight

2 red onions, cut into large chunks

2 garlic cloves, thinly sliced

2 tablespoons extra virgin olive oil

pepper to taste

2 large leeks, thickly sliced

170 g asparagus spears, cut across in half

300 g rigatoni or penne

CHEESE SAUCE

2$\frac{1}{3}$ cups low-fat milk

4 tablespoons cornstarch

70 g 25% reduced-fat mature Cheddar cheese, grated

2 teaspoons whole-grain mustard

pepper to taste

1 Preheat the oven to 425°F (220°C). Place the squash and onions in a roasting pan and scatter over the garlic. Drizzle with the oil and season with pepper. Toss to coat the vegetables with the oil, then place the pan in the oven and roast for 15 minutes.

2 Remove the pan from the oven and add the leeks and asparagus. Toss gently to mix with the other vegetables, then return to the oven. Roast for a further 20 minutes or until all the vegetables are tender and beginning to brown.

3 Meanwhile, cook the pasta in a large saucepan of boiling water for 10–12 minutes, or according to the package instructions.

4 Meanwhile, to make the sauce, measure 5 tablespoons milk into a jug, add the cornstarch and stir to make a smooth paste. Heat the remaining milk in a saucepan until almost boiling. Stir the hot milk into the cornstarch mixture, then return to the saucepan and heat gently, stirring, until the mixture boils and thickens. Simmer for 2 minutes. Remove the sauce from the heat and add two-thirds of the cheese and the mustard. Season with pepper.

5 Remove the vegetables from the oven. Drain the pasta well then pour over the vegetables and stir to combine. Stir in the sauce. Sprinkle the remaining cheese over the top. Return to the oven and bake for 10–15 minutes or until golden and bubbling. Serve hot.

Fb GI

preparation time **20 mins**

cooking time **50 mins**

serves **4**

PER SERVING

494 calories

23 g protein

15 g total fat
4 g saturated fat

19 mg cholesterol

68 g total carbohydrate
18 g sugars

8 g fibre

258 mg sodium

HEALTH HINT

The bright orange flesh of butternut squash is an indicator of its high beta carotene content. Squash is also a good source of vitamin C and a useful source of vitamin E.

spicy garlic vegetable stir-fry

Has your passion for vegetables faded lately? This lively stir-fry will make the sparks fly again! Fresh, crisp broccoli, bright red pepper and tender baby corn are flash-fried with tantalizing Asian seasonings for a speedy side dish.

1 Combine ¼ cup stock, soy sauce, cornstarch and chili paste, if using, in a small bowl until smooth. Set aside. Crush the garlic cloves by smashing with the side of a knife; peel.

2 Coat a large nonstick wok or deep frying pan with nonstick cooking spray. Add the oil and set the wok over high heat until hot but not smoking. Stir-fry the ginger and garlic until fragrant, about 1 minute. Remove with a slotted spoon and set aside.

3 Add the broccoli to the wok and stir-fry just until it begins to soften, about 4 minutes. Transfer to a bowl. Add the corn, red pepper and water chestnuts and stir-fry just until they begin to soften, about 3 minutes. Return the broccoli to the wok and add the remaining stock.

4 Cover and cook until the vegetables are crisp-tender, about 3 minutes. Whisk the cornstarch mixture again and add to the wok with the ginger and garlic. Stir-fry until the sauce thickens and boils, about 1 minute. Sprinkle with sesame seeds and serve.

1½ cups reduced-salt chicken stock

2 tablespoons reduced-salt soy sauce, or to taste

2 tablespoons cornstarch

½ teaspoon chili paste or chili powder (optional)

2 garlic cloves

1½ teaspoons peanut or vegetable oil

4 tablespoons peeled, finely chopped fresh ginger

2 cups broccoli florets

1 can (398 ml) baby corn, drained

1 large red pepper, cut into thin strips

1 can (199 ml) sliced water chestnuts, drained

1 tablespoon sesame seeds, toasted, to garnish

preparation time **15 mins**

cooking time **10 mins**

serves **4**

PER SERVING

165 calories

8 g protein

5 g total fat

1 g saturated fat

0 mg cholesterol

23 g total carbohydrate

7 g sugars

6 g fibre

774 mg sodium

COOK'S TIP

Stir-frying is a fast, easy and healthy way to cook, but it pays to be prepared. Cut up and measure all ingredients before you heat the wok. Make sure all vegetables are cut into similar-size pieces so they cook evenly. Stir-fry vegetables with similar cooking times together. Most of all, don't crowd the pan: If you add too many vegetables, they will steam rather than fry, and they'll end up soggy.

veggie burgers

A few simple ingredients make really tasty meat-free burgers. If you want to barbecue them, the best method is to cook the patties in advance and just heat them up over the coals, as this prevents them from sticking to the grill.

3 tablespoons extra virgin olive oil
1 large onion, finely chopped
1 garlic clove, finely chopped
300 g carrots, coarsely grated
300 g zucchinis, coarsely grated
1½ teaspoons ground cumin
1½ teaspoons ground coriander
4 tablespoons reduced-fat
    peanut butter
2 tablespoons chopped
    fresh coriander
pepper to taste
1⅓ cups fresh whole-wheat
    breadcrumbs
1 egg, beaten

TO SERVE

2 tomatoes, seeded and chopped
2 tablespoons tomato ketchup,
    chutney or relish
pepper to taste
4 sesame seed hamburger buns
4 teaspoons low-fat mayonnaise
4 iceberg lettuce leaves, shredded
1 shallot, thinly sliced

1 Heat 2 tablespoons oil in a large nonstick frying pan. Add the onion and garlic and cook over medium heat for 5 minutes, stirring frequently, until the onion is soft and beginning to brown. Add the carrots and zucchinis and fry for a further 10 minutes, stirring, until the vegetables soften. Stir in the ground cumin and coriander, peanut butter, fresh coriander and pepper and mix well. Remove the pan from the heat and set aside to cool slightly.

2 Mix in the breadcrumbs and egg until thoroughly combined. The mixture should bind together well. Shape the mixture into 4 thick patties about 10 cm in diameter.

3 Wipe the pan with paper towel, then add and heat the remaining oil. Fry the patties over low to medium heat for 5 minutes on each side, or until they are firm and golden.

4 To serve, stir the tomatoes and ketchup together with a little pepper. Split the hamburger buns in half and toast the cut sides. Spread ½ teaspoon mayonnaise on each piece of bun, then place some lettuce and a patty on top of half of the buns. Spread with the tomato mixture and top with the shallot slices. Replace the tops of the buns and serve.

preparation time **20 mins**
cooking time **25 mins**
serves **4**

PER SERVING

553 calories

19 g protein

24 g total fat
4 g saturated fat

57 mg cholesterol

66 g total carbohydrate
18 g sugars

12 g fibre

804 mg sodium

HEALTH HINT

Peanut butter contributes protein to these burgers, as does the wheat from the whole-wheat breadcrumbs. Peanut butter is high in fat, but this is largely in a healthy monounsaturated form. However, it is best to use a reduced-fat variety if you are watching your weight.

cold sesame noodles and vegetables

A long-time favourite at Chinese restaurants, cold sesame noodles make a great side dish (double the portions for a main dish). Sesame paste has been replaced with peanut butter and sesame oil.

1 Cook the noodles in a large saucepan of boiling water according to the package instructions, until al dente. Drain, reserving ½ cup of the cooking water.

2 Meanwhile, combine the coriander, peanut butter, soy sauce, honey, vinegar, sesame oil, garlic and cayenne pepper in a food processor or blender and purée. Transfer to a large bowl.

3 Whisk in the reserved pasta cooking water. Add the linguine, carrots, pepper, celery and green onions and toss well to combine the ingredients. Chill the noodles in the refrigerator for at least 1 hour before serving.

250 g whole-wheat noodles or linguine

⅓ cup fresh coriander

2 tablespoons reduced-fat peanut butter

2 tablespoons reduced-salt soy sauce

2½ teaspoons clear honey

1 tablespoon rice vinegar or cider vinegar

1 tablespoon sesame oil

2 cloves garlic, peeled

¼ teaspoon cayenne pepper

2 carrots, slivered

1 red pepper, slivered

1 large celery stalk, slivered

2 green onions, slivered

preparation time **15 mins**

cooking time **10 mins**
plus 1 hour chilling

serves **6**

PER SERVING

211 calories

8 g protein

6 g total fat
1 g saturated fat

0 mg cholesterol

31 g total carbohydrate
5 g sugars

7 g fibre

312 mg sodium

COOK'S TIP

The pasta cooking water, which carries some of the pasta's starch, is used here to "stretch" the sauce. It's a traditional Italian technique for thinning or smoothing a sauce so that it coats the noodles better. And the water replaces what might otherwise be a lot of extra fat.

grilled asparagus and peppers

Here, spears of asparagus, green onions and peppers are cooked in a ridged cast-iron grill pan, then mixed with oven-baked Parmesan croutons. If you haven't got a ridged grill pan, the vegetables can be sizzled under the broiler.

500 g asparagus spears, woody ends trimmed

2 large red peppers, halved and seeded

220 g green onions

2 tablespoons extra virgin olive oil

shavings of Parmesan cheese, about 15 g in total, to garnish

PARMESAN CROUTONS

2 thick slices whole-wheat bread, crusts removed and diced

1 tablespoon extra virgin olive oil

pepper to taste

2½ tablespoons Parmesan cheese, freshly grated

LEMON AND BASIL DRESSING

2 tablespoons freshly squeezed lemon juice

2 tablespoons extra virgin olive oil

16 fresh basil leaves, torn into pieces

1 garlic clove, very finely chopped

pepper to taste

1 Preheat the oven to 350°F (180°C). Heat a ridged cast-iron grill pan. Place the asparagus, peppers and green onions in a bowl, add the olive oil and toss to coat.

2 Arrange the asparagus and peppers in the hot grill pan, in one layer, and cook for 10 minutes or until tender, adding the green onions after the asparagus and peppers have been cooking for a few minutes. Turn the vegetables frequently so they cook and colour evenly. (You may have to grill the vegetables in 2 batches, depending on the size of the pan.)

3 Meanwhile, to make the croutons, place the bread in a bowl with the oil and pepper to season and toss well. Spread out on a baking sheet and bake for about 5 minutes. Sprinkle over the Parmesan cheese and bake for a further 5 minutes or until golden and crisp.

4 Whisk together the dressing ingredients in a salad bowl, adding pepper to taste. Roughly slice the grilled vegetables, add to the bowl and stir to coat with the dressing. Scatter the croutons over the top and garnish with a few shavings of Parmesan cheese. Serve while still warm.

30 **Fb**

preparation time **10 mins**
cooking time **20 mins**
serves **4**

PER SERVING

350 calories

10 g protein

29 g total fat
6 g saturated fat

12 mg cholesterol

13 g total carbohydrate
8 g sugars

5 g fibre

250 mg sodium

HEALTH HINT

Whole-wheat bread is an important part of a healthy diet as it is a very good source of starchy (complex) carbohydrate. It also contributes vitamins and minerals, particularly calcium, and dietary fibre.

squash and chickpea stew

The orange colour of squash signals beta carotene, a plant pigment that's a potent disease-fighter. And this is a meatless stew, so the total fat content is minimal. Like all good stews, this is a fine make-ahead recipe.

1 Preheat the oven to 350°F (180°C). Heat the olive oil in a nonstick flameproof casserole dish over medium heat. Add the onion and garlic and cook, stirring frequently, until the onion is golden-brown, about 7 minutes.

2 Add the butternut squash, curry powder and ground coriander, stirring to coat. Add the tomatoes, chickpeas, raisins and ½ cup water. Bring to a boil over medium heat.

3 Cover the casserole with the lid, transfer to the oven, and bake until the squash is tender, about 20 minutes. (The recipe can be made ahead to this point and refrigerated. Reheat in a 340°F (170°C) oven, adding a little more water if necessary.) Stir in the chopped fresh coriander just before serving.

1 tablespoon olive oil

1 large onion, halved and thinly sliced

3 cloves garlic, finely chopped

500 g butternut squash, peeled and cut into 2 cm chunks

1½ teaspoons curry powder

1 teaspoon ground coriander

1 can (398 ml) canned tomatoes, coarsely chopped

1 can (540 ml) chickpeas, rinsed and drained

¼ cup raisins

¼ cup chopped fresh coriander, to garnish

preparation time **15 mins**

cooking time **30 mins**

serves **4**

PER SERVING

197 calories

8 g protein

6 g total fat
1 g saturated fat

0 mg cholesterol

27 g total carbohydrate
17 g sugars

6 g fibre

154 mg sodium

HEALTH HINT

Butternut squash is a spectacular source of cardio-protective beta carotene. Compared with other types of squash, butternut squash is the richest source of this nourishing antioxidant, as evidenced by the deep orange flesh. If you are unable to find butternut squash, other types of squash are also highly nutritious.

breads
& pizzas

254

basic loaf

 This recipe makes a very good basic loaf, but it is also infinitely flexible. You can make any number of breads, just by using different types of flour or adding herbs, nuts, cheese, olives, seeds, dried fruit and berries, or shape it into rolls.

3¼ cups white bread flour

2½ cups whole-wheat bread flour, preferably stone-ground, plus a little extra to dust

1 teaspoon salt

1 envelope dried yeast, about 8 g

1¾ cups tepid water

1 Sift the white and whole-wheat flours into a large bowl. Add salt. Stir in the dried yeast, then make a well in the centre and pour in the tepid water. Using your hands, gradually draw the flour into the water, mixing well to make a dough.

2 Gather the dough into a ball that feels firm and leaves the sides of the bowl clean; if necessary, add a little more flour or a little more water.

3 Turn the dough out onto a lightly floured work surface and knead for about 10 minutes or until smooth and elastic. Place the dough in a large, lightly greased bowl and cover with plastic wrap. Leave to rise in a warm place for about 1 hour or until doubled in size.

4 Turn out the risen dough onto a floured work surface and knock it back with your knuckles. Gently knead the dough into a neat ball shape, then place it on a large greased baking sheet. Cover with a damp dish towel and leave to rise in a warm place for 1 hour or until doubled in size again.

5 Toward the end of the rising time, preheat the oven to 425°F (220°C). Uncover the loaf and dust with a little whole-wheat flour, then make 4 slashes across the top with a small serrated knife. Bake for 35 minutes or until the bread sounds hollow when removed from the sheet and tapped on the base.

6 Transfer the loaf to a wire rack and cool completely before slicing. It can be kept for up to 5 days.

preparation time **20 mins**

rising time **2 hours**

cooking time **35 mins**

makes **1 large round loaf** (cuts into about 12 slices)

PER SLICE

192 calories

7 g protein

1 g total fat
0.1 g saturated fat

0 mg cholesterol

38 g total carbohydrate
0.3 g sugars

4 g fibre

204 mg sodium

HEALTH HINT

Stone-ground flour is milled by traditional methods, which keep the wheat grains cool and thus preserve almost all the nutrients in the whole grain.

quick whole-wheat bread

C Fb

preparation time **10 mins**

rising time **30 mins**

cooking time **40 mins**

makes **1 large loaf**
(cuts into about 14 slices)

PER SLICE

106 calories	
4 g protein	
1 g total fat	
0.1 g saturated fat	
0 mg cholesterol	
21 g total carbohydrate	
0.3 g sugars	
4 g fibre	
175 mg sodium	

HEALTH HINT

Yeast is particularly rich
in folate and contains
a number of other
B vitamins.

With only one rising and no kneading, this is a whole-wheat bread that couldn't be simpler to make. High in fibre, and with a dense, moist texture, this filling bread makes excellent toast.

1 Lightly grease a 23 x 13 cm (9 x 5 in.) loaf pan or line it with parchment paper. Set aside while you make the dough.

2 Sift the flour into a large mixing bowl. Add salt. Stir in the yeast and make a well in the centre. Stir the sugar or honey into the tepid water, then pour into the well in the dry ingredients.

3 Mix together, then beat vigorously with your hand (or with a wooden spoon if you prefer) for about 2 minutes or until the dough comes away from the side of the bowl; it will be very soft and sticky.

4 Pour the dough into the prepared pan, cover with a damp dish towel and leave in a warm place for about 30 minutes or until the dough has risen almost to the top of the pan.

5 Toward the end of the rising time, preheat the oven to 400°F (200°C). Uncover the pan and dust the top of the loaf evenly with the white flour. Bake for 30–40 minutes or until well risen and brown. It should feel light and sound hollow when turned out of the pan and tapped on the base.

6 Transfer the loaf to a wire rack and, if necessary, return it to the oven for 5 minutes to crisp the sides and base. Leave on the wire rack to cool. It can be kept for up to 5 days.

3¼ cups whole-wheat bread flour,
  preferably stone-ground

1 teaspoon salt

1 envelope dried yeast, about 8 g

1 teaspoon brown sugar or
  clear honey

1¾ cups tepid water

1 tablespoon white all-purpose
  flour to dust

light rye bread

Rye flour is lower in gluten than wheat, so it produces a close-textured, moist loaf. Caraway seeds are a traditional seasoning, complementing the nutty rye flavour to make an excellent bread that goes well with soft cheeses.

3¼ cups rye flour
1 cup white bread flour
½ teaspoon salt
1 teaspoon caster (superfine) sugar
1 envelope dried yeast, about 8 g
2 teaspoons caraway seeds
2 tablespoons extra virgin olive oil
¾ cup tepid water

1 Sift the rye and white flours into a bowl. Add salt and sugar, then stir in the yeast and caraway seeds. Stir the olive oil into the tepid water, then pour this over the flour mixture. Mix the ingredients together with a wooden spoon at first, then with your hand, to make a stiff but sticky and slightly grainy dough.

2 Turn the dough out onto a floured work surface and knead for about 10 minutes or until smooth. The dough should be very firm. Shape it into an oval loaf about 18 cm long, and place it on a greased baking sheet. Cover loosely with plastic wrap and leave to rise in a warm place for about 1 hour or until almost doubled in size. It will be slightly cracked on top.

3 Toward the end of the rising time, preheat the oven to 400°F (200°C). Uncover the loaf and bake for 40–45 minutes or until it is lightly browned and sounds hollow when removed from the sheet and tapped on the base.

4 Transfer to a wire rack and leave to cool. Once cold, place the loaf in a plastic bag and leave overnight (this allows the crust to soften). After this, the loaf can be kept for 2 days.

preparation time **15 mins**

rising time **1 hour**

cooking time **45 mins**

makes **1 small loaf**
(cuts into about
24 thin slices)

PER SLICE

66 calories

2 g protein

2 g total fat
0.3 g saturated fat

0 mg cholesterol

10 g total carbohydrate
0.4 g sugars

2 g fibre

51 mg sodium

HEALTH HINT

Caraway seeds are said to stimulate the production of saliva and aid in the digestion of food.

multi-grain seeded loaf

 Serve this nutty-textured loaf very fresh, cut into wedges. It's good with a hearty bowl of soup or cheese and pickles. The mix of seeds can be varied to your own taste, or you can use just one kind.

Fb

preparation time **25 mins**

rising time **2 hours**

cooking time **35 mins**

makes **1 round loaf**
(cuts into 8 wedges)

PER WEDGE

380 calories

12 g protein

11 g total fat
1 g saturated fat

0.1 mg cholesterol

58 g total carbohydrate
1 g sugars

6 g fibre

614 mg sodium

HEALTH HINT

Pumpkin seeds are one of the richest vegetarian sources of zinc, a mineral that is essential for the functioning of the immune system. They are a good source of protein and unsaturated fat and a useful source of iron, magnesium and fibre.

1 Sift the white, whole-wheat and buckwheat flours into a large bowl. Stir in the polenta, salt, yeast and sugar.

2 Mix together the sunflower and pumpkin seeds and linseeds, then set aside 1 tablespoon for the topping. Stir the rest into the flour mixture.

3 Make a well in the dry ingredients and pour in the oil and most of the water. Work the dry ingredients into the liquid to make a soft dough, adding water as needed. Turn out onto a lightly floured work surface and knead for 10 minutes, until smooth and elastic.

4 Place in a large, lightly greased bowl and cover with a damp dish towel. Leave in a warm place for 1½ hours, until doubled.

5 Turn the dough out onto a lightly floured surface and knock it back with your knuckles, then knead firmly for a few minutes. Shape into a 20 cm round and place on a lightly greased baking sheet. Cover with oiled plastic wrap and leave to rise for 20–30 minutes or until well risen and springy to the touch.

6 Preheat the oven to 450°F (230°C). Uncover the loaf and, using a sharp knife, cut the top deeply to mark it into 8 wedges. Brush with milk and sprinkle with the reserved seeds.

7 Bake for 15 minutes, then reduce the oven temperature to 400°F (200°C). Bake for a further 15–20 minutes or until the loaf is golden-brown and sounds hollow when removed from the sheet and tapped on the base. Cool on a wire rack. This bread is best eaten on the day it is made.

3 cups white bread flour

1½ cups whole-wheat bread flour

½ cup buckwheat flour

½ cup polenta

2 teaspoons salt

1 envelope dried yeast, about 8 g

1 teaspoon brown sugar

4 tablespoons sunflower seeds

2 tablespoons pumpkin seeds

2 tablespoons linseeds

2 tablespoons sunflower oil

1¾ cups tepid water

a little low-fat milk to glaze

sourdough bread

Instead of commercial yeast, delicious sourdough bread is made with a "starter," which uses the yeasts that occur naturally in the atmosphere and on flour. Despite the time needed to "grow" the starter, it's not a difficult bread to make.

STARTER

1 cup white bread flour, preferably unbleached organic flour

⅓ cup tepid water, preferably spring water

TO "FEED"

2–3 cups white bread flour, preferably unbleached organic flour

tepid water, preferably spring water

DOUGH

5 cups white bread flour, preferably unbleached organic flour

1 teaspoon salt

1 cup tepid water, preferably spring water, or as needed

1 To make the starter, place the flour and tepid water in a bowl and stir together to make a sticky paste. Cover with a damp dish towel (not plastic wrap) and leave on the kitchen counter for 2 days, dampening the dish towel again as needed to keep it moist. If after 2 days the mixture looks bubbly and has a milky smell, you can proceed to the first "feed." (It may take up to 4 days to reach this stage.) If there are patches of mould or the paste smells sour or bad, throw it away and begin again with a new batch of starter.

2 To "feed" the starter, stir 1 cup flour and enough tepid water into the starter to make a soft, paste-like dough. Cover the bowl as before and leave for 24 hours. At this point the starter will look very active and bubbly. Stir well, then discard half the starter. Stir another 1 cup flour and enough tepid water into the starter to make a soft, paste-like dough. Cover again and leave for 12 hours. If the starter looks very bubbly and lively, it is ready to use. If it seems only slightly bubbly, give it one more feed of 1 cup flour and tepid water and wait 6 hours.

3 To make the dough, place the flour and salt in a large bowl. Mix together and make a well in the centre. Transfer 2 cups of the starter into a separate bowl and mix it with the tepid water, then pour it into the well in the flour. Gradually work the flour into the liquid mixture to make a soft dough. You may need to add a little more water as you work if the dough feels dry or crumbly, or more flour if it sticks to your hands or the bowl.

4 Turn the dough out onto a floured work surface and knead for about 10 minutes or until very pliable. Return it to the cleaned bowl, cover with a damp dish towel and leave to rise in a warm place for 3–8 hours or until doubled in size. Rising time depends on the room temperature and on the strength of your starter. (A new starter will give a slower rise and less volume than one that is well established.)

5 Turn out the risen dough onto a floured work surface and knock it back with your knuckles to its original size. Shape the dough into a ball and set it in a basket or colander lined with a heavily floured linen dish towel. Cover with a damp dish towel and leave to rise for 2–6 hours or until doubled in size.

preparation time **35 mins**

rising time **5–14 hours**

cooking time **35 mins** plus 4–6 days for the starter to develop

makes **1 large round loaf** (cuts into about 20 slices)

PER SLICE

113 calories

4 g protein

0.4 g total fat
0.1 g saturated fat

0 mg cholesterol

23 g total carbohydrate
0.1 g sugars

1 g fibre

122 mg sodium

HEALTH HINT

Sourdough starters can last for decades, and seem to be resistant to contamination. This may be due to an antibiotic action similar to that of the moulds in cheeses such as Stilton and Roquefort.

6 Toward the end of the rising time, preheat the oven to 425°F (220°C). Invert the dough onto a large greased baking sheet and make a single slash across the top of the loaf with a sharp knife. Bake for about 35 minutes or until the bread sounds hollow when removed from the sheet and tapped on the base.

7 Transfer the bread to a wire rack and leave to cool. It can be kept for up to 5 days, and is wonderful toasted.

Variations Leftover sourdough starter can be stored in an airtight container in the refrigerator. Before using it to make another loaf, bring it back to room temperature, then feed it once as in the main recipe and leave for about 6 hours. Each time you make a loaf, you will have leftover starter. This can be kept in the refrigerator, provided you feed it every 4 days to keep it alive. It will improve in flavour with time. Any starter you do not need or want can be discarded, or given to a friend. • Instead of spring water, you can use water that has been filtered, boiled and cooled. • To make a French-style sourdough bread, replace ¹/₂ cup white bread flour with 5¹/₂ tablespoons whole-wheat bread flour. • To make a heavier, German-style sourdough bread, replace half the white bread flour with rye flour.

focaccia

This light Italian flat bread is prepared from a soft dough enriched with olive oil. This recipe uses just enough olive oil to give a good texture and flavour. Focaccia makes an ideal accompaniment to Italian meats, cheeses and salads.

4 cups white bread flour
1 teaspoon salt
1 envelope dried yeast, about 8 g
5 tablespoons extra virgin olive oil
1¼ cups tepid water
½ teaspoon coarse sea salt

1 Place the flour in a large bowl and stir in the salt and yeast. Make a well in the centre and pour in 4 tablespoons olive oil and the water. Gradually mix the flour in; use a wooden spoon, then your hand, to make a soft, slightly sticky dough.

2 Turn the dough onto a floured surface and knead for about 10 minutes, until smooth and elastic. Keep the dough moving by turning, punching and folding it to prevent it from sticking. Sprinkle the surface with a little extra flour if necessary, but try not to add too much as this will make the dough dry.

3 Shape into a ball and slap onto a greased baking sheet, then roll it out (or push it out with your hands) into a round about 20 cm in diameter and 2 cm thick. Cover loosely with a clean dish towel, tuck the ends under the sheet, and leave in a warm place for about 45 minutes or until doubled in thickness.

4 Preheat the oven to 450°F (230°C). Uncover the dough. Pour a little hand-hot water into a cup, then dip your fingers into the water and press into the risen dough to make deep dents all over the top; wet your fingers each time, to leave the top of the loaf moist. Brush the remaining olive oil over the bread and sprinkle with the sea salt.

5 Bake the focaccia for about 15 minutes or until golden-brown. Transfer to a wire rack to cool for 15 minutes, then wrap it in a clean dish towel to soften the crust. Serve warm or allow to cool completely. The bread can be kept in a plastic bag for up to 2 days.

preparation time **15 mins**
rising time **45 mins**
cooking time **15 mins**
makes **1 round flat bread**
(cuts into 8 wedges)

PER SLICE

276 calories

6 g protein

10 g total fat
1 g saturated fat

0 mg cholesterol

41 g total carbohydrate
0.1 g sugars

2 g fibre

456 mg sodium

HEALTH HINT

Olive oil is high in monounsaturated fat, which may help to lower blood cholesterol levels.

bagels

These little bread rings are delicious teamed with savoury fillings such as smoked salmon and a soft cheese, or egg and salad. The double cooking method gives bagels their unique softness and slightly chewy crust.

preparation time **30 mins**

rising time **1 hour**

cooking time **20 mins**

makes **12 bagels**

PER BAGEL

152 calories

6 g protein

3 g total fat
1 g saturated fat

54 mg cholesterol

25 g total carbohydrate
1 g sugars

3 g fibre

319 mg sodium

HEALTH HINT

Serving the bagels with a vitamin-C rich fruit, or including a vitamin-C rich salad in the bagel filling, will help the body to absorb the iron that the bagels provide.

1 Place the flours in a large mixing bowl and stir in the salt, yeast and caraway seeds. Make a well in the centre.

2 Lightly whisk 2 eggs with the treacle and oil, and pour into the well in the flour. Add the water and mix to a soft dough.

3 Turn out onto a lightly floured surface and knead for 10 minutes or until smooth and elastic. Place the dough in a large greased bowl, cover with a damp dish towel and leave to rise in a warm place for 40 minutes or until doubled in size.

4 Turn out the dough onto the floured work surface and knead it lightly, then divide it into 12 equal pieces. Form each into a 20 cm long sausage, then shape it into a ring. Dampen the ends with a little water, slightly overlap them and then gently pinch together to seal.

5 Arrange the bagels on a lightly oiled baking sheet, cover with oiled plastic wrap and leave to rise in a warm place for 20 minutes or until they are slightly puffy.

6 Preheat the oven to 400°F (200°C). Bring a large saucepan of lightly salted water to a boil. Drop the bagels into the water, one at a time, and poach for 20 seconds. Lift them out with a large slotted spoon and return to the baking sheet.

7 Lightly beat the remaining egg and brush it over the bagels to glaze. Bake for 14–15 minutes or until well risen and golden-brown. Transfer to a wire rack to cool. The bagels can be kept in an airtight container for up to 3 days.

2¾ cups white bread flour

1¾ cups rye flour

1½ teaspoons salt

1 envelope dried yeast, about 8 g

1 teaspoon caraway seeds

3 eggs

1 teaspoon treacle

2 teaspoons sunflower oil

¾ cup tepid water

spiced pumpkin tea bread

Here's a delicious, richly coloured tea bread that is moist enough to eat without butter. It makes a great addition to a healthy lunchbox, being rich in essential antioxidants, vitamins and minerals.

340 g peeled pumpkin, diced

6 tablespoons honey, plus 2 teaspoons to glaze

²/₃ cup sultanas

1 cup whole-wheat self-raising flour

1¹/₂ cups white self-raising flour

2 teaspoons ground allspice

²/₃ cup reduced-salt margarine

1 tablespoon pumpkin seeds to sprinkle

1 Preheat the oven to 350°F (180°C). Line a 23 x 13 cm (9 x 5 in.) loaf pan with parchment paper.

2 Steam the pumpkin, or cook it in just a little boiling water, for 10 minutes or until tender. Drain thoroughly, then mash with a potato masher until smooth. Add 6 tablespoons honey and the sultanas and beat well.

3 Sift the whole-wheat and white flours and the allspice into a large bowl. Rub the margarine in with your fingertips until the mixture resembles fine breadcrumbs.

4 Add the pumpkin mixture and beat well with a wooden spoon until evenly mixed. Tip the mixture into the prepared pan and smooth the surface. Sprinkle with pumpkin seeds. Bake for 50–60 minutes or until the loaf is well risen, golden-brown and firm to the touch.

5 Allow the loaf to cool in the pan for 10 minutes, then turn out onto a wire rack. Gently brush with the remaining honey while still warm. This tea bread is best served slightly warm, or cool completely and eat within a day of making.

preparation time **15 mins**

cooking time
1 hour 10 mins

makes **1 large loaf**
(cuts into about 12 slices)

PER SLICE

261 calories

4 g protein

11 g total fat
2 g saturated fat

0 mg cholesterol

37 g total carbohydrate
20 g sugars

3 g fibre

227 mg sodium

HEALTH HINT

Pumpkin has a high water content, which makes it low in calories—just 15 per 100 g. It provides carbohydrates, potassium, calcium and vitamin C. An excellent source of beta carotene, pumpkin also provides several other antioxidants, including lutein and zeaxanthin.

banana cinnamon muffins

These delicious, moist muffins with a crunchy sweet topping are low in fat and contain bananas, oat bran, soy milk and soy flour—all beneficial for anyone eating for a healthy heart. Enjoy them warm at breakfast or at morning coffee.

1 Preheat the oven to 350°F (180°C). Line a 12 cup deep muffin pan with paper muffin cups.

2 Mix together 2 teaspoons oat bran, 1 teaspoon cinnamon and the golden brown sugar, and set aside for the topping. Place the remaining oat bran in a bowl with the soy milk and leave to soak for 5 minutes.

3 Peel and roughly mash the bananas. Add the brown sugar, oil, vanilla extract and egg white, and beat well together.

4 Sift the all-purpose and soy flours, baking powder and remaining cinnamon into a large bowl. Make a well in the centre and stir in the soaked oat bran and the banana mixture. Mix lightly but thoroughly, just until smooth.

5 Spoon the mixture into the paper cups and sprinkle with the topping. Bake for 20–25 minutes or until well risen and golden-brown. Lift the muffins out onto a wire rack to cool a little. Serve fresh, preferably still slightly warm from the oven. These muffins are best eaten on the day they are made.

1 cup oat bran
2 teaspoons ground cinnamon
1 tablespoon golden brown sugar
¾ cup soy milk
3 bananas
⅔ cup brown sugar
4 tablespoons sunflower oil
2 teaspoons vanilla extract
1 egg white
2 cups all-purpose flour
½ cup soy flour
1 tablespoon baking powder

preparation time **15 mins**
cooking time **25 mins**
makes **12 muffins**

PER MUFFIN

205 calories

6 g protein

6 g total fat
1 g saturated fat

0 mg cholesterol

32 g total carbohydrate
15 g sugars

3 g fibre

213 mg sodium

HEART SUPERFOOD

Diets that are rich in soy protein are believed to help reduce high blood cholesterol levels. Several studies suggest that soy products may also help to reduce the risk of heart disease, certain cancers and osteoporosis, as well as alleviating some of the symptoms associated with menopause.

summer berry muffins

Fresh summer berries add delicious flavour, colour and nutrition to these tempting muffins. They are best fresh from the oven, but are also good once cooled—an ideal addition to a lunchbox, or for breakfast on the go.

1 Preheat the oven to 400°F (200°C). Use paper muffin cups to line 9 cups of a muffin pan—each cup should measure about 7 cm across the top and be about 3 cm deep.

2 Sift the whole-wheat and all-purpose flours and baking powder into a large bowl. Gently fold in the mixed berries.

3 Melt the margarine gently in a small saucepan, then add the sugar, egg and milk and mix until smooth. Pour this over the flour mixture and gently fold together just enough to combine the ingredients. The mixture should remain quite lumpy.

4 Spoon the mixture into the paper muffin cups, filling each about two-thirds full. (Half-fill the empty cups with water.) Bake for 18–20 minutes or until the muffins are risen and golden-brown.

5 Transfer to a wire rack to cool slightly, then serve warm or allow to cool completely before serving. The muffins can be kept in an airtight container for 1–2 days.

Variations Instead of a mixture of white and whole-wheat flours, use all whole-wheat flour. • For a hint of spice, add 1½ teaspoons mixed spice, ground ginger or cinnamon with the flour. • Replace the berries with other fresh fruit, such as chopped apples, apricots, peaches or strawberries or dried fruit, such as sultanas, raisins, chopped apricots, dates or figs. • To make pear and cinnamon oatmeal muffins, mix 1½ cups whole-wheat self-raising flour, ¾ cup oatmeal, 1 teaspoon baking powder and 1½ teaspoons ground cinnamon in a bowl. Fold in 2 peeled and chopped pears. In a separate bowl, mix together 4 tablespoons melted reduced-salt margarine, ¼ cup caster (superfine) sugar, 2 eggs and ⅔ cup freshly squeezed orange juice. Pour this over the flour mixture and fold the ingredients together. Spoon into 9 paper muffin cups and bake as in the main recipe. • For mini muffins, divide the mixture among 30 mini paper muffin cups and bake for 10 minutes.

1 cup whole-wheat all-purpose flour
1 cup white all-purpose flour
1 tablespoon baking powder
140 g mixed berries, such as blueberries and raspberries
4 tablespoons reduced-salt margarine
⅓ cup brown sugar
1 egg, beaten
¾ cup low-fat milk

preparation time **10 mins**
cooking time **20 mins**
makes **9 muffins**

PER MUFFIN

177 calories	
5 g protein	
7 g total fat	
1 g saturated fat	
25 mg cholesterol	
25 g total carbohydrate	
9 g sugars	
2 g fibre	
312 mg sodium	

HEALTH HINT

Fresh berries are naturally low in fat. They contain dietary fibre and make a good contribution to vitamin C intake. Raspberries also supply vitamin E, and blueberries, like cranberries, contain a compound that helps to prevent urinary tract infections.

ricotta herb scones

These savoury scones are made with soft cheese and plenty of fresh herbs— ideally a mixture of Italian parsley, chives, thyme and rosemary, although any combination will do. They are nicest warm, with soup or salad.

4 cups self-raising flour

¼ teaspoon salt

several grinds of black pepper

220 g reduced-fat ricotta

1 egg

4 tablespoons chopped mixed fresh herbs, such as Italian parsley, chives, thyme, rosemary, basil

1 cup low-fat milk, or more as needed, plus extra to glaze

1 tablespoon sesame seeds to sprinkle

1 Preheat the oven to 375°F (190°C). Sift the flour into a mixing bowl and stir in the salt and black pepper.

2 Place the ricotta, egg and herbs in another bowl and stir well until smooth. Add to the flour and stir in with a round-bladed knife. Work in 1 cup milk, or a little more if needed, to make a slightly soft but not sticky dough.

3 Turn the dough out onto a lightly floured work surface and knead gently for 1 minute or until smooth. Divide into 8 equal portions and shape each into a rough-looking ball.

4 Place the scones on a large greased baking sheet, arranging them so they do not touch. Brush lightly with milk to glaze, then sprinkle with sesame seeds. Bake for 20–25 minutes or until the scones are lightly browned and sound hollow when they are tapped on the base.

5 Transfer to a wire rack to cool slightly, then eat warm or allow to cool completely before serving. The scones can be kept in an airtight container for 24 hours.

preparation time **15 mins**

cooking time **25 mins**

makes **8 scones**

PER SCONE

258 calories

11 g protein

5 g total fat
2 g saturated fat

40 mg cholesterol

42 g total carbohydrate
3 g sugars

2 g fibre

545 mg sodium

HEALTH HINT

Herbs like parsley, chives, rosemary, oregano, basil and coriander add a nutrition bonus to your meals. They are fat-free and exceedingly rich in vitamins, minerals, fibre and hundreds of phyto-chemicals, with virtually no calories. Weight for weight, parsley has almost twice as much vitamin C as oranges. Dill has six times more beta-carotene than cantaloupe or pumpkin. But—as a garnish—we consume only one or two grams of herbs while we can happily consume a 120 gram orange.

potato scones

Served fresh from the oven while still warm, scones are a popular treat. Here, mashed potatoes are added to the mixture, which makes these savoury scones wonderfully moist. It's a great way of using up leftover potatoes.

30 **C**

preparation time **10 mins**

cooking time **20 mins**

makes **6 scone wedges**

PER WEDGE

197 calories	
5 g protein	
5 g total fat	
1 g saturated fat	
1 mg cholesterol	
32 g total carbohydrate	
2 g sugars	
2 g fibre	
545 mg sodium	

HEALTH HINT

Potatoes, while not particularly high in vitamin C, provide fibre and potassium and are also low in fat. But be careful. Potatoes have a high GI rating.

1 Preheat the oven to 425°F (220°C). Sift the flour, mustard powder and baking powder into a large bowl and add salt. Rub in the margarine with your fingertips until the mixture resembles fine breadcrumbs.

2 Place ¼ cup milk and mashed potatoes in another bowl and mix well. Add to the dry ingredients and stir with a fork, adding another 1–2 tablespoons milk, if needed, to make a soft dough.

3 Turn the dough out onto a floured work surface and knead lightly for a few seconds or until smooth, then roll out to a 15 cm round about 2 cm thick. Place on a greased baking sheet. Using a sharp knife, cut the top deeply to mark it into 6 wedges.

4 Brush with milk or egg, then sprinkle with oatmeal. Bake for 15–20 minutes or until well risen and golden-brown.

5 Transfer to a wire rack and break into wedges. Serve warm or leave to cool. The scones can be kept in an airtight container for 3 days and reheated to serve: set on a baking sheet, cover with foil and warm in the oven for about 5 minutes.

Variations Instead of oatmeal, dust the scones with a mixture of 2 teaspoons all-purpose flour and ⅛ teaspoon paprika before baking. • For potato and feta scones, instead of margarine, stir 70 g feta cheese, finely crumbled, and 2 tablespoons snipped fresh chives into the dry ingredients.

2 cups self-raising flour

¼ teaspoon mustard powder

1½ teaspoons baking powder

¼ teaspoon salt

2 tablespoons reduced-salt margarine

¼ cup low-fat milk, or more as needed

¾ cup cold mashed potatoes (without any milk or butter added)

milk or beaten egg to glaze

2 teaspoons oatmeal to sprinkle

cinnamon raisin bread

This milk-enriched fruity loaf tastes good plain or can be served spread with a little honey or jam. It's also wonderful toasted for breakfast, when the gentle aroma of warm cinnamon makes a soothing start to the day.

3¼ cups whole-wheat bread flour
2 teaspoons ground cinnamon
1 envelope dried yeast, about 8 g
1 cup raisins
¼ cup caster (superfine) sugar
¼ cup reduced-salt margarine
1 cup low-fat milk, plus
    1 tablespoon to glaze
1 egg, lightly beaten

1 Grease and lightly flour a 23 x 13 cm (9 x 5 in.) loaf pan. Sift the flour and cinnamon into a large mixing bowl. Stir in the yeast, raisins and sugar, and make a well in the centre.

2 Gently heat the margarine and 1 cup milk in a small saucepan until the margarine has melted and the mixture is just tepid. Pour into the well in the dry ingredients and add the beaten egg. Mix together to make a soft dough.

3 Turn the dough out onto a lightly floured surface and knead for 10 minutes or until smooth and elastic. Shape the dough into a rectangular shape and place in the prepared pan. Cover with oiled plastic wrap or a clean dish towel and leave to rise in a warm place for about 1 hour or until doubled in size.

4 Toward the end of the rising time, preheat the oven to 425°F (220°C). Uncover the loaf and brush with the remaining milk to glaze. Bake for about 30 minutes or until it sounds hollow when removed from the pan and tapped on the base. Cover the loaf with foil toward the end of the cooking time if the top is browning too much.

5 Turn out onto a wire rack and leave to cool. The bread can be kept, wrapped in foil, for 2–3 days.

preparation time **15 mins**
rising time **1 hour**
cooking time **30 mins**
makes **1 large loaf**
(cuts into about 16 slices)

PER SLICE

164 calories

5 g protein

4 g total fat
1 g saturated fat

14 mg cholesterol

28 g total carbohydrate
11 g sugars

4 g fibre

34 mg sodium

HEALTH HINT

Dried fruit, such as raisins, is a concentrated source of energy. Raisins are also a useful source of fibre and potassium.

preparation time **10 mins**

cooking time **15 mins**

serves **4**

PER SERVING

410 calories

23 g protein

13 g total fat
5 g saturated fat

32 mg cholesterol

50 g total carbohydrate
12 g sugars

8 g fibre

751 mg sodium

HEALTH HINT

With its abundance of
vegetables, this pizza
provides a range of
nutrients—especially
vitamin C from the
tomatoes—which
promote the absorption
of iron in the body.
And the reduced-fat
mozzarella supplies
calcium, which helps
prevent osteoporosis.

pepperoni pizza

*Here's proof—you can enjoy a slice of pepperoni pizza and do your heart good.
A few heart-smart substitutions and lots of vegetables make this much more
healthy than a pizzeria's, and you get to savour the aroma as it bakes.*

1 Preheat the oven to 425°F (220°C). Line a 30 cm (12 in.)
pizza tray or a large baking sheet with parchment paper.

2 Heat the oil in a large saucepan. Add mushrooms, onion,
garlic and oregano and fry over a medium heat until the
mushrooms are golden-brown, about 7 minutes. Stir in the
tomatoes, sprinkle with the vinegar, and cover. Remove from
the heat and let stand for 3 minutes.

3 Meanwhile, place the pizza base on the pizza tray. Spread
over the tomato paste. Top with the vegetable mixture,
pepperoni and mozzarella, then sprinkle over the parsley.

4 Bake until the crust is golden-brown and crisp and the
cheese is melted and bubbly, about 10 minutes. Remove from
the oven and serve hot.

1 teaspoon extra-light olive oil

140 g button mushrooms,
 trimmed and sliced

1 large onion, cut into thin wedges

2 garlic cloves, crushed

2 teaspoons fresh oregano or
 1 teaspoon dried oregano

4 Italian tomatoes, sliced

2 teaspoons balsamic vinegar

1 ready-made thick pizza base,
 about 300 g

¾ cup no-salt-added tomato paste

30 g pepperoni (about 16 slices)

1 cup grated reduced-fat
 mozzarella cheese

4 tablespoons chopped parsley
 to sprinkle

double-cheese pizza bites

What a delicious way to welcome your guests! These mini pizzas are loaded with fresh tomato slices, two kinds of cheese, black olives and fresh herbs. And because they're on the light side, everyone will still have room for dinner.

3¼ cups all-purpose flour, plus extra for sprinkling

1 teaspoon sugar

½ teaspoon salt

1 envelope dried yeast, about 8 g

1 cup tepid water

1 tablespoon extra virgin olive oil

2 cups cherry tomatoes, thinly sliced

1 cup reduced-fat mozzarella cheese, grated

4 tablespoons freshly grated Parmesan cheese

12 kalamata olives, pitted and cut into slivers, to sprinkle

¼ cup fresh oregano leaves to sprinkle

1 Place the flour in a large bowl and stir in the sugar, salt and yeast. Make a well in the centre and pour in the tepid water and oil. Gradually mix the flour into the water and oil; use a wooden spoon, then your hand, to make a soft dough.

2 Turn the dough onto a floured surface and knead for about 10 minutes, until smooth and elastic. Sprinkle the surface with a little extra flour if necessary, but try not to add too much as this will make the dough dry. Shape into a ball, cover with a clean dish towel and leave to rise for 10 minutes.

3 Preheat the oven to 450°F (230°C). Line two baking sheets with parchment paper. Divide the dough into 4 pieces. Wrap 3 pieces in plastic wrap and refrigerate. Cut the remaining piece into 12 equal pieces and shape each into a 4 cm ball. Arrange on the baking sheets and flatten into 7 cm rounds. Lightly coat with nonstick cooking spray.

4 Top each with 2–3 tomato slices, 1 teaspoon mozzarella cheese and a little Parmesan cheese. Sprinkle with a few olive slivers and oregano leaves. Bake until the crust is golden-brown and crisp and the cheese is melted and bubbly, about 10 minutes. Repeat to use up the remaining dough. Serve hot.

preparation time **40 mins**

rising time **10 mins**

cooking time **20 mins**

makes **48 pizza bites**

PER PIZZA

40 calories

2 g protein

1 g total fat
0.4 g saturated fat

2 mg cholesterol

6 g total carbohydrate
1 g sugars

0.4 g fibre

55 mg sodium

HEALTH HINT

Olives contain healthy monounsaturated fat, which tends to lower LDL (the "bad") cholesterol, thus helping to prevent the formation of artery-clogging plaque, which increases the risk of heart disease.

tuna and tomato pizza

Add canned tuna to a good tomato sauce, spread it on a ready-made pizza base and you have a delicious, healthy pizza in no time at all. It makes a flavourful change from the usual cheese-laden pizzas.

1 Preheat the oven to 425°F (220°C). Heat 1 teaspoon oil in a small saucepan. Add the onion and cook over a medium heat for 4 minutes or until softened. Add the tomatoes and their juice, oregano, sugar and pepper. Bring to a boil, then leave to bubble for 10 minutes, stirring occasionally.

2 Place the pizza bases on 2 baking sheets. Spread 1 tablespoon tomato sauce over each base. Spoon the tomato mixture over the pizzas, then lay the tuna over the top. Add the capers and sliced olives, and drizzle the remaining oil over the top.

3 Bake the pizzas for 10 minutes or until the bases are golden-brown and crisp. Garnish with the torn basil leaves and serve.

3 teaspoons extra virgin olive oil

1 onion, finely chopped

1 can (398 ml) chopped tomatoes

1/2 teaspoon dried oregano

1/8 teaspoon sugar

pepper to taste

2 ready-made thick pizza bases, about 300 g each

2 tablespoons tomato sauce

1 can (170 g) tuna in water, drained and flaked into chunks

4 teaspoons capers

8 black olives, pitted and sliced

fresh basil leaves to garnish

preparation time **10 mins**

cooking time **25 mins**

serves **4**

PER SERVING

543 calories

24 g protein

10 g total fat
2 g saturated fat

21 mg cholesterol

87 g total carbohydrate
13 g sugars

8 g fibre

1026 mg sodium

HEALTH HINT

Canned tomatoes and tomato sauce are healthy ingredients. They are both rich sources of the phytochemical lycopene (other good sources include pink grapefruit, watermelon and guava), which can help to protect against several types of cancer and heart disease.

desserts, cakes & cookies

peach and berry cobbler

Want to put big smiles on their faces? Bring this luscious dessert straight from the oven to the table. Dripping with fruit and topped with pecan dumplings, it's sure to please. And don't worry if they ask for seconds—it's a low-fat treat.

1.5 kg peaches, peeled and sliced

2 cups blackberries or raspberries

¾ cup firmly packed brown sugar

1 tablespoon cornstarch

2 tablespoons freshly squeezed
    lemon juice

2 cups self-raising flour

⅓ cup pecans, toasted
    and chopped

¼ teaspoon nutmeg

½ cup cold reduced-salt margarine

¾ cup plus 2 tablespoons
    low-fat milk

2 tablespoons sugar

1 Preheat the oven to 350°F (180°C). Coat a 30 x 20 cm (13 x 9 in.) baking pan with nonstick cooking spray. In a large bowl, toss the peaches, blackberries, ½ cup brown sugar, cornstarch and lemon juice. Turn into the baking pan. Bake for 30 minutes.

2 Meanwhile, combine the flour, pecans, remaining brown sugar and nutmeg in a large bowl. Cut in the margarine with a pastry blender or two knives until the mixture resembles very coarse crumbs. Add ¾ cup milk and stir with a fork until a thick batter forms, adding water if necessary.

3 Drop the batter on top of the fruit, spacing evenly, to make 12 dumplings. Lightly brush the dumplings with the remaining milk and sprinkle with sugar.

4 Bake until a skewer inserted in the centre of a dumpling comes out with moist crumbs sticking to it, 25–30 minutes. Serve warm or at room temperature.

preparation time **25 mins**

cooking time **1 hour**

serves **12**

PER SERVING

269 calories

5 g protein

9 g total fat

1 g saturated fat

1 mg cholesterol

42 g total carbohydrate

25 g sugars

4 g fibre

210 mg sodium

COOK'S TIP

If you don't have self-raising flour, substitute 2 cups sifted all-purpose flour mixed with 1 tablespoon baking powder and ½ teaspoon salt. When fresh berries are not available, use 1.25 kg frozen blackberries or raspberries.

steamed kumquat honey pudding

A pleasingly light yet traditional pudding for wintry days, this offers all the pleasure of a steamed pudding without unhealthy saturated fat. Layers of sliced kumquats add a deliciously tangy citrus flavour.

Fb

preparation time **15 mins**
cooking time **1¾ hours**
serves **6**

PER SERVING

337 calories	
10 g protein	
8 g total fat	
2 g saturated fat	
110 mg cholesterol	
57 g total carbohydrate	
36 g sugars	
4 g fibre	
386 mg sodium	

HEALTH HINT

Milk provides calcium and phosphorus—both important for strong bones and teeth—as well as protein and many B vitamins.

1 Place the honey in a 1 litre (1 quart) pudding basin and swirl it so that the honey coats the bottom half. Set aside.

2 Place breadcrumbs in a large mixing bowl. Stir in sugar, flour and baking powder. Add egg, milk and margarine and mix together to form a stiff cake-like mixture.

3 Place a quarter of the pudding mixture in the basin and arrange half the kumquat slices on top. Add half the remaining mixture and top with the remaining kumquat. Finish with the pudding mixture. Press down lightly to smooth the surface.

4 Bring a steamer or deep saucepan of water to a boil. Cover the pudding basin with aluminum foil and tie string around the rim. Use more string to make a handle. Place the basin in the steamer. The water should come halfway up the basin. Cover and steam for 1¾ hours, adding water as necessary.

5 About 20 minutes before serving, make the custard. Place the eggs, sugar and 4 tablespoons milk in a bowl and beat. Place the remaining milk in a saucepan and heat until bubbles appear around the edge. Pour the milk over the egg mixture, stirring, then strain it all back into the saucepan. Cook over low heat, stirring constantly, until the custard thickens enough to coat the spoon thinly. Do not allow to boil. Stir in the vanilla extract.

6 When the pudding is cooked, carefully remove the basin from the steamer. Remove the foil, place a plate over the top of the basin and invert it. Serve the pudding hot with the custard.

2 tablespoons clear honey
2 cups fresh fine white breadcrumbs
½ cup golden brown sugar
¼ cup self-raising flour
1 teaspoon baking powder
1 egg, beaten
2 tablespoons low-fat milk
2 tablespoons reduced-salt margarine
220 g kumquats, sliced (with skin)

CUSTARD

2 eggs
1 tablespoon sugar
1¼ cups low-fat milk
1 teaspoon vanilla extract

sticky date and walnut pudding

On a cold winter day, nothing could be more welcoming than a pudding full of dates and toasted walnuts. It is easy to make and has a lovely moist texture. A tangy pineapple and marmalade sauce makes a perfect accompaniment.

1 cup dried pitted dates, chopped
4 tablespoons low-fat milk
½ cup reduced-salt margarine
½ cup brown sugar
2 eggs, lightly beaten
1 cup self-raising flour
¼ teaspoon ground cinnamon
½ teaspoon ground ginger
½ cup walnuts, toasted and
    roughly chopped

PINEAPPLE AND MARMALADE SAUCE

1 can (398 ml) pineapple pieces in
    natural juice, finely chopped
1 teaspoon arrowroot
5 tablespoons fine-cut orange
    marmalade

1 Preheat the oven to 350°F (180°C). Lightly grease a 1 litre (1 quart) pudding basin lined with a disc of parchment paper.

2 Place the dates in a bowl and pour over 2 tablespoons milk. Stir to coat, then leave to soak.

3 Place the margarine, sugar, eggs and remaining milk in a bowl. Sift over the flour, cinnamon and ginger, and beat with an electric mixer for 2 minutes or until smooth. Fold in the soaked dates and walnuts.

4 Spoon the mixture into the pudding basin. Set the basin in a baking pan and pour in boiling water to come 1 cm up the sides of the basin. Cover the pan and basin with a tent of foil.

5 Bake for about 1 hour or until the pudding is lightly risen and a skewer comes out clean. If not, bake a further 10 minutes.

6 Meanwhile, make the sauce. Drain the pineapple, reserving ⅔ cup of the juice. Blend the arrowroot with a little of the juice in a small saucepan, then stir in the remaining juice. Bring to a boil and simmer for 1 minute or until thickened and clear. Stir the pineapple and marmalade into the sauce and simmer for a further 2–3 minutes, stirring occasionally.

7 Turn the pudding onto a serving plate. Spoon a little sauce over and serve with the remaining sauce in a bowl.

preparation time **25 mins**
cooking time **1 hour**
serves **8**

PER SERVING

382 calories

6 g protein

16 g total fat
2 g saturated fat

54 mg cholesterol

55 g total carbohydrate
42 g sugars

4 g fibre

199 mg sodium

HEART SUPERFOOD

Walnuts have a high unsaturated fat content, particularly as linoleic acid. Some studies have suggested that regularly including a small quantity of walnuts in the diet can help to reduce high blood cholesterol levels and reduce the risk of heart attacks.

apricot and rum brioche pudding

This glamorous version of bread and butter pudding is based on brioche and custard spiked with rum or brandy for a seductive flavour. Sultanas, dried apricots and apricot preserve provide lots of sweetness, so no sugar is needed.

1 Spread the brioche slices with the preserve. (If the preserve is a little thick, warm it gently so that it can be spread easily.) Cut the slices in half diagonally or into squares.

2 Arrange the pieces of brioche in a lightly greased 1 litre (1 quart) ovenproof dish, scattering the sultanas and dried apricots between the layers.

3 Place the eggs in a mixing bowl. Add the milk, vanilla extract and rum or brandy, and whisk together until well combined. Pour the mixture over the brioche, then gently press the brioche down into the liquid. Leave to soak for 20 minutes.

4 Preheat the oven to 350°F (180°C). If desired, pull up the edges of some of the brioche slices to make a peaked effect. Bake the pudding for 30–35 minutes or until it is just firm to the touch. Serve immediately.

Variation If preferred, you can omit the brandy or rum and add another teaspoon vanilla extract.

8 medium-sized slices brioche loaf, about 200 g in total
5 tablespoons apricot preserve
½ cup sultanas
100 g dried apricots, chopped
2 eggs
1¾ cups low-fat milk
1 teaspoon vanilla extract
1 tablespoon dark rum or brandy

preparation time **10 mins**
cooking time **35 mins**
plus 20 mins soaking
serves **4**

PER SERVING

420 calories

14 g protein

9 g total fat
4 g saturated fat

139 mg cholesterol

68 g total carbohydrate
55 g sugars

3 g fibre

324 mg sodium

HEALTH HINT

Dried apricots are a useful source of fibre and also contain some beta carotene, iron and potassium. Regularly using dried apricots in recipes and enjoying them as a snack will help to boost your intake of these essential nutrients.

hazelnut meringue cake

Simply add candles to turn this light but gooey meringue into a birthday cake. As it has a pastry cream and fresh raspberry filling, it's much lower in fat and calories than conventional celebration cakes.

½ cup hazelnuts
4 egg whites
1 cup caster (superfine) sugar
220 g fresh raspberries
icing sugar, sifted, to decorate

VANILLA PASTRY CREAM

1¼ cups low-fat milk, plus
    2 tablespoons extra
    if needed
1 vanilla pod, slit open lengthwise
3 egg yolks
2 tablespoons caster (superfine) sugar
2 tablespoons all-purpose flour
2 tablespoons cornstarch

1 Preheat the broiler, then toast the hazelnuts until golden. Leave to cool. Roughly chop a few and set aside for decoration. Finely chop or grind the remaining hazelnuts.

2 Preheat the oven to 275°F (140°C). Line 2 baking sheets with parchment paper and draw a 20 cm circle on each piece of paper.

3 Place the egg whites in a large bowl and beat with an electric mixer until they form stiff peaks. Gradually add the caster sugar a tablespoon at a time, then continue to beat for 1–2 minutes or until the meringue is very thick and glossy. Fold in the hazelnuts with a large metal spoon.

4 Divide the meringue mixture between the baking sheets and spread evenly within the drawn circles. Bake for 40 minutes, then turn the baking sheets around in the oven so that the meringues colour evenly. Bake for another 35 minutes or until the meringues are set and can be removed easily from the paper. Loosen them from the paper, then leave to cool completely on the baking sheets.

5 While the meringues are cooking, make the pastry cream. Pour 1¼ cups milk into a medium saucepan and bring to a boil. Add the vanilla pod, then remove from the heat and leave to infuse for 30 minutes.

6 Place the egg yolks and sugar in a medium bowl and beat with a whisk for 2–3 minutes or until pale. Sift in the flour and cornstarch and whisk to combine. Remove the vanilla pod from the milk and scrape the seeds into the milk with a sharp knife; discard the pod. Bring the milk just to a boil, then gradually stir it into the egg yolk mixture.

7 Pour the mixture back into the saucepan and bring to a boil, stirring constantly with a wooden spoon or whisk. When thick, simmer gently for 1 minute, still stirring constantly. Remove from the heat. Cover the surface of the pastry cream with wet parchment paper and leave to cool. (Both the meringues and pastry cream can be made a day in advance; store the meringues in an airtight container and the pastry cream in a covered bowl in the refrigerator.)

8 Assemble the cake no more than 1 hour before serving. Place one of the meringues on a serving plate, flat side facing

preparation time **40 mins**
cooking time **1¼ hours**
plus cooling
serves **6**

PER SERVING

332 calories

9 g protein

9 g total fat
1 g saturated fat

109 mg cholesterol

55 g total carbohydrate
49 g sugars

3 g fibre

75 mg sodium

HEART SUPERFOOD

Hazelnuts have excellent levels of copper and magnesium and also provide thiamine, potassium, vitamin B$_6$, folic acid, phosphorus and zinc.

upward, and spread over the pastry cream. If the cream is too thick to spread, beat in the extra milk. Sprinkle with two-thirds of the raspberries, then top with the second meringue. Decorate with the remaining raspberries, the reserved toasted hazelnuts and a light dusting of icing sugar. Cut into thick slices with a sharp knife to serve.

Variations To make mini meringues, use ground hazelnuts or pistachios in the meringue mixture and shape it into ovals with 2 spoons, placing them on baking sheets lined with parchment paper. Bake for 50–60 minutes. Dip the base of each meringue in melted chocolate and sandwich pairs together with a mixture of $^2/_3$ cup Greek-style yogourt or ricotta cheese and $^2/_3$ cup whipped reduced-fat cream. • For a chocolate and chestnut meringue cake, melt 90 g good-quality dark chocolate in a bowl set over a saucepan of hot water. Spread it over the flat side of one meringue and leave to set. Mix 1 can (199 ml) sweetened chestnut purée with 1 cup cooking cream, and spread over the chocolate. Top with the other meringue, and decorate with chocolate curls.

mocha ricotta tiramisu

This delectable version of the popular Italian dessert includes the traditional lady fingers cookies soaked in coffee and liqueur. A creamy mixture of sweetened ricotta and yogourt is sprinkled with grated dark chocolate.

8 lady fingers cookies, about 70 g in total

1 teaspoon espresso instant coffee

½ cup boiling water

2 tablespoons coffee liqueur or brandy

1 teaspoon caster (superfine) sugar

200 g reduced-fat ricotta cheese

200 g Greek-style* yogourt

4 tablespoons icing sugar, sifted

1 teaspoon vanilla extract

30 g good-quality dark chocolate (at least 70% cocoa solids), grated, to decorate

*If you can't find Greek-style yogourt, make your own by straining plain whole-milk yogourt through cheese cloth to remove the excess moisture.

1 Break each of the lady fingers into 3 pieces, then divide evenly among four 250 ml (1 cup) glass tumblers or dessert glasses.

2 Place the coffee in a measuring cup and add the boiling water. Add the liqueur or brandy and caster sugar, and stir to dissolve. Pour evenly over the lady fingers. Leave to soak while you make the topping.

3 Place the ricotta, yogourt, icing sugar and vanilla extract in a bowl and beat with an electric mixer until smooth and creamy. Pile on top of the soaked lady fingers.

4 Sprinkle the top of each dessert with grated chocolate. Cover and chill for at least 30 minutes (but no more than 3–4 hours) before serving.

preparation time **20 mins** plus 30 mins chilling

serves **4**

PER SERVING

290 calories

10 g protein

11 g total fat
7 g saturated fat

62 mg cholesterol

35 g total carbohydrate
30 g sugars

0.3 g fibre

174 mg sodium

HEALTH HINT

Ricotta cheese is much lower in fat and calories than creamy mascarpone, which is traditionally used in this dessert. Adding Greek-style yogourt to the ricotta provides creaminess without loading the fat content.

lemon mousse with strawberries

Sampling this mousse is like spooning up sunshine; jewel-like layers of berries are an unexpected delight. We've lightened up the mousse by substituting gelatin and fat-free yogourt for the usual quantities of eggs and cream.

preparation time **15 mins**

cooking time **5 mins**
plus 3 hours chilling

serves **8**

PER SERVING

129 calories

3 g protein

3 g total fat

1 g saturated fat

32 mg cholesterol

22 g total carbohydrate

22 g sugars

1 g fibre

25 mg sodium

HEALTH HINT

Although the vitamin C in the lemon juice is diminished somewhat by being heated, one serving still provides a useful amount of this antioxidant vitamin.

COOK'S TIP

When you're squeezing lemons for lemonade or other recipes, take a moment to grate the rind before you cut the lemons. Wrap the rind tightly in plastic wrap and freeze it until needed.

1 Hull the strawberries and slice thickly.

2 Sprinkle the gelatin over ¼ cup cold water in a small bowl. Allow to stand for 5 minutes to soften.

3 Place another ¼ cup water, the sugar, lemon rind, lemon juice, oil and egg in a medium saucepan and whisk together until well combined. Cook over a low heat, whisking constantly, until the mixture is hot, about 5 minutes. Whisk in the softened gelatin and cook, whisking constantly, until the gelatin has dissolved, about 1 minute.

4 Remove from the heat, transfer to a medium bowl and cool to room temperature, whisking occasionally. Whisk in the yogourt. Alternately layer the strawberries and lemon mousse in 8 dessert bowls and chill until set, about 3 hours. Serve.

2 cups strawberries
1 envelope gelatin, about 7 g
¾ cup sugar
2 teaspoons grated lemon rind
½ cup freshly squeezed lemon juice
1 tablespoon extra light olive oil
1 large egg
1⅓ cups fat-free plain yogourt

raspberry frozen yogourt

*This **frozen yogourt**, exotically flavoured with rosewater and crème de cassis, is much lower in sugar than store-bought frozen yogourt. Serve scoops on their own, or pile into sundae glasses with fresh fruit and sprigs of mint.*

500 g raspberries

5 tablespoons seedless raspberry preserve

2 tablespoons rosewater

2 tablespoons crème de cassis (optional)

2 cups Greek-style* yogourt

4 tablespoons icing sugar, or to taste

24 raspberries, about 100 g, to decorate (optional)

fresh mint leaves to decorate (optional)

* If you can't find Greek-style yogourt, make your own by straining plain whole-milk yogourt through cheese cloth to remove the excess moisture.

1 Place the raspberries in a medium saucepan and add the raspberry preserve. Warm over a low heat for about 5 minutes or until the raspberries are pulpy, stirring occasionally.

2 Press the raspberries and juice through a nylon sieve into a bowl; discard the seeds in the sieve. Stir in the rosewater and crème de cassis, if using. Whisk in the yogourt until smoothly blended. Taste the mixture and sweeten with the icing sugar.

3 Pour into an ice cream machine and freeze according to the manufacturer's instructions. When you have a smooth and creamy frozen mixture, spoon it into a large freezerproof container. Freeze for at least 1 hour. If you do not have an ice cream machine, pour the mixture straight into a large freezerproof container and freeze for 1 hour or until set round the edges. Beat until the mixture is smooth, then return to the freezer. Freeze for 30 minutes, then beat again. Repeat the freezing and beating several times more until the frozen yogourt has a smooth consistency, then leave it to freeze for at least 1 hour.

4 If storing in the freezer for longer than 1 hour, transfer the frozen yogourt to the refrigerator 20 minutes before serving to soften slightly. Decorate with raspberries and mint, if desired.

30 — C — Fb — GI

preparation time **10 mins**

cooking time **5 mins** plus freezing

serves **8**

PER SERVING

152 calories

4 g protein

5 g total fat
3 g saturated fat

18 mg cholesterol

23 g total carbohydrate
22 g sugars

4 g fibre

44 mg sodium

HEALTH HINT

Although Greek-style yogourt is regarded as very rich and creamy-tasting, it has relatively few calories compared to 35% whipping cream.

little custard pots with cherries

These creamy baked custards, flavoured with vanilla and accompanied by a cherry compote, are sure to be popular with all ages. Take care not to overcook the custards—they should be just set when you take them out of the oven.

preparation time **10 mins**

cooking time **50 mins** plus 15 mins infusing

serves **6**

PER SERVING

176 calories

9 g protein

4 g total fat

1 g saturated fat

147 mg cholesterol

27 g total carbohydrate

25 g sugars

1 g fibre

82 mg sodium

COOK'S TIP

The cherry compote can be used warm, or you can wait until it is at room temperature before spooning it over the custards and serving.

1 Place the milk and vanilla pod in a medium saucepan and heat until almost boiling. Remove from the heat, cover and set aside to infuse for 15 minutes.

2 Preheat the oven to 325°F (160°C). Place the whole eggs, egg yolks, caster sugar and cornstarch in a bowl and lightly whisk together.

3 Bring the milk back to boiling point, then remove the vanilla pod and pour the hot milk over the egg mixture, whisking all the time. Strain the mixture into a large measuring cup, then divide among 6 lightly greased 120 ml (½ cup) ramekins.

4 Set the ramekins in a baking pan and pour enough hot water into the pan to come halfway up the sides of the ramekins. Bake for 30–35 minutes or until lightly set—the custards should still be slightly wobbly. Lift them out of the hot water and place on a wire rack to cool. Once cold, chill until ready to serve.

5 To make the compote, place the golden brown sugar and ⅓ cup water in a saucepan and heat until the sugar dissolves. Bring to a boil, then reduce the heat and add the cherries. Cover and simmer for 4–5 minutes, stirring occasionally. Lift out the cherries with a slotted spoon and place in a serving bowl.

6 Mix the arrowroot with 1 tablespoon cold water. Stir into the cherry juices in the saucepan and simmer for 1 minute, stirring. Allow to cool for a few minutes, then pour over the cherries.

7 Spoon a little of the cherry compote over the top of each custard pot, and serve the rest of the compote in the bowl.

2⅓ cups low-fat milk

½ vanilla pod, slit open lengthwise

2 eggs

2 egg yolks

3 tablespoons caster (superfine) sugar

½ teaspoon cornstarch

CHERRY COMPOTE

2 tablespoons golden brown sugar

450 g cherries, pitted

2 teaspoons arrowroot

double raspberry sorbet

Go ahead raspberry lovers, take a bite. This velvety smooth sorbet and rich sauce give you a double dose of your favourite fruit—and you can make it from frozen berries any time of year.

1 cup sugar

1.5 kg frozen raspberries, slightly thawed

1 tablespoon freshly squeezed lemon juice

1 Place the sugar and 1 cup water in a medium saucepan. Bring to a boil, stirring until the sugar dissolves. Simmer gently for 5 minutes, then remove from the heat.

2 Place the raspberries and lemon juice in a food processor or blender and process until smooth. Press through a nylon sieve into a large bowl; discard the seeds in the sieve.

3 Stir the sugar syrup into the raspberries. Cover and chill for about 1 hour. Reserve $1/2$ cup to use as the sauce.

4 Pour the remaining mixture into an ice cream machine and freeze according to the manufacturer's instructions. Transfer to a large freezerproof container, cover and freeze until ready to serve. If you do not have an ice cream machine, chill a 30 x 20 cm (13 x 9 in.) baking pan in the freezer. Pour in the raspberry mixture and freeze until slushy, about $1 1/2$ hours, stirring every 30 minutes. Place in a food processor and process until smooth. Transfer to a large freezerproof container, cover and freeze until firm, about 4 hours. Stand at room temperature for 10 minutes. Divide between 8 dessert dishes. Drizzle each with 1 tablespoon reserved sauce and serve.

preparation time **25 mins**

cooking time **8 mins**
plus freezing

serves **8**

PER SERVING

170 calories

2 g protein

1 g total fat
0 g saturated fat

0 mg cholesterol

38 g total carbohydrate
37 g sugars

10 g fibre

4 mg sodium

HEALTH HINT

One cup of fresh raspberries contains no fat and only 60 calories, while also providing fibre and vitamin C. Raspberries are also high in pectin, the soluble fibre that helps control blood cholesterol levels, and contain ellagic acid, a phytochemical that is thought to neutralize carcinogens.

Pimm's melon cup

 This fruit salad is inspired by the classic summer drink. A mixture of melon, berries, pear and cucumber is marinated in Pimm's and then served in the cantaloupe shells. A decoration of pretty borage flowers is a traditional finish.

1 Cut the melons in half horizontally and scoop out the seeds. Using a melon baller or a small spoon, scoop out the flesh and place it in a large bowl. Reserve the melon shells.

2 Add the strawberries, pear and cucumber to the melon in the bowl. Reserve some slices of starfruit for decoration and chop the rest. Add to the bowl. Sprinkle the Pimm's over the fruit. Add the mint and stir gently. Cover with plastic wrap and place in the refrigerator to marinate for 20 minutes.

3 Smooth out the melon shells with a spoon. Pile the fruit mixture into the shells and decorate with the reserved slices of starfruit and the flowers, if using.

Variation Turn this into a fruit and vegetable salad using just 1 melon, the strawberries and cucumber plus an apple instead of the pear and 100 g seedless green grapes. Omit the Pimm's. Make a bed of salad greens, including some watercress and chopped green onion, on each plate and pile the fruit on top. Add a scoop of cottage cheese and sprinkle with chopped fresh mint and toasted pine nuts.

1 small cantaloupe
1 small honeydew melon
200 g strawberries, hulled and sliced
1 pear, cut into 2 cm chunks
½ cucumber, diced 1 cm thick
1 starfruit, cut into 5 mm slices
⅓ cup Pimm's
2 tablespoons shredded fresh mint
flowers to decorate (optional)

C **Fb**

preparation time **25 mins** plus 20 mins marinating

serves **4**

PER SERVING

181 calories

4 g protein

1 g total fat
0 g saturated fat

0 mg cholesterol

33 g total carbohydrate
32 g sugars

7 g fibre

134 mg sodium

HEALTH HINT

Moderate alcohol consumption is now associated with a lower risk of death from coronary heart disease. Recommended intake is no more than 2 standard drinks for men and no more than 1 standard drink for women a day. Avoid excessive drinking on weekends and at parties.

rich chocolate torte

A generous amount of good-quality dark chocolate makes this cake beautifully moist and rich. It's perfect with a cup of coffee, or warm for dessert, with a spoonful of reduced-fat cream or yogourt and some fresh berries.

preparation time **20 mins**
cooking time **25 mins**
serves **10**

PER SERVING

225 calories

4 g protein

14 g total fat
5 g saturated fat

87 mg cholesterol

22 g total carbohydrate
18 g sugars

0.4 g fibre

68 mg sodium

HEART SUPERFOOD

Scientists at the University of California have discovered that chocolate, particularly dark chocolate, contains significant amounts of phenols. These substances work as an antioxidant, helping to prevent the oxidation of harmful LDL cholesterol, which is the cholesterol responsible for clogging the arteries.

1 Preheat the oven to 350°F (180°C). Grease a 25 cm (10 in.) springform cake pan and line it with greased parchment paper.

2 Break up the chocolate and place it in a heatproof bowl with the margarine. Set the bowl over a saucepan of almost boiling water, making sure the water does not touch the base of the bowl. Leave to melt, then remove from the heat and stir the mixture until smooth.

3 Meanwhile, place the eggs and sugar in a large bowl and beat with an electric mixer until the mixture has increased considerably in volume and leaves a trail on the surface when the beaters are lifted out. (If using a whisk or egg beater, set the bowl over a saucepan of almost boiling water, making sure the water is not touching the base of the bowl.)

4 Add the chocolate mixture and fold in with a large metal spoon. Gradually sift the flour over the top of the mixture, folding it in until it is just combined.

5 Turn the mixture into the prepared cake pan, gently spreading it to the edges to level the surface. Bake for 15–20 minutes or until the top of the cake feels just firm to the touch. Leave to cool in the pan.

6 Remove the cake from the pan and peel away the parchment paper. Cut into thin wedges for serving, decorating each with a Cape gooseberry or strawberry, if desired. Dust with the sifted icing sugar and cocoa powder. The cake can be kept in the refrigerator for 2–3 days.

Variations You could use ground almonds instead of flour. • If you're making the torte for a special occasion, drizzle 4 tablespoons brandy or an orange liqueur such as Cointreau over the top of the cake after baking, then leave to cool.

170 g good-quality dark chocolate (at least 70% cocoa solids)

⅓ cup reduced-salt margarine

4 eggs

½ cup dark brown sugar

¼ cup all-purpose flour

10 Cape gooseberries, papery skins folded back, or strawberries, hulled, to decorate (optional)

icing sugar to decorate

cocoa powder to decorate

daffodil cake

Usher in spring by baking a daffodil cake—a fragrant, delicate sponge cake with swirls of yellow and white in every slice. This festive treat is lightly flavoured with orange, and it boasts one mere gram of fat per serving.

4 large eggs, separated
1½ cups caster (superfine) sugar
2 teaspoons grated orange rind
1 tablespoon vanilla extract
6 large egg whites
1 teaspoon cream of tartar
1⅓ cups all-purpose flour, sifted
⅓ cup icing sugar, sifted, to decorate

1 Preheat the oven to 375°F (190°C). Place the yolks, ¼ cup sugar and orange rind in a large bowl. Beat with an electric mixer at high speed until the mixture is thick and lemon-coloured, about 10 minutes. Add the vanilla and beat in.

2 Place the egg whites in a separate large bowl and beat with clean beaters at high speed until foamy. Add the cream of tartar and beat until soft peaks form. Add the remaining sugar, 2 tablespoons at a time, and beat until the sugar dissolves and stiff, glossy peaks form.

3 Sift ⅓ cup flour over the egg whites and gently fold in with a whisk just until the flour is no longer visible. Repeat three times until all the flour is used. Spoon one-third of the egg white mixture into the yolk mixture and gently fold in.

4 Spoon heaping tablespoons of the yellow and white mixtures by turns into a 28 or 30 cm (11 or 12 in.) ring pan. Swirl a thin spatula or knife through the mixture to give a marbled effect. Lightly swirl the top of the cake, too. Bake until the cake springs back when lightly touched, about 35 minutes.

5 Leaving the cake in the pan, invert it and place over the neck of a bottle to cool completely. (Cooling the cake in the pan the right way up will cause it to sink.) Run a knife around the cake to loosen it. Turn it out onto a plate and dust with icing sugar.

preparation time **20 mins**
cooking time **35 mins**
serves **16**

PER SERVING

156 calories	
5 g protein	
2 g total fat	
1 g saturated fat	
63 mg cholesterol	
31 g total carbohydrate	
23 g sugars	
0.5 g fibre	
36 mg sodium	

COOK'S TIP

When beating egg whites, always use a clean bowl and clean beaters. Even a trace of fat or egg yolk can cause the egg whites to collapse or prevent them from forming stiff peaks. Cream of tartar added to the egg whites gives the cake a fine grain and helps to keep it from pulling away from the side of the pan.

raspberry and passion fruit sponge roll

 This light, almost fat-free sponge, rolled up around a raspberry and passion fruit filling, makes a very pretty dessert. It's ideal with sweet raspberries. Serve with homemade custard, if desired.

30 C Fb

preparation time **20 mins**
cooking time **10 mins**
serves **8**

PER SERVING

194 calories

6 g protein

3 g total fat
1 g saturated fat

94 mg cholesterol

36 g total carbohydrate
23 g sugars

5 g fibre

28 mg sodium

HEALTH HINT

Passion fruit offers one of the highest fibre counts of any fruit. In addition, it supplies moderate amounts of vitamin C and riboflavin and the minerals potassium, magnesium and zinc.

1 To make the fruit filling, place half the raspberries and the icing sugar in a bowl and crush lightly with a fork. Stir in the passion fruit pulp.

2 To make the sponge, preheat the oven to 400°F (200°C). Grease a 30 x 20 cm (13 x 9 in.) Swiss roll pan and line the bottom with parchment paper.

3 Place the eggs and sugar in a large bowl and beat with an electric mixer until the mixture is very thick and pale, and leaves a trail on the surface when the beaters are lifted out.

4 Sift half the flour over the mixture and gently fold in with a large metal spoon. Sift over the remaining flour and fold in together with the tepid water.

5 Pour the mixture into the prepared pan and shake gently to spread it evenly into the corners. Bake for 10–12 minutes or until the sponge is well risen and pale golden, and springs back when pressed lightly.

6 Turn out onto a sheet of parchment paper that is slightly larger than the sponge. Peel off the lining paper. Remove the crusty edges of the sponge with a sharp knife and make a score mark 2 cm from one of the shorter edges all the way along.

7 Spread the fruit filling over the hot sponge, leaving a 1 cm border all around. Scatter over the remaining half of the raspberries. Carefully roll up the sponge, starting from the edge with the score mark. Place the roll, seam-side down, on a plate.

8 Serve warm or cold, cut into slices. Decorate each serving with a few extra raspberries and a sprig of mint.

24 raspberries, about 100 g, to decorate
sprigs of fresh mint to decorate

FRUIT FILLING
350 g raspberries
4 tablespoons icing sugar, sifted
pulp from 4 passion fruits

SPONGE
3 large eggs
²⁄₃ cup caster (superfine) sugar
1 cup all-purpose flour
1 tablespoon tepid water

citrus meringue pie

*A modern twist on lemon meringue pie, this recipe uses lime and orange as
well as lemon in the filling. The case is made with crushed cookie crumbs held
together with egg white, rather than melted butter, to reduce the fat content.*

COOKIE CASE
150 g wheat bran cookies
1 egg white, whisked lightly to loosen

CITRUS FILLING
grated rind and juice of 1 large lemon
grated rind and juice of 1 large lime
juice of 1 large orange
⅓ cup cornstarch
2 large egg yolks
⅓ cup caster (superfine) sugar

MERINGUE TOPPING
3 large egg whites
⅓ cup caster (superfine) sugar

1 Preheat the oven to 350°F (180°C). Place the cookies in a
plastic bag and crush with a rolling pin. Tip into a mixing
bowl, add the egg white and stir until moistened.

2 Spoon the cookie mixture into a lightly greased, nonstick
23 cm (9 in.) springform cake pan. Using the back of a spoon,
press the crumbs in a thin layer over the bottom and sides of
the pan. Bake for 7–10 minutes or until firm. Leave to cool.

3 To make the filling, combine the rind and juice of the lemon
and lime with the orange juice in a heatproof bowl. Stir in
the cornstarch to make a smooth paste. Bring 1¼ cups water
to a boil in a saucepan. Pour the water over the juice mixture,
stirring constantly, then return to the pan. Bring to a boil over
medium heat, stirring. Reduce the heat and simmer, stirring
frequently, for 1 minute or until thick and smooth.

4 Remove the pan from the heat and cool for a minute.
Meanwhile, place the egg yolks and sugar in a small bowl
and combine. Add a little of the hot citrus mixture and stir,
then pour this into the remaining citrus mixture and stir until
thoroughly combined. Pour into the prepared cookie case.

5 To make the meringue topping, place the egg whites in
a bowl and beat with an electric mixer until stiff. Gradually
add the sugar and beat until stiff, glossy peaks form.

6 Spoon the egg whites over the top of the citrus filling
to cover evenly, swirling the egg whites attractively. Bake
for about 15 minutes or until the meringue is golden-brown.
Leave the pie to cool before serving.

preparation time **30 mins**
cooking time **30 mins**
serves **8**

PER SERVING

205 calories

4 g protein

5 g total fat
2 g saturated fat

56 mg cholesterol

38 g total carbohydrate
24 g sugars

1 g fibre

109 mg sodium

HEALTH HINT

Eggs are one of the few
sources of vitamin D. It is
found in the yolk and is
not destroyed by cooking.
The vitamin A and vitamin
B content of eggs is also
concentrated in the yolk
rather than the white.

very fruity Christmas pudding

Lighter than the traditional pudding, this Christmas pudding is packed with fruit and soaked in sherry or brandy and orange juice so it's extra juicy. Served with brandy sauce, it won't leave you feeling uncomfortably full.

1 Place all the dried fruit in a bowl. Add the orange rind and juice and sherry or brandy, and set aside to soak.

2 Grease a 1.5 litre (2½ pint) pudding basin and place a disc of parchment paper on the bottom.

3 Beat together the margarine and sugar with an electric mixer until light and fluffy, then gradually beat in the eggs. Stir in the apple, carrot, almonds and soaked fruits. Sift over the flour and mixed spice, add the breadcrumbs and mix together.

4 Spoon the mixture into the pudding basin and smooth the top. Lay a doubled sheet of parchment paper and then of aluminum foil on top. Fold to make a pleat in the centre, then smooth down around the basin. Tie securely with string.

5 Bring a steamer or deep pan of water to a boil. Place the basin inside and steam for 3 hours, adding water as needed.

6 Remove the basin and take off the foil and paper. Cover with a dish towel and cool completely. Wrap in fresh parchment paper and foil. Store in a cool, dark place for up to 3 months.

7 On the day of serving, steam the pudding for a further 1½ hours. To make the sauce, blend the cornstarch with ⅓ cup milk. Heat the remaining milk until almost boiling, then pour over the cornstarch mixture, stirring. Return to the pan and stir over medium heat until thickened. Simmer for a further 1–2 minutes, still stirring. Add the sugar and brandy and stir to dissolve. Taste for sweetness, adding a little more sugar if necessary. Turn out the pudding onto a serving plate. Serve with the hot brandy sauce in a gravy boat.

preparation time **40 mins**

cooking time
4 hours 40 mins

serves **10**

PER SERVING

458 calories

10 g protein

13 g total fat

2 g saturated fat

47 mg cholesterol

72 g total carbohydrate

58 g sugars

5 g fibre

243 mg sodium

COOK'S TIP

The brandy-laced sauce, made with low-fat milk and cornstarch, provides a much healthier alternative to cream or brandy butter.

⅔ cup currants

⅔ cup raisins

⅔ cup sultanas

½ cup dried pitted dates, chopped

½ cup dried apricots, chopped

⅔ cup dried cranberries

grated rind and juice of
   1 large orange

4 tablespoons sherry or brandy

½ cup reduced-salt margarine

½ cup firmly packed dark
   brown sugar

2 eggs, beaten

1 dessert apple, peeled, cored
   and diced

1 large carrot, finely grated

⅓ cup flaked almonds, toasted

½ cup self-raising flour

2 teaspoons mixed spice

1¼ cups fresh white breadcrumbs

BRANDY SAUCE

⅓ cup cornstarch

4 cups low-fat milk

4 tablespoons caster (superfine)
   sugar, or to taste

4 tablespoons brandy

upside-down pear pudding

This comforting pudding is perfect for a Sunday lunch on a chilly day. Pears and blackberries are topped with an orange-scented sponge mixture and baked, then the pudding is turned out upside-down, so the luscious fruit is on top.

2 tablespoons golden syrup

3 ripe pears

1 cup blackberries or raspberries

½ cup reduced-salt margarine

½ cup firmly packed dark brown sugar

2 eggs, beaten

1⅓ cups self-raising flour

finely grated rind of 1 small orange

2 tablespoons low-fat milk,
    or as needed

Greek-style* yogourt to serve
    (optional)

*If you can't find Greek-style yogourt, make your own by straining plain whole-milk yogourt through cheese cloth to remove the excess moisture.

1 Preheat the oven to 350°F (180°C). Grease a deep 20 cm (8 in.) round cake pan and line the bottom with parchment paper.

2 Heat the golden syrup gently in a small saucepan until it is runny, then pour it over the bottom of the pan. Peel, halve and core the pears. Arrange them, cut side down and in one layer, around the bottom of the pan. Scatter over the blackberries or raspberries.

3 Place the margarine and sugar in a large bowl and beat with an electric mixer until pale and fluffy. Gradually add the eggs and beat well. Fold in the flour, orange rind and 2 tablespoons milk with a large metal spoon to give a soft, dropping consistency. Add a little more milk if needed. Spoon the sponge mixture evenly over the fruit in the pan and level the surface.

4 Bake for 50–60 minutes or until risen and golden-brown. If the pudding seems to be browning too much toward the end of the cooking time, cover loosely with aluminum foil.

5 Leave to cool in the pan for about 10 minutes, then place an inverted serving plate on top. Turn the pan and plate over, holding them firmly together, so the pudding falls out onto the plate. Serve warm, cut into wedges, with yogourt, if desired.

Variations You could use 6 canned pear halves in natural juice, well drained, instead of fresh pears, and substitute maple syrup for the golden syrup. • Try an upside-down pineapple and blueberry pudding, replacing the pears and blackberries with 4 canned pineapple rings in natural juice, well drained, and 170 g fresh blueberries. • Or make an upside-down ginger and plum pudding. Instead of pears and blackberries, arrange 6 halved plums in the base of the pan. For the sponge mixture, use ⅔ cup each of white and whole-wheat self-raising flour. Omit the orange rind and add 1½ teaspoons ground ginger and 3–4 pieces preserved ginger in syrup, finely chopped.

 Fb

preparation time **25 mins**

cooking time **1 hour**

serves **6**

PER SERVING

417 calories
6 g protein
19 g total fat
4 g saturated fat
72 mg cholesterol
58 g total carbohydrate
33 g sugars
4 g fibre
339 mg sodium

HEALTH HINT

Golden syrup is a residual syrup from sugar milling. It is made up of the sugars sucrose, glucose and fructose, but because it contains more water and less sucrose than table sugar, it is not as sweet.

iced fairy cakes

Fairy cakes are easy to prepare and always popular with children. Using ricotta cheese in the topping makes a lighter, fresher alternative to the more usual glacé icing. The cakes are best iced shortly before serving.

½ cup reduced-salt margarine
½ cup caster (superfine) sugar
2 eggs
1 cup white self-raising flour
¼ cup whole-wheat self-raising flour
½ teaspoon baking powder
finely grated rind of ½ orange
30 g dried apricots, thinly sliced,
    to decorate

ORANGE RICOTTA ICING
1 cup reduced-fat ricotta cheese
½ cup icing sugar
finely grated rind of ½ orange

1 Preheat the oven to 350°F (180°C). Line a 12 cup and a 6 cup cupcake pan or muffin pan with cupcake cups.

2 Place the margarine, sugar and eggs in a large bowl. Sift the white and whole-wheat flours and the baking powder into the bowl. Add the orange rind and beat with an electric mixer for 2 minutes or until smooth and creamy.

3 Spoon the mixture into the cupcake cups. Bake for about 20 minutes or until just firm to the touch. Transfer to a wire rack to cool. (The cakes can be stored in an airtight container for up to 2 days before being iced.)

4 To make the icing, place the ricotta in a bowl and sift over the icing sugar. Add the orange rind and beat with a wooden spoon until well mixed.

5 Spread a little icing over the top of each cake and decorate with a couple of dried apricot slices. Serve as soon as possible after icing.

preparation time **20 mins**
cooking time **20 mins**
makes **18 cakes**

PER CAKE

139 calories
3 g protein
7 g total fat
2 g saturated fat
30 mg cholesterol
16 g total carbohydrate
11 g sugars
1 g fibre
128 mg sodium

HEALTH HINT

Dried apricots are one of the richest fruit sources of iron, and they provide soluble fibre.

COOK'S TIP

Using a mixture of whole-wheat flour and all-purpose flour increases the fibre content of these cakes without making them too heavy.

preparation time **8 mins**

cooking time **1 min**

serves **4**

PER SERVING

247 calories

6 g protein

6 g total fat

4 g saturated fat

23 mg cholesterol

43 g total carbohydrate

40 g sugars

2 g fibre

52 mg sodium

HEALTH HINT

Bananas are great energy providers and one of the best fruit sources of potassium, a mineral we need in order to keep a stable balance of water in our bodies. Apart from pure carbohydrate, bananas also provide fibre plus useful amounts of vitamins B_6 and C, magnesium and copper.

cinnamon banana caramels

Any fruit—fresh, canned or frozen—can be used to make this instant version of crème brûlée. The fruit is topped with Greek-style yogourt—lower in fat than cream—then with golden brown sugar, and grilled to a rich caramel topping.

1 Preheat the broiler. Peel the bananas and cut each one into about 16 slices. Divide the slices among four 250 ml (1 cup) ramekins and sprinkle with the ground cinnamon. Divide the yogourt between the ramekins, spooning it over the banana slices to cover them completely. Sprinkle 1 tablespoon sugar evenly over each dessert.

2 Place the ramekins on a baking sheet and place them under the broiler. Cook for about 1 minute or until the sugar melts into the yogourt—keep watching to make sure that it does not burn. Remove from the oven and leave to cool for a few minutes before serving.

Variations Instead of yogourt, you could use reduced-fat ricotta cheese or reduced-fat cream. • Try chopped peaches or nectarines, or a mixture of summer fruits, prepared the same way. Plums, rhubarb, cherries and raspberries can also be used, but these fruits are best if they are lightly stewed in a minimum amount of water until tender, then cooled, before the yogourt topping goes on.

4 bananas

¼ teaspoon ground cinnamon

1¼ cups Greek-style* yogourt

4 tablespoons golden brown sugar

*If you can't find Greek-style yogourt, make your own by straining plain whole-milk yogourt through cheese cloth to remove the excess moisture.

gingerbread

This delicious, lightly spiced gingerbread is hard to resist. Enjoy a slice with a cup of tea or try it for dessert, with custard or a little reduced-fat cream or plain yogourt plus, perhaps, a spoonful of fresh apple compote.

½ cup firmly packed dark brown sugar
⅓ cup reduced-salt margarine
½ cup treacle
⅔ cup white all-purpose flour
⅔ cup whole-wheat all-purpose flour
½ cup rye flour
1 teaspoon baking soda
1 tablespoon ground ginger
1 teaspoon mixed spice
2 eggs, lightly beaten
⅔ cup low-fat milk

1 Preheat the oven to 325°F (160°C). Lightly grease a 23 x 13 cm (9 x 5 in.) loaf pan and line the bottom with parchment paper.

2 Place the sugar, margarine and treacle in a medium saucepan and heat gently until melted and well blended, stirring occasionally. Remove from the heat and cool slightly.

3 Sift the white, whole-wheat and rye flours, baking soda, ginger and mixed spice into a large bowl. Make a well in the centre and pour in the melted mixture, together with the eggs and milk. Beat together until smooth (the mixture will be very runny). Pour into the pan.

4 Bake for 1¼–1½ hours or until risen, firm to the touch and nicely browned. Leave the cake to cool in the pan for a few minutes, then turn it out onto a wire rack to cool completely. Gingerbread can be kept, wrapped in foil or in an airtight container, for up to 1 week.

preparation time **15 mins**
cooking time **1½ hours**
serves **10**

PER SERVING

256 calories

5 g protein

9 g total fat
2 g saturated fat

44 mg cholesterol

40 g total carbohydrate
23 g sugars

2 g fibre

229 mg sodium

HEALTH HINT

Compared with wheat flour, rye flour has much less gluten, which explains why rye breads such as pumpernickel tend to have a heavier texture. Rye flour contains high quantities of pentosans (long-chain sugars), which have a high water-binding capacity. Baked goods made with rye flour retain moisture, which means they swell in the stomach, giving a sensation of fullness.

fruit and pistachio baklava

Here is an updated version of the traditional Greek pastry, made with a filling of dates, dried mango and pistachio nuts. Although this baklava uses less fat and honey than usual, it is most definitely a special sweet snack.

preparation time **30 mins**

cooking time **30 mins**

makes **20 squares**

PER SQUARE

158 calories

2 g protein

6 g total fat

1 g saturated fat

0 mg cholesterol

24 g total carbohydrate

16 g sugars

1 g fibre

115 mg sodium

HEALTH HINT

The nutrients in fresh fruit are concentrated when they are dried, so they are much higher in minerals, dietary fibre and some vitamins such as beta carotene. Most of their vitamin C, however, is lost after drying but they nevertheless remain nutritious cooking ingredients.

1 Gently heat the margarine and oil in a small saucepan until melted and blended. Remove the pan from the heat and set aside. Mix together the dried mango, dates, pistachios and cinnamon in a bowl. Set aside.

2 Preheat the oven to 425°F (220°C). Lightly grease a shallow 28 x 18 cm (11 x 7 in.) pan with some melted margarine mixture.

3 Place 1 sheet filo pastry in the bottom of the pan, allowing the pastry to come up the sides if necessary, and brush sparingly with the melted margarine. Layer over 4 more sheets of filo, brushing each one lightly with the melted margarine. Spread with one-third of the fruit mixture and half the honey.

4 Repeat the layering of filo sheets and fruit mixture twice. Top with the remaining 5 sheets of filo, brushing each sheet with melted margarine. Trim the edges of the pastry to fit the pan.

5 Mark the surface of the pastry into 20 squares using a sharp knife. Bake for 15 minutes, then reduce the oven to 350°F (180°C). Bake 10–15 minutes or until crisp and golden-brown.

6 Meanwhile, gently warm the remaining honey and orange juice in a small saucepan until blended, stirring constantly.

7 Remove the cake pan from the oven and pour the honey and orange mixture evenly over the cooked baklava. Leave it to cool in the pan. When cold, cut into the marked squares for serving.

2 tablespoons reduced-salt margarine

2 tablespoons sunflower oil

80 g dried mango, finely chopped

1/2 cup dried pitted dates, finely chopped

1/2 cup pistachios, finely chopped

1 1/2 teaspoons ground cinnamon

20 sheets filo pastry, about 18 x 30 cm each

2/3 cup clear honey

1/4 cup freshly squeezed orange juice

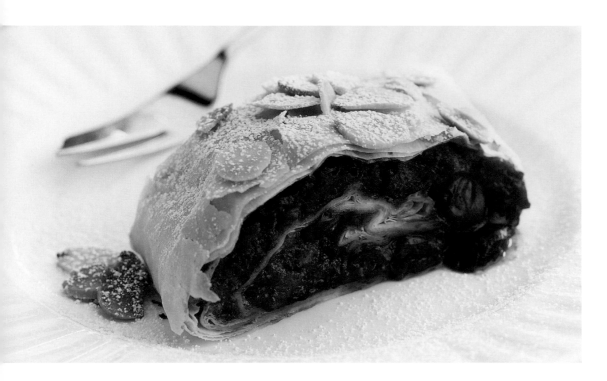

cherry and almond strudel

Austria's famous melt-in-the-mouth pastry looks very impressive, but is surprisingly easy to make. Ground almonds and breadcrumbs absorb the juice from the cherries, so the layers of filo pastry bake wonderfully light and crisp.

3 sheets filo pastry, 30 x 50 cm each

2 tablespoons reduced-salt margarine, melted

15 g flaked almonds

1 tablespoon icing sugar, sifted, to decorate

Greek-style* yogourt to serve (optional)

FRUIT FILLING

⅓ cup fresh white breadcrumbs

⅓ cup ground almonds

¼ cup brown sugar

finely grated rind of 1 orange

670 g cherries, pitted and halved if large

---

* If you can't find Greek-style yogourt, make your own by straining plain whole-milk yogourt through cheese cloth to remove the excess moisture.

1 Preheat the oven to 400°F (200°C). Lightly grease a nonstick baking sheet. To make the fruit filling, place the breadcrumbs, almonds, brown sugar and orange rind in a large bowl and stir together. Add the cherries and mix well.

2 Lay a sheet of filo pastry out on a clean dish towel and brush lightly with melted margarine. Place a second sheet of filo on top and brush with margarine. Repeat with the third sheet.

3 Spoon the fruit filling evenly over the pastry, leaving a 2 cm margin clear around the edges. Fold in the edges along the short sides.

4 With the help of the dish towel, roll up from a long side to make a thick sausage shape. Transfer to the prepared sheet, placing the seam underneath and curving the strudel slightly to fit, if necessary. Brush with the remaining margarine, then scatter over the flaked almonds.

5 Bake for 20 minutes or until the pastry and almonds are golden-brown. Dust with the icing sugar and serve hot or warm, with a little Greek-style yogourt, if desired.

preparation time **30 mins**

cooking time **20 mins**

serves **6**

PER SERVING
198 calories
4 g protein
9 g total fat
1 g saturated fat
0 mg cholesterol
26 g total carbohydrate
19 g sugars
3 g fibre
97 mg sodium

HEART SUPERFOOD

Almonds are a good source of vitamin E, a powerful antioxidant that helps to protect against heart disease.

carrot cake with light cream cheese icing

Go ahead, take another bite. This cake is delicious, and really good for you! Each bite provides beta carotene, which helps protect your heart. And you don't need to be a pastry chef in a four-star restaurant to make it.

1 Preheat the oven to 350°F (180°C). Coat a 25 cm (10 in.) fluted ring pan with nonstick cooking spray. Dust the pan with a little flour, tapping out any excess.

2 Place the flour, mixed spice and baking soda in a large bowl and stir together. Make a well in the centre. Place the buttermilk, oil, sugar, eggs and vanilla extract in a bowl and whisk until blended and frothy. Pour into the well in the dry ingredients and stir just until combined. Fold in the carrots.

3 Pour the mixture into the prepared pan and level the surface. Lightly tap the pan to break up any large air bubbles. Bake until a skewer inserted in the centre comes out clean, about 50 minutes. Leave the cake to cool in the pan for 10 minutes, then turn it out onto a wire rack to cool completely.

4 To make the icing, place the vanilla extract, cream cheese and buttermilk in a medium bowl and beat with an electric mixer until softened. Gradually add the icing sugar and blend just until the icing is smooth. Place the cake on a serving plate and cover with the icing, letting some drip down the sides. Refrigerate the cake until ready to serve.

3 ¾ cups self-raising flour
2 tablespoons mixed spice
1 ½ teaspoons baking soda
2 cups buttermilk
½ cup vegetable oil
1 ½ cups sugar
3 large eggs
2 teaspoons vanilla extract
3 cups finely grated carrot, about 8 medium carrots

LIGHT CREAM CHEESE ICING

2 teaspoons vanilla extract
250 g reduced-fat cream cheese, at room temperature
1 tablespoon buttermilk
2 cups icing sugar, sifted

preparation time **20 mins**
cooking time **50 mins**
serves **16**

PER SERVING

388 calories

8 g protein

12 g total fat
4 g saturated fat

58 mg cholesterol

64 g total carbohydrate
40 g sugars

2 g fibre

452 mg sodium

HEALTH HINT

Cooking carrots, as in this recipe, breaks down the cellular walls that hold the heart-healthy beta carotene, thus increasing the availability of this vital nutrient to the body.

COOK'S TIP

This heart-smart cake recipe uses about one-third the oil of the traditional recipe, only 3 eggs instead of 5, and buttermilk for extra moistness.

Spanish orange and almond cake

Made with whole oranges—simmered until very tender and then finely chopped—and ground almonds, this classic Spanish cake has a moist, light texture and a wonderful fresh flavour.

1 Place the chopped oranges in a small saucepan. Add 1 tablespoon water, then cover the pan and simmer gently for 30 minutes or until the oranges are soft and all the excess liquid has evaporated. Leave to cool.

2 Preheat the oven to 350°F (180°C). Line the bottom and sides of a 23 cm (9 in.) springform cake pan with parchment paper. Finely chop the oranges in a food processor or blender, or with a sharp knife.

3 Place the egg whites in a large bowl and beat with an electric mixer until they form stiff peaks. Gradually add half the caster sugar, then beat for 1 minute.

4 Place the egg yolks and the remaining caster sugar in another bowl and, using the same beaters, beat for 2–3 minutes or until pale and quite thick. Add the oranges and beat to combine well. Carefully fold in the ground almonds with a large metal spoon.

5 Stir in 3 spoonfuls of the egg whites to loosen the mixture, then gently fold in the remaining whites. Transfer the mixture to the pan and level the surface. Sprinkle with the flaked almonds.

6 Bake for 50–55 minutes or until the cake is golden and a skewer inserted in the centre comes out clean. Check the cake after 20 minutes and again at 30 minutes, and cover lightly with aluminum foil if it is browning too quickly.

7 Leave the cake to cool in the pan, then turn it out, peel away the lining paper and transfer to a serving plate. Dust with icing sugar before serving. The cake can be kept in an airtight container for up to 2 days.

Variations This cake is delicious served with a mixture of ²/₃ cup whipped, reduced-fat cream and 150 g ricotta cheese. • Instead of ground almonds alone, use a mixture of 1¼ cups each of ground almonds and semolina or instant polenta. Because this cake will be a little drier, drizzle over 2–4 tablespoons Grand Marnier, Amaretto liqueur or freshly squeezed orange juice rather than dusting with icing sugar.

2 oranges, about 280 g, washed and roughly chopped (with skin), pips discarded
5 eggs, separated
1 cup caster (superfine) sugar
2½ cups ground almonds
2 tablespoons flaked almonds
icing sugar, sifted, to decorate

preparation time **30 mins**
cooking time
1 hour 25 mins
serves **10**

PER SERVING

275 calories

8 g protein

17 g total fat
2 g saturated fat

108 mg cholesterol

24 g total carbohydrate
24 g sugars

3 g fibre

30 mg sodium

HEALTH HINT

Using whole oranges boosts the fibre and vitamin C content of this cake. Studies have shown a connection between a regular intake of vitamin C and the maintenance of intellectual function in elderly people. Also, this cake is suitable for those on gluten-free or wheat-free diets as it is made without flour.

blueberry cheesecake

Compared with most cheesecakes, this version isn't particularly high in fat, as it uses low-fat cottage cheese instead of the traditional cream cheese, and is lightened by folding in whisked egg whites before baking.

120 g wheat bran cookies

2 tablespoons rolled oats

2 tablespoons reduced-salt margarine, melted

1²⁄₃ cups low-fat cottage cheese

5 tablespoons reduced-fat ricotta cheese

3 eggs

1 tablespoon cornstarch

finely grated rind of 1 large lemon

1 cup icing sugar, sifted

140 g blueberries

60 g blueberries, to decorate

fresh mint leaves, to decorate

1 tablespoon icing sugar, sifted, to decorate

1 Preheat the oven to 350°F (180°C). Line the bottom of a 20 cm (8 in.) springform cake pan with parchment paper.

2 Place the cookies in a plastic bag and crush with a rolling pin. Tip into a bowl, add the oats and margarine, and mix.

3 Spread this mixture evenly over the bottom and just up the sides of the prepared pan, pressing down firmly, and set aside.

4 Place the cottage cheese in a food processor or blender and blend until smooth. Add the ricotta cheese, 1 egg, 2 egg yolks, cornstarch and lemon rind. Blend briefly until evenly mixed. Tip the mixture into a bowl.

5 Beat the 2 egg whites with an electric mixer in another bowl to form soft peaks. Slowly add the icing sugar and beat until thick and glossy. Gently fold half the egg whites into the cheese mixture. Fold in the blueberries, then the remaining whites.

6 Pour the mixture over the base and bake for 30 minutes. Cover loosely with foil and reduce the heat to 325°F (160°C). Bake for a further hour or until the cheesecake feels just set in the centre. Turn off the oven and leave the cheesecake inside to cool for 30 minutes, with the door slightly ajar.

7 Transfer the cheesecake to a wire rack to cool completely, then chill until ready to serve. Remove it from the pan, peel off the lining paper and place it on a serving plate. Decorate with blueberries and a few mint leaves, and dust with icing sugar.

preparation time **25 mins**

cooking time **1½ hours**

serves **8**

PER SERVING

294 calories

14 g protein

13 g total fat
4 g saturated fat

94 mg cholesterol

33 g total carbohydrate
23 g sugars

2 g fibre

199 mg sodium

HEALTH HINT

Blueberries are a good source of vitamin C and, like cranberries, they contain compounds that have been shown to inhibit the bacteria that can cause urinary tract infections. Studies have suggested that these compounds may also help to protect against cataracts and glaucoma.

preparation time **15 mins**

cooking time **45 mins**

makes **16 slices**

PER SLICE

228 calories

4 g protein

8 g total fat
1 g saturated fat

31 mg cholesterol

36 g total carbohydrate
21 g sugars

1 g fibre

171 mg sodium

HEART SUPERFOOD

Walnut oil is a rich source of heart-friendly monounsaturated and polyunsaturated fats and the antioxidant vitamin E. It may help lower the risk of heart disease by increasing high-density lipoprotein (HDL), or "good," cholesterol.

cappuccino chiffon cake

When chiffon cakes first appeared in the 1940s, the focus was on how easy they were to mix. Today, however, we also value the fact that they are sweet treats that are lower in fat and cholesterol than most.

1 Preheat the oven to 325°F (160°C). Place the flour, sugar, baking powder and cinnamon in a medium bowl and mix. Place the oil, 2 egg yolks, coffee, cocoa powder and vanilla extract in a large bowl and beat with an electric mixer until smooth. Fold in the flour mixture with a large metal spoon.

2 Place the 6 egg whites in another bowl and beat with clean beaters until frothy. Add the cream of tartar and beat until stiff peaks form. Gently fold into the cake mixture.

3 Spoon the mixture into an ungreased 25 cm (10 in.) ring pan. Bake until a skewer inserted in the centre of the cake comes out clean, about 45 minutes.

4 Leaving the cake in the pan, invert it and place over the neck of a bottle to cool completely. (Cooling the cake in the pan the right way up will cause it to sink.) Run a knife around the cake to loosen it. Turn it out onto a plate and dust with icing sugar.

2¼ cups all-purpose flour

1½ cups caster (superfine) sugar

1 tablespoon baking powder

¾ teaspoon cinnamon

½ cup walnut oil or extra-light olive oil

2 large eggs, separated, plus 4 large egg whites

¾ cup brewed espresso coffee, at room temperature

2 tablespoons cocoa powder

1 teaspoon vanilla extract

½ teaspoon cream of tartar

2 tablespoons icing sugar, sifted, to dust

Black Forest mousse cake

This very light cake is almost fat-free, being based on egg whites beaten to firm peaks and folded together with flour, sugar and cocoa powder. Cocoa delivers the rich chocolate flavour without the fat of chocolate.

½ cup all-purpose flour

6 tablespoons cocoa powder

½ cup caster (superfine) sugar

5 large egg whites

1 teaspoon vanilla extract

340 g sweet dark cherries, pitted and halved

1 tablespoon icing sugar, sifted, to dust

4 tablespoons reduced-fat cream to serve (optional)

1 tablespoon cherry preserve to serve (optional)

1–2 tablespoons kirsch or rum to serve (optional)

1 Preheat the oven to 350°F (180°C). Line the bottom of a deep 23 cm round cake pan with parchment paper.

2 Sift the flour, cocoa powder and half the caster sugar into a medium bowl.

3 Place the egg whites in a large bowl and beat with an electric mixer until they form soft peaks. Gradually add the remaining sugar, 1 tablespoon at a time, and the vanilla extract, and beat until the egg whites are glossy and smooth, and form firm peaks.

4 Sprinkle the flour and cocoa mixture over the egg whites and fold in gently but thoroughly with a metal spoon, taking care not to deflate the egg whites too much. Spoon the mixture into the pan. Smooth the surface gently. Sprinkle the cherries evenly over the top of the cake.

5 Bake for 20–25 minutes or until the cake has risen and is just firm to the touch yet still moist on top—a skewer inserted in the centre should come out clean. Remove from the oven and leave to cool.

6 Dust with icing sugar to decorate. If desired, mix together the cream, cherry preserve and kirsch or rum to taste and serve with the cake.

preparation time **15 mins**

cooking time **25 mins**

serves **6**

PER SERVING

156 calories

6 g protein

1 g total fat
0.5 g saturated fat

0 mg cholesterol

32 g total carbohydrate
24 g sugars

1 g fibre

59 mg sodium

HEALTH HINT

Egg white provides protein, but has none of the fat or cholesterol found in egg yolk.

banana cake

Quick and easy to prepare, this cake makes a healthy snack for hungry children or a handy addition to lunchboxes. And it's a great way to use up bananas that have been sitting in the fruit bowl for too long.

1 Preheat the oven to 350°F (180°C). Grease a deep 18 cm (7 in.) round cake pan and line the bottom with parchment paper. Peel the bananas, then mash with a fork.

2 Sift the flour and baking powder into a large bowl and stir in the sugar. Mix together the oil, milk and eggs in a separate bowl and add to the flour mixture. Stir in the sultanas and mashed bananas, then pour the mixture into the pan.

3 Bake for 50–55 minutes or until the cake is well risen and a skewer inserted in the centre comes out clean. Leave to cool for 15 minutes, then loosen the edge of the cake with a knife and turn it out onto a wire rack to cool completely. The cake can be kept in an airtight container for up to 4 days.

Variation You can substitute other dried fruit for the sultanas, such as dried cranberries, chopped dried figs or apricots, or a mix of chopped exotic dried fruit such as mango and papaya.

2 large, ripe bananas, about 400 g in total
2 cups self-raising flour
1 teaspoon baking powder
¼ cup brown sugar
⅓ cup sunflower oil
⅓ cup low-fat milk
2 eggs
1 cup sultanas

Fb

preparation time **10 mins**
cooking time **55 mins**
serves **8**

PER SERVING

337 calories

7 g protein

12 g total fat
2 g saturated fat

54 mg cholesterol

52 g total carbohydrate
26 g sugars

3 g fibre

346 mg sodium

HEALTH HINT

This cake is much lower in sugar than a conventional banana cake. Using sunflower oil instead of butter makes it low in saturated fat, too.

chocolate chunk and nut cookies

These cookies are simply irresistible eaten while still warm, when the chocolate chunks are soft and melting. Macadamia nuts add a crunchy texture, but can be omitted if you prefer. Like the chocolate, the nuts should be in large pieces.

½ cup reduced-salt margarine

⅓ cup firmly packed brown sugar

½ teaspoon vanilla extract

1 egg, beaten

⅔ cup white self-raising flour

½ cup whole-wheat all-purpose flour

4 tablespoons cocoa powder

¼ teaspoon baking powder

120 g good-quality dark chocolate (at least 70% cocoa solids), roughly chopped

⅓ cup macadamia nuts, roughly chopped

4 tablespoons low-fat milk

1 Preheat the oven to 375°F (190°C). Line 2 baking sheets with parchment paper. Place the margarine, sugar and vanilla extract in a large bowl and beat with an electric mixer until light and fluffy. Add the egg and beat well.

2 Sift the self-raising and all-purpose flours, cocoa powder and baking powder over the creamed mixture, and stir to combine thoroughly. Add the chocolate, nuts and milk, and mix together.

3 Place tablespoonfuls of the mixture on the baking sheets, arranging them well apart so they have space to spread during baking. Flatten slightly with the back of a fork, then bake for about 15 minutes or until soft and springy.

4 Leave the cookies to cool slightly on the baking sheets, then transfer to a wire rack. Serve them while still slightly warm or leave until cold. They can be kept in an airtight container for up to 5 days.

Variations Use walnuts or pecans instead of macadamia nuts.
• For cherry and almond cookies, use white all-purpose flour instead of the cocoa powder, and substitute 60 g dried sour cherries and 60 g flaked almonds for the chocolate chunks and macadamia nuts. If you want a pronounced almond flavour, use ¼ teaspoon almond extract instead of vanilla extract.

preparation time **15 mins**

cooking time **15 mins**

makes **12 cookies**

PER COOKIE

235 calories

3 g protein

15 g total fat
4 g saturated fat

19 mg cholesterol

23 g total carbohydrate
12 g sugars

1 g fibre

127 mg sodium

HEALTH HINT

Plain chocolate is a good source of copper and provides useful amounts of iron. The scientific name of the cocoa bean tree is *Theobroma cacao*, which means "food of the gods." Casanova was reputed to drink hot chocolate before his nightly conquests—in fact, he was said to prefer chocolate to champagne.

oatmeal and raisin cookies

Both children and adults will love these crisp, melt-in-the-mouth cookies. They are a wholesome treat, packed with oatmeal and raisins for extra flavour and nutrition. It's worth making a double batch and freezing some.

⅓ cup reduced-salt margarine
½ cup firmly packed brown sugar
1 egg, beaten
1 cup self-raising flour
½ cup quick oatmeal
1⅓ cups raisins

1 Preheat the oven to 350° (180°C). Place the margarine and sugar in a bowl and beat with an electric mixer until pale and fluffy. Gradually beat in the egg. Sift over the flour, then add the oatmeal and raisins and fold in with a large metal spoon.

2 Drop heaping teaspoonfuls of the mixture onto 3 greased baking sheets, leaving enough space around each spoonful to allow it to spread during baking.

3 Bake for 10–15 minutes or until golden-brown. Cool slightly on the baking sheets, then transfer to a wire rack and leave to cool completely. These cookies can be kept in an airtight container for 3–4 days or frozen for 2 months.

Variation For a warmer flavour, you can sift in 1–1½ teaspoons mixed spice, cinnamon or ginger with the flour.

preparation time **15 mins**
cooking time **15 mins**
makes **18 cookies**

PER COOKIE

136 calories

2 g protein

5 g total fat
1 g saturated fat

12 mg cholesterol

22 g total carbohydrate
15 g sugars

1 g fibre

86 mg sodium

HEART SUPERFOOD

Oatmeal is an excellent source of soluble fibre, which can help to reduce high blood cholesterol levels, thereby reducing the risk of heart disease. Soluble fibre also helps to slow the absorption of carbohydrate into the bloodstream, resulting in a gentler rise and fall in blood sugar levels.

sweet whole-wheat cookies

preparation time **15 mins**

cooking time **12 mins**
plus 30 mins chilling

makes **25 cookies**

These crunchy, golden cookies are full of nutty, slightly sweet flavours. They are sliced from a long piece of dough, which you can make ahead and store in the refrigerator or freezer. So you can bake the cookies all at once or in batches.

PER COOKIE

51 calories	
1 g protein	
2 g total fat	
0.3 g saturated fat	
0.1 mg cholesterol	
8 g total carbohydrate	
3 g sugars	
1 g fibre	
62 mg sodium	

HEALTH HINT

All forms of sugar contain 4 calories per gram. A cup of white sugar contains 770 calories, while a cup of densely packed brown sugar contains 820 calories.

1 Sift the flour, baking powder and baking soda into a mixing bowl. Add the oatmeal, bran and sugar, and mix well to combine.

2 Add the margarine and rub it in with your fingertips until the mixture resembles breadcrumbs. Add 4 tablespoons milk and stir in well so the mixture forms a soft dough. If the mixture is a little dry, add the remaining 1 tablespoon milk.

3 Turn the dough out onto a sheet of plastic wrap and shape it into a log about 25 cm long. Wrap the plastic around the dough and roll it gently back and forward to make a smooth shape. Twist the ends of the plastic together to seal. Chill the dough for about 30 minutes. (It can be kept for up to 4 days in the refrigerator.)

4 Preheat the oven to 375°F (190°C). Unwrap the dough and, using a very sharp knife, cut it across into slices 1 cm thick. Use parchment paper to line a baking sheet and place the dough slices on it. Bake for about 12 minutes or until lightly browned.

5 Transfer the cookies to a wire rack and leave to cool completely. They can be kept in an airtight container for up to 5 days.

1 cup whole-wheat all-purpose flour
1 teaspoon baking powder
$\frac{1}{2}$ teaspoon baking soda
$\frac{1}{4}$ cup quick oatmeal
$\frac{1}{4}$ cup bran
$\frac{1}{2}$ cup dark brown sugar
$\frac{1}{4}$ cup reduced-salt margarine
5 tablespoons low-fat milk,
    or as needed

fudgy chocolate brownies

Most people's ideal brownie is one that is moist in the centre, with a deep chocolate flavour. This recipe uses chocolate and cocoa powder to give plenty of chocolate flavour, and dark brown sugar for the desired fudgy texture.

90 g good-quality dark chocolate (at least 70% cocoa solids)

½ cup reduced-salt margarine

½ cup caster (superfine) sugar

½ cup brown sugar

1 teaspoon vanilla extract

2 eggs and 1 egg yolk, at room temperature, beaten together

1 cup all-purpose flour

4 tablespoons cocoa powder

1 Preheat the oven to 350°F (180°C). Grease a shallow 20 cm (8 in.) square cake pan and line the bottom with parchment paper.

2 Break up the chocolate and place it in a large heatproof bowl with the margarine. Set the bowl over a saucepan of simmering water, making sure the water is not touching the bottom of the bowl. Leave to melt, then remove from the heat and stir the mixture until smooth. Set aside to cool.

3 Stir in the caster sugar, dark brown sugar and vanilla extract. Gradually beat in the eggs. Sift over the flour and cocoa powder, and stir until evenly blended. Do not overmix.

4 Pour the mixture into the pan. Bake for about 30 minutes or until risen but still slightly soft in the middle—a skewer inserted in the centre should come out with a few moist crumbs sticking to it. The surface will look cracked. It is important not to overcook or the brownies will be dry.

5 Leave in the pan for 5 minutes, then turn out onto a wire rack and leave to cool. When cold, peel off the lining paper and cut into 16 squares. If possible, wrap the brownies in foil and leave until the next day before eating. They can be kept like this for 3–4 days.

preparation time **15 mins**

cooking time **35 mins**

makes **16 brownies**

PER BROWNIE

157 calories

2 g protein

8 g total fat
2 g saturated fat

40 mg cholesterol

20 g total carbohydrate
14 g sugars

0.4 g fibre

41 mg sodium

HEALTH HINT

These brownies are a healthier version of a traditionally high-fat favourite. The fat content is reduced by substituting cocoa powder for some of the chocolate. Cocoa powder contains 5 times as much iron as chocolate.

chocolate-nut meringue cookies

Here's an astounding achievement: chocolate-nut cookies with less than one gram of fat each! The secret is meringue. These cookies contain no butter or margarine and no egg yolks, yet they're tender and rich tasting.

1 Preheat the oven to 300°F (150°C). Line 2 baking sheets with parchment paper. Toast the walnuts in a small saucepan, stirring frequently, until crisp and fragrant, about 7 minutes. When cool enough to handle, coarsely chop.

2 Sift together ½ cup icing sugar, cocoa powder and cinnamon.

3 Place the egg whites in a large bowl and beat with an electric mixer until stiff peaks form. Gently fold in the cocoa mixture with a spatula. Gently fold in the nuts.

4 Drop generous teaspoonfuls of the mixture onto the baking sheets, spacing them 2 cm apart. Bake until set, about 20 minutes. Remove and cool on a wire rack. Dust with the remaining icing sugar just before serving.

⅓ cup walnuts
½ cup plus 2 tablespoons icing sugar
1 tablespoon cocoa powder
¼ teaspoon cinnamon
2 large egg whites

preparation time **10 mins**
cooking time **30 mins**
makes **36 cookies**

PER COOKIE

18 calories

0.4 g protein

1 g total fat
0.1 g saturated fat

0 mg cholesterol

3 g total carbohydrate
3 g sugars

0.1 g fibre

4 mg sodium

HEART SUPERFOOD

Despite their relatively high calorie count, walnuts and other nuts eaten in small amounts every day can help keep cholesterol levels low.

COOK'S TIP

Meringues are sensitive to humidity (they'll absorb moisture and become sticky), so bake them on a fairly dry day. Place them in an airtight container once they've cooled completely. If you live in a humid climate, seal the meringues in a freezer bag and freeze them.

index

t